SOUL-STIRRING SONGS & HYMNS

Compiled by
John R. Rice, D. D.
Joy Rice Martin, M. F. A.

"Speaking to yourselves in psalms and hymns and spiritual songs, singing and making melody in your heart to the Lord."
—Ephesians 5:19

SWORD OF THE LORD PUBLISHERS
224 Bridge Avenue, Box 1099
Murfreesboro, Tennessee   37130

TABLE OF CONTENTS

FOREWORD

Soul-Stirring Songs and Hymns has been compiled with an earnest endeavor to make the very best songbook possible for all churches and groups of Christians who hold to the historic Christian faith, who preach the Gospel of Christ and hope to get people saved.

In the days of great revivals men wrote revival songs. But the well of gospel melody ran nearly dry when evangelism had less emphasis. Only about two new gospel songs have been universally popular in the last fifty years. No invitation songs are now used of less than seventy years ago!

So here we have some new, revival-type songs, not available elsewhere, as well as much loved hymns and the best well-known gospel songs.

In all songs of Christian service we are warned to beware of 'the form of godliness without the power thereof.' In Ephesians 5:19 we are commanded, "Speaking to yourselves in psalms and hymns and spiritual songs, singing and making melody in your heart to the Lord." And again in Colossians 3:16 are these instructions: "Let the word of Christ dwell in you richly in all wisdom; teaching and admonishing one another in psalms and hymns and spiritual songs, singing with grace in your hearts to the Lord."

Oh, then, may these songs and hymns admonish as well as make melody in our hearts to the Lord as we sing.

So we send the book out with an earnest prayer to God that in every kind of service it may help Christians in praise, in petition and in heart's love and may woo the unsaved with sweet words and haunting melodies to trust in our beloved Saviour the Lord Jesus Christ.

The Publishers

EDITORIAL COMMITTEE

REV. BILL HARVEY, soloist, composer, director of music for many evangelistic meetings and conferences.

DR. JACK HYLES, pastor, First Baptist Church, Hammond, Indiana.

EVANGELIST BUD LYLES, "Voice of Revival" radio broadcast announcer and music coordinator, soloist.

MRS. J. ALLAN MACMULLEN, pastor's wife and music coordinator, M.A. in music from Bob Jones University.

MRS. TOM MALONE, director of music and pastor's wife, Emmanuel Baptist Church; music instructor, Midwestern Baptist Schools, Pontiac, Michigan.

MRS. ROGER MARTIN, instructor in music, Tennessee Temple Schools, Chattanooga, Tennessee; M.F.A. in music and speech, Bob Jones University.

Jesus, I My Cross Have Taken

1

Henry F. Lyte

Ascribed to Wolfgang A. Mozart
Arr. by Hubert P. Main

1. Je - sus, I my cross have ta - ken, All to leave, and fol - low Thee;
2. Let the world de-spise and leave me, They have left my Sav - ior, too;
3. Man may troub-le and dis - tress me, 'Twill but drive me to Thy breast;
4. Haste thee on from grace to glo - ry, Armed by faith, and winged by prayer;

Des - ti - tute, de-spised, for - sa - ken, Thou, from hence, my all shalt be:
Hu - man hearts and looks de - ceive me; Thou art not, like man, un-true;
Life with tri - als hard may press me, Heav'n will bring me sweet-er rest.
Heav'n's e-ter - nal day's be - fore thee, God's own hand shall guide thee there.

Per - ish ev - 'ry fond am - bi - tion, All I've sought, and hoped, and known;
And, while Thou shalt smile up-on me, God of wis - dom, love, and might,
O 'tis not in grief to harm me, While Thy love is left to me;
Soon shall close thy earth-ly mis - sion, Swift shall pass thy pil - grim days,

Yet how rich is my con - di - tion, God and heav'n are still my own!
Foes may hate, and friends may shun me; Show Thy face, and all is bright.
O 'twere not in joy to charm me, Were that joy un - mixed with Thee.
Hope shall change to glad fru - i - tion, Faith to sight, and prayer to praise.

Favorite hymn of Dr. John R. Rice and Mr. Arthur DeMoss.

2 Glory to His Name

ELISHA A. HOFFMAN

JOHN H. STOCKTON

1. Down at the cross where my Sav-ior died, Down where for cleansing from
2. I am so won-drous-ly saved from sin, Je - sus so sweet-ly a-
3. Oh, pre-cious foun-tain that saves from sin, I am so glad I have
4. Come to this foun-tain so rich and sweet; Cast thy poor soul at the

sin I cried, There to my heart was the blood ap-plied; Glo-ry to His name.
bides with-in, There at the cross where He took me in; Glo-ry to His name.
en - tered in; There Jesus saves me and keeps me clean; Glo-ry to His name.
Sav-ior's feet; Plunge in to-day, and be made com-plete; Glo-ry to His name.

FINE

D. S.—*There to my heart was the blood ap-plied; Glo-ry to His name.*

CHORUS

D. S.

Glo - ry to His name,... Glo - ry to His name;...

3 Must Jesus Bear the Cross Alone?

THOMAS SHEPHERD

GEORGE N. ALLEN

1. Must Je - sus bear the cross a - lone, And all the world go free?
2. The con - se - crat - ed cross I'll bear, Till death shall set me free,
3. Up - on the crys - tal pave-ment, down At Je - sus' pierc - ed feet,
4. O pre - cious cross! O glo - rious crown! O res - ur - rec - tion day!

Must Jesus Bear the Cross Alone?

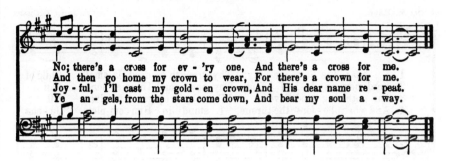

No; there's a cross for ev - 'ry one, And there's a cross for me.
And then go home my crown to wear, For there's a crown for me.
Joy - ful, I'll cast my gold - en crown, And His dear name re - peat.
Ye an - gels, from the stars come down, And bear my soul a - way.

When I Survey the Wondrous Cross   4

ISAAC WATTS

Arr. by LOWELL MASON

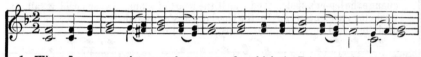

1. When I sur - vey the won - drous cross, On which the Prince of glo - ry died,
2. For - bid it, Lord! that I should boast, Save in the death of Christ my God:
3. See, from His head, His hands, His feet, Sor - row and love flow min - gled down:
4. Were the whole realm of na - ture mine, That were a pres - ent far too small;

My rich - est gain I count but loss, And pour contempt on all my pride.
All the vain things that charm me most, I sac - ri - fice them to His blood.
Did e'er such love and sor - row meet, Or thorns com - pose so rich a crown?
Love so a - maz - ing, so di - vine, De - mands my soul, my life, my all.

Favorite hymn of Dr. Bill Rice and composer John W. Peterson.

5 Jesus Paid It All

ELVINA M. HALL

JOHN T. GRAPE

1. I hear the Sav-ior say, "Thy strength in-deed is small, Child of
2. Lord, now in-deed I find Thy pow'r, and Thine a-lone, Can
3. For noth-ing good have I Where-by Thy grace to claim— I'll
4. And when, be-fore the throne, I stand in Him com-plete, "Je-sus

CHORUS

weakness, watch and pray, Find in Me thine all in all."
change the lep-er's spots, And melt the heart of stone. Je-sus paid it all,
wash my garments white In the blood of Cal-v'ry's Lamb.
died my soul to save," My lips shall still re-peat.

All to Him I owe; Sin had left a crimson stain, He washed it white as snow.

6 Majestic Sweetness Sits Enthroned

SAMUEL STENNETT

THOMAS HASTINGS

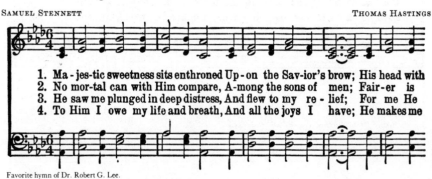

1. Ma-jes-tic sweetness sits enthroned Up-on the Sav-ior's brow; His head with
2. No mor-tal can with Him compare, A-mong the sons of men; Fair-er is
3. He saw me plunged in deep distress, And flew to my re-lief; For me He
4. To Him I owe my life and breath, And all the joys I have; He makes me

Favorite hymn of Dr. Robert G. Lee.

Majestic Sweetness Sits Enthroned

radiant glories crowned, His lips with grace o'erflow, His lips with grace o'erflow.
He than all the fair Who fill the heav'nly train, Who fill the heav'nly train.
bore the shameful cross, And carried all my grief, And car-ried all my grief.
tri - umph o-ver death, And saves me from the grave, And saves me from the grave.

Beneath the Cross of Jesus

7

ELIZABETH C. CLEPHANE

FREDERICK C. MAKER

1. Be-neath the cross of Je - sus I fain would take my stand,
2. Up - on that cross of Je - sus Mine eye at times can see
3. I take, O cross, thy shad - ow For my a - bid-ing place;

The shad - ow of a might-y Rock With-in a wea-ry land;
The ver - y dy - ing form of One Who suf-fered there for me;
I ask no oth - er sun-shine than The sun-shine of His face;

A home with-in the wil - der-ness, A rest up - on the way,
And from my smit - ten heart with tears, Two won-ders I con-fess,—
Con-tent to let the world go by, To know no gain nor loss,

From the burn-ing of the noon-tide heat, And the bur-den of the day.
The won-ders of His glo-rious love And my own worth-less-ness.
My sin - ful self my on - ly shame, My glo - ry all the cross!

I Gave My Life for Thee

FRANCES R. HAVERGAL

PHILIP P. BLISS

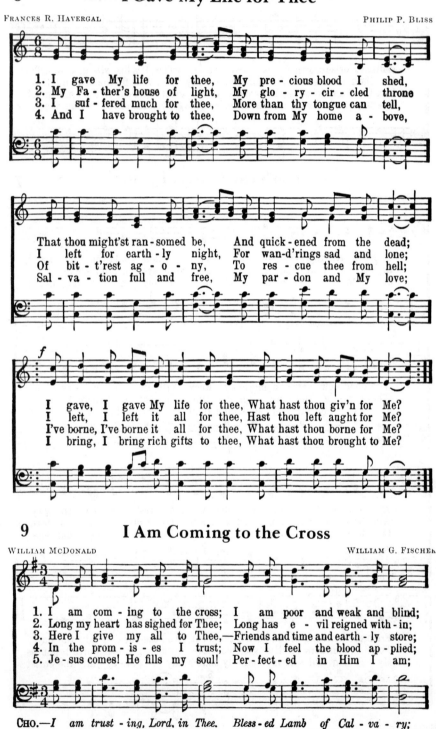

1. I gave My life for thee, My pre-cious blood I shed,
2. My Fa-ther's house of light, My glo-ry-cir-cled throne
3. I suf-fered much for thee, More than thy tongue can tell,
4. And I have brought to thee, Down from My home a-bove,

That thou might'st ran-somed be, And quick-ened from the dead;
I left for earth-ly night, For wan-d'rings sad and lone;
Of bit-t'rest ag-o-ny, To res-cue thee from hell;
Sal-va-tion full and free, My par-don and My love;

I gave, I gave My life for thee, What hast thou giv'n for Me?
I left, I left it all for thee, Hast thou left aught for Me?
I've borne, I've borne it all for thee, What hast thou borne for Me?
I bring, I bring rich gifts to thee, What hast thou brought to Me?

9

I Am Coming to the Cross

WILLIAM McDONALD

WILLIAM G. FISCHER

1. I am com-ing to the cross; I am poor and weak and blind;
2. Long my heart has sighed for Thee; Long has e-vil reigned with-in;
3. Here I give my all to Thee,—Friends and time and earth-ly store;
4. In the prom-is-es I trust; Now I feel the blood ap-plied;
5. Je-sus comes! He fills my soul! Per-fect-ed in Him I am;

CHO.—I am trust-ing, Lord, in Thee. Bless-ed Lamb of Cal-va-ry;

I Am Coming to the Cross

D. C. CHORUS

I am count-ing all but dross; I shall full sal-va-tion find.
Je-sus sweet-ly speaks to me,— "I will cleanse you from all sin."
Soul and bod-y Thine to be,— Whol-ly Thine for-ev-er-more.
I am pros-trate in the dust; I with Christ am cru-ci-fied.
I am ev-'ry whit made whole: Glo-ry, glo-ry to the Lamb!

Hum-bly at Thy cross I bow. Save me, Je-sus, save me now.

Near the Cross

10

FANNY J. CROSBY

WILLIAM H. DOANE

1. Je-sus, keep me near the cross, There a pre-cious foun-tain
2. Near the cross, a trem-bling soul, Love and mer-cy found me;
3. Near the cross! O Lamb of God, Bring its scenes be-fore me;
4. Near the cross I'll watch and wait, Hop-ing, trust-ing ev-er,

Free to all— a heal-ing stream, Flows from Cal-v'ry's moun-tain.
There the Bright and Morn-ing Star Sheds its beams a-round me.
Help me walk from day to day, With its shad-ows o'er me.
Till I reach the gold-en strand, Just be-yond the riv-er.

CHORUS

In the cross, in the cross, Be my glo-ry ev-er;

Till my rap-tured soul shall find Rest be-yond the riv-er.

11 He Died for Me

JOHN NEWTON

EDWIN O. EXCELL

1. I saw One hang-ing on a tree, In ag - o - ny and blood;
2. Sure, nev - er, till my lat - est breath, Can I for - get that look:
3. My con-science felt and owned the guilt, And plunged me in de - spair;
4. A - las! I knew not what I did,—But now my tears are vain:
5. A sec - ond look He gave, which said, "I free - ly all for - give:

He fixed His lan - guid eyes on me, As near His cross I stood.
It seemed to charge me with His death, Tho' not a word He spoke.
I saw my sins His blood had spilt And helped to nail Him there.
Where shall my trem-bling soul be hid? For I the Lord have slain.
This blood is for thy ran - som paid, I die that thou may'st live."

CHORUS.

Oh, can it be, up - on a tree The Sav - ior died for me?

My soul is thrilled, My heart is filled, To think He died for me!

Copyright 1917. Renewal 1944 in "Praiseworthy" by G. J. Excell Loftus. Assigned to Hope Publishing
Co. All Rights Reserved. Used by Permission.

Room at the Cross for You

IRA F. STANPHILL.   IRA F. STANPHILL.

1. The cross up-on which Je-sus died Is a shel-ter in
2. Tho mil-lions have found Him a friend And have turned from the
3. The hand of my Sav-ior is strong, And the love of my

which we can hide; And its grace so free is suf-
sins they have sinned, The Sav-ior still waits to
Sav-ior is long; Through sun-shine or rain, through

fi-cient for me, And deep is its foun-tain— as wide as the sea.
o-pen the gates And wel-come a sin-ner be-fore it's too late.
loss or in gain, The blood flows from Cal-v'ry to cleanse ev-'ry stain.

CHORUS

There's room at the cross for you, There's room at the cross for you; Tho

mil-lions have come, There's still room for one—Yes, there's room at the cross for you.

13 Blessed Redeemer

Avis B. Christiansen

Harry D. Loes

1. Up Cal-vary's mountain one dreadful morn, Walked Christ my Saviour, weary and worn;
2. "Fa-ther, forgive them!" thus did He pray, E'en while His life-blood flowed fast a-way;
3. O how I love Him, Sav-iour and Friend, How can my prais-es ev - er find end!

Fac-ing for sin-ners death on the cross, That He might save them from endless loss.
Pray-ing for sin-ners while in such woe— No one but Je - sus ev - er loved so.
Thro' years un-num-bered on heaven's shore, My tongue shall praise Him for-ev-er-more.

CHORUS

Bless-ed Re-deem - er! pre-cious Re-deem - er! Seems now I
Bless-ed Re-deem-er! bless - ed Re-deem - er!

see Him on Cal - va-ry's tree; Wound-ed and bleed - ing, for sin-ners
Wound-ed and bleed-ing,

plead - ing— Blind and un-heed - - ing— dy-ing for me!
for sin-ners plead-ing— Blind and un-heed - ing—

Kneel at the Cross

14

Words and Melody Chas. E Moody

Arr. for J. T. B. Pub. Co.

1. Kneel at the cross, Christ will meet you there, Come while He waits for you;
2. Kneel at the cross, There is room for all Who would His glo-ry share;
3. Kneel at the cross, Give your i-dols up, Look un-to realms a-bove;

List to His voice, Leave with Him your care And be-gin life a-new.
Bliss there a-waits, Harm can ne'er be-fall Those who are anchored there.
Turn not a-way To life's sparkling cup, Trust on-ly in His love.

CHORUS

Kneel............ at the cross,............Leave............
Kneel at the cross, Kneel at the cross, Leave ev-'ry care

ev-'ry care;......... .... · Kneel............ at the
Leave ev-'ry care; Kneel at the cross,

cross .... Je-sus will meet you there............
Kneel at the cross, meet you there.

15 The Way of the Cross Leads Home

JESSIE B. POUNDS

CHARLES H. GABRIEL

1. I must needs go home by the way of the cross, There's no oth-er
2. I must needs go on in the blood-sprinkled way, The path that the
3. Then I bid fare-well to the way of the world, To walk in it

way but this; I shall ne'er get sight of the Gates of Light,
Sav-ior trod, If I ev-er climb to the heights sub-lime,
nev-er-more; For my Lord says "Come," and I seek my home,

If the way of the cross I miss.
Where the soul is at home with God.
Where He waits at the o-pen door.

CHORUS.

The way of the cross leads home, The way of the cross leads home;
leads home, leads home;
It is sweet to know as I on-ward go, The way of the cross leads home.

Lead Me to Calvary

16

JENNIE E. HUSSEY

WILLIAM J. KIRKPATRICK

1. King of my life, I crown Thee now, Thine shall the glo - ry be;
2. Show me the tomb where Thou wast laid, Ten-der-ly mourned and wept;
3. Let me like Ma - ry, thro' the gloom, Come with a gift to Thee;
4. May I be will - ing, Lord, to bear Dai - ly my cross for Thee;

Lest I for - get Thy thorn-crowned brow, Lead me to Cal - va - ry.
An - gels in robes of light ar - rayed Guarded Thee whilst Thou slept.
Show to me now the emp - ty tomb, Lead me to Cal - va - ry.
E - ven Thy cup of grief to share, Thou hast borne all for me.

CHORUS

Lest I for - get Geth-sem - a - ne; Lest I for - get Thine ag - o - ny;

Lest I for - get Thy love for me, Lead me to Cal - va - ry.

17 One Day!

J. Wilbur Chapman

Charles H. Marsh

1. One day when heav-en was filled with His prais-es, One day when
2. One day they led Him up Cal-va-ry's moun-tain, One day they
3. One day they left Him a-lone in the gar-den, One day He
4. One day the grave could con-ceal Him no lon-ger, One day the
5. One day the trump-et will sound for His com-ing, One day the

sin was as black as could be,... Je-sus came forth to be
nailed Him to die on the tree;.. Suf-fer-ing an-guish, de-
rest-ed, from suf-fer-ing free;.. An-gels came down o'er His
stone rolled a-way from the door;.. Then He a-rose, o-ver
skies with His glo-ries will shine; Won-der-ful day, my be-

born of a vir-gin—Dwelt amongst men, my ex-am-ple is He!...
spised and re-ject-ed: Bear-ing our sins, my Re-deem-er is He!...
tomb to keep vig-il; Hope of the hope-less, my Sav-ior is He!...
death He had con-quered; Now is as-cend-ed, my Lord ev-er-more!.
lov-ed ones bring-ing; Glo-ri-ous Sav-ior, this Je-sus is mine!.

CHORUS

Liv-ing, He loved me; dy-ing, He saved me; Bur-ied, He

car-ried my sins far a-way;.. Ris-ing, He jus-ti-fied

One Day!

cres. > > > > > *rit.* > > >

free-ly for-ev-er: One day He's com-ing—oh, glo-ri-ous day!

Take the Name of Jesus With You

LYDIA BAXTER

WILLIAM H. DOANE

1. Take the name of Je-sus with you, Child of sor-row and of woe;
2. Take the name of Je-sus ev-er, As a shield from ev-'ry snare;
3. O the precious name of Je-sus! How it thrills our souls with joy,
4. At the name of Je-sus bow-ing, Fall-ing pros-trate at His feet,

It will joy and com-fort give you, Take it, then, wher-e'er you go.
If temp-ta-tions round you gath-er, Breathe that ho-ly name in prayer.
When His lov-ing arms re-ceive us, And His songs our tongues em-ploy!
King of kings in Heav'n we'll crown Him, When our jour-ney is com-plete.

CHORUS

Pre-cious name, O how sweet! Hope of earth and joy of Heav'n;
Precious name, O how sweet!

Pre-cious name, O how sweet!... Hope of earth and joy of Heav'n.
Precious name, O how sweet, how sweet!

When I See the Blood

JOHN FOOTE

J. G. FOOTE

1. Christ our Re-deem-er died on the cross, Died for the sin-ner,
2. Chief-est of sin-ners, Je-sus will save; All He has prom-ised,
3. Judg-ment is com-ing, all will be there, Each one re-ceiv-ing
4. O great com-pas-sion! O bound-less love! O lov-ing kind-ness,

paid all his due; Sprin-kle your soul with the blood of the Lamb,
that He will do; Wash in the foun-tain o-pened for sin,
just-ly his due; Hide in the sav-ing sin-cleans-ing blood,
faith-ful and true! Find peace and shel-ter un-der the blood,

And I will pass, will pass o-ver you.

CHORUS

When I see the blood, When I see the blood, When I see the blood, When I see the blood,

When I see the blood, When I see the blood, When I see the blood, When I see the blood,

rit.

blood, I will pass, I will pass o-ver you.

see the blood, o-ver you.

What a Wonderful Savior!

ELISHA A. HOFFMAN

ELISHA A. HOFFMAN

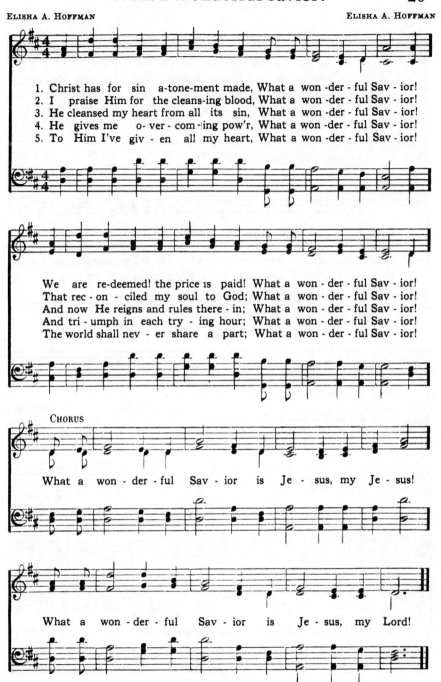

1. Christ has for sin a-tone-ment made, What a won-der-ful Sav-ior!
2. I praise Him for the cleans-ing blood, What a won-der-ful Sav-ior!
3. He cleansed my heart from all its sin, What a won-der-ful Sav-ior!
4. He gives me o-ver-com-ing pow'r, What a won-der-ful Sav-ior!
5. To Him I've giv-en all my heart, What a won-der-ful Sav-ior!

We are re-deemed! the price is paid! What a won-der-ful Sav-ior!
That rec-on-ciled my soul to God; What a won-der-ful Sav-ior!
And now He reigns and rules there-in; What a won-der-ful Sav-ior!
And tri-umph in each try-ing hour; What a won-der-ful Sav-ior!
The world shall nev-er share a part; What a won-der-ful Sav-ior!

CHORUS

What a won-der-ful Sav-ior is Je-sus, my Je-sus!

What a won-der-ful Sav-ior is Je-sus, my Lord!

21   Are You Washed in the Blood?

ELISHA A. HOFFMAN   ELISHA A. HOFFMAN

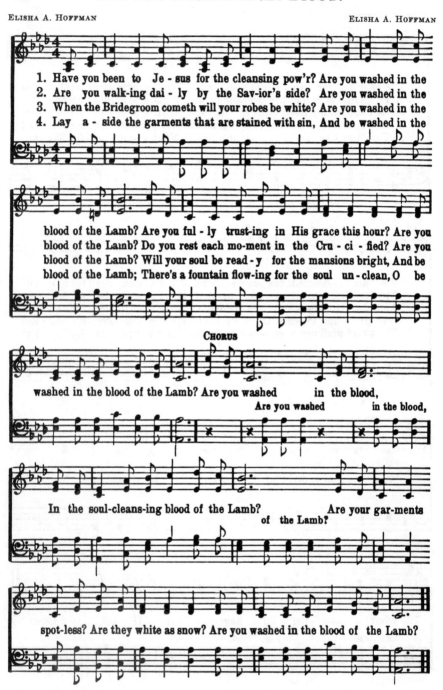

1. Have you been to Je-sus for the cleansing pow'r? Are you washed in the
2. Are you walk-ing dai-ly by the Sav-ior's side? Are you washed in the
3. When the Bridegroom cometh will your robes be white? Are you washed in the
4. Lay a - side the garments that are stained with sin, And be washed in the

blood of the Lamb? Are you ful-ly trust-ing in His grace this hour? Are you
blood of the Lamb? Do you rest each mo-ment in the Cru-ci-fied? Are you
blood of the Lamb? Will your soul be read-y for the mansions bright, And be
blood of the Lamb; There's a fountain flow-ing for the soul un-clean, O be

CHORUS

washed in the blood of the Lamb? Are you washed in the blood,
Are you washed in the blood,

In the soul-cleans-ing blood of the Lamb? Are your gar-ments
of the Lamb?

spot-less? Are they white as snow? Are you washed in the blood of the Lamb?

There Is Power in the Blood

LEWIS E. JONES

LEWIS E. JONES

1. Would you be free from the bur-den of sin? There's pow'r in the blood,
2. Would you be free from your pas-sion and pride? There's pow'r in the blood,
3. Would you be whit-er, much whiter than snow? There's pow'r in the blood,
4. Would you do serv-ice for Je-sus your King? There's pow'r in the blood,

pow'r in the blood; Would you o'er e-vil a vic-to-ry win? There's
pow'r in the blood; Come for a cleans-ing to Cal-va-ry's tide; There's
pow'r in the blood; Sin-stains are lost in its life-giv-ing flow; There's
pow'r in the blood; Would you live dai-ly His prais-es to sing? There's

CHORUS.

won-der-ful pow'r in the blood. There is pow'r, pow'r, Wonder-working pow'r
there is

In the blood of the Lamb; There is pow'r, pow'r,
In the blood of the Lamb; there is

Won-der-work-ing pow'r In the pre-cious blood of the Lamb.

23 There Is a Fountain

WILLIAM COWPER EARLY AMERICAN MELODY

1. There is a foun-tain filled with blood Drawn from Im-man- uel's veins;
2. The dy - ing thief re - joiced to see That foun - tain in his day;
3. Dear dy - ing Lamb, Thy pre-cious blood Shall nev - er lose its pow'r,
4. E'er since, by faith, I saw the stream Thy flow-ing wounds sup-ply,
5. Then in a no-bler, sweet-er song, I'll sing Thy pow'r to save,

And sin - ners, plunged be-neath that flood, Lose all their guilt-y stains:
And there may I, though vile as he, Wash all my sins a - way:
Till all the ran-somed Church of God Be saved, to sin no more:
Re - deem-ing love has been my theme, And shall be till I die:
When this poor lisp-ing, stamm'ring tongue Lies si - lent in the grave:

Lose all their guilt-y stains, Lose all their guilt-y stains; And
Wash all my sins a - way, Wash all my sins a - way; And
Be saved, to sin no more, Be saved, to sin no more; Till
And shall be till I die, And shall be till I die; Re-
Lies si - lent in the grave, Lies si - lent in the grave; When

sin - ners, plunged be - neath that flood, Lose all their guilt - y stains.
there may I, though vile as he, Wash all my sins a - way.
all the ran-somed Church of God Be saved, to sin no more.
deem-ing love has been my theme, And shall be till I die.
this poor lisp - ing, stam-m'ring tongue Lies si - lent in the grave.

Favorite song of Dr. Tom Malone and Dr. Harold Sightler.

The Old Rugged Cross

GEORGE BENNARD

GEORGE BENNARD

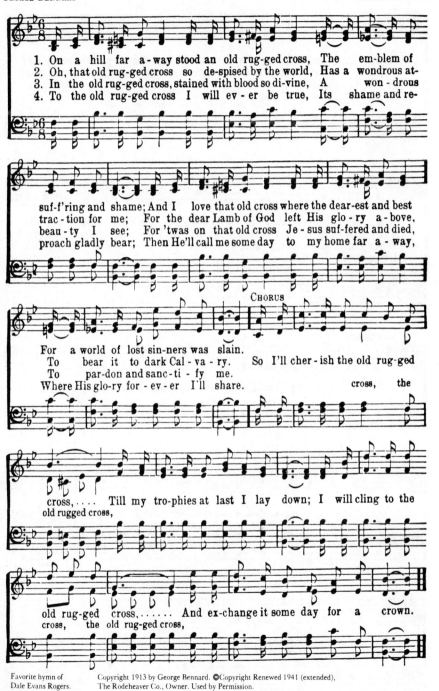

1. On a hill far away stood an old rug-ged cross, The em-blem of
2. Oh, that old rug-ged cross so de-spised by the world, Has a wondrous at-
3. In the old rug-ged cross, stained with blood so di-vine, A won-drous
4. To the old rug-ged cross I will ev-er be true, Its shame and re-

suf-f'ring and shame; And I love that old cross where the dear-est and best
trac-tion for me; For the dear Lamb of God left His glo-ry a-bove,
beau-ty I see; For 'twas on that old cross Je-sus suf-fered and died,
proach gladly bear; Then He'll call me some day to my home far a-way,

CHORUS

For a world of lost sin-ners was slain.
To bear it to dark Cal-va-ry. So I'll cher-ish the old rug-ged
To par-don and sanc-ti-fy me.
Where His glo-ry for-ev-er I'll share. cross, the

cross,.... Till my tro-phies at last I lay down; I will cling to the
old rugged cross,

old rug-ged cross,...... And ex-change it some day for a crown.
cross, the old rug-ged cross,

Copyright 1913 by George Bennard. ©Copyright Renewed 1941 (extended),
The Rodeheaver Co., Owner. Used by Permission.

25   At the Cross

ISAAC WATTS
REF., RALPH E. HUDSON

RALPH E. HUDSON

1. A - las, and did my Sav - ior bleed? And did my Sov-'reign die?
2. Was it for crimes that I have done, He groaned up - on the tree?
3. Well might the sun in dark-ness hide, And shut his glo - ries in,
4. But drops of grief can ne'er re - pay The debt of love I owe:

Would He de - vote that sa - cred head For such a worm as I?
A - maz - ing pit - y! grace unknown! And love be - yond de - gree!
When Christ, the might-y Mak - er, died For man the crea-ture's sin.
Here, Lord, I give my - self a - way, 'Tis all that I can do!

CHORUS

At the cross, at the cross where I first saw the light, And the

bur - den of my heart rolled a - way, (rolled a-way,) It was there by faith

I re-ceived my sight, And now I am hap - py all the day!

And Can It Be That I Should Gain?   26

Charles Wesley

Thomas Campbell

1. And can it be that I should gain An in - terest in the
2. He left His Fa - ther's throne a - bove, So free, so in - fi -
3. Long my im - pris - oned spir - it lay Fast bound in sin and

Sav-iour's blood? Died He for me, who caused His pain? For me, who
nite His grace; Emp-tied Him - self of all but love, And bled for
na-ture's night; Thine eye dif - fused a quick-'ning ray, I woke, the

Him to death pur-sued? A-maz-ing love! how can it be That
A - dam's help-less race; 'Tis mer-cy all, im-mense and free; For,
dun - geon flamed with light; My chains fell off, my heart was free; I

REFRAIN

Thou, my God, shouldst die for me? A - maz-ing love! how
O my God, it found out me. A - maz-ing love!
rose, went forth, and fol-lowed Thee.

can it be That Thou, my God, shouldst die for me.
How can it be That Thou, my God,

Favorite hymn of Dr. Bob Jones, III.

Nothing but the Blood

ROBERT LOWRY

ROBERT LOWRY

1. What can wash a - way my sin? Noth-ing but the blood of Je - sus;
2. For my par - don this I see— Noth-ing but the blood of Je - sus;
3. Noth - ing can for sin a - tone— Noth-ing but the blood of Je - sus;
4. This is all my hope and peace— Noth-ing but the blood of Je - sus;

What can make me whole a - gain? Noth-ing but the blood of Je - sus.
For my cleans-ing, this my plea— Noth-ing but the blood of Je - sus.
Naught of good that I have done— Noth-ing but the blood of Je - sus.
This is all my right-eous - ness— Noth-ing but the blood of Je - sus.

REFRAIN

Oh! pre - cious is the flow That makes me white as snow;

No oth - er fount I know, Noth-ing but the blood of Je - sus.

Wounded for Me

W. G. OVENS AND
GLADYS W. ROBERTS

W. G. OVENS

1. Wound-ed for me, wound-ed for me, There on the cross
2. Dy - ing for me, dy - ing for me. There on the cross
3. Ris - en for me, ris - en for me, Up from the grave
4. Liv - ing for me, liv - ing for me, Up in the skies
5. Com - ing for me, com - ing for me, One day to earth

Wounded for Me

He was wound-ed for me; Gone my trans-gres-sions, and
He was dy-ing for me; Now in His death my re-
He has ris-en for me; Now ev-er-more from death's
He is liv-ing for me; Dai-ly He's plead-ing and
He is com-ing for me; Then with what joy His dear

dim.

now I am free, All be-cause Je-sus was wound-ed for me.
demp-tion I see, All be-cause Je-sus was dy-ing for me.
sting I am free, All be-cause Je-sus has ris-en for me.
pray-ing for me, All be-cause Je-sus is liv-ing for me.
face I shall see, Oh, how I praise Him! He's com-ing for me.

Alas! and Did My Savior Bleed?   29

Isaac Watts   Hugh Wilson

1. A-las! and did my Sav-ior bleed? And did my Sov-'reign die?
2. Was it for crimes that I have done He groaned up-on the tree?
3. Well might the sun in dark-ness hide, And shut his glo-ries in,
4. But drops of grief can ne'er re-pay The debt of love I owe;

Would He de-vote that sa-cred head For such a worm as I?
A-maz-ing pit-y! grace un-known! And love be-yond de-gree!
When Christ, the might-y Mak-er, died For man the crea-ture's sin.
Here, Lord, I give my-self to Thee,—'Tis all that I can do.

Hallelujah for the Cross!

HORATIUS BONAR, ARR.   JAMES McGRANAHAN

1. The cross it stand-eth fast, Hal-le-lu-jah, hal-le-lu-jah! De-fy-ing
2. It is the old cross still, Hal-le-lu-jah, hal-le-lu-jah! Its tri-umph
3. 'Twas here the debt was paid, Hal-le-lu-jah, hal-le-lu-jah! Our sins on

ev-ery blast, Hal-le-lu-jah, hal-le-lu-jah! The winds of hell have blown, The
let us tell, Hal-le-lu-jah, hal-le-lu-jah! The grace of God here shone Thro'
Je-sus laid, Hal-le-lu-jah, hal-le-lu-jah! So round the cross we sing Of

world its hate hath shown, Yet it is not over-thrown, Hal-le-lu-jah for the cross!
Christ the bless-ed Son, Who did for sin a-tone, Hal-le-lu-jah for the cross!
Christ our of-fer-ing, Of Christ our liv-ing King, Hal-le-lu-jah for the cross!

OBBLIGATO DUET SOP. (or TEN.) and ALTO

Hal-le-lu-jah,   hal-le-lu-jah,   Hal-le-

SOPRANO & ALTO*

CHORUS mp   Hal-le-lu-jah,   hal-le-lu-jah, Hal-le-

TENOR & BASS

*If desired, the Soprano and Alto may sing the upper staff, omitting the middle staff.

Hallelujah for the Cross!

lu - jah for the cross! Hal - le - lu - jah,

lu - jah for the cross, hal-le - lu-jah for the cross! Hal - le - lu - jah,

hal - le - lu - jah, It shall nev - er suf - fer loss!

hal - le - lu - jah, It shall nev-er suf - fer, nev - er suf - fer loss!

FULL CHORUS

Hal - le - lu - jah, hal - le - lu - jah, Hal - le - lu - jah for the cross!

cres. *ff*

Hal - le - lu - jah, hal - le - lu - jah, It shall nev - er suf - fer loss!

He Lives

Alfred H. Ackley

Alfred H. Ackley

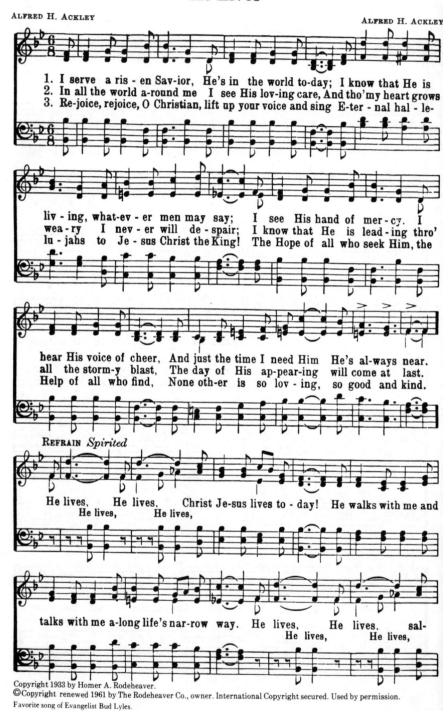

1. I serve a ris-en Sav-ior, He's in the world to-day; I know that He is
2. In all the world a-round me I see His lov-ing care, And tho' my heart grows
3. Re-joice, rejoice, O Christian, lift up your voice and sing E-ter-nal hal-le-

liv-ing, what-ev-er men may say; I see His hand of mer-cy. I
wea-ry I nev-er will de-spair; I know that He is lead-ing thro'
lu-jahs to Je-sus Christ the King! The Hope of all who seek Him, the

hear His voice of cheer, And just the time I need Him He's al-ways near.
all the storm-y blast, The day of His ap-pear-ing will come at last.
Help of all who find, None oth-er is so lov-ing, so good and kind.

REFRAIN *Spirited*

He lives, He lives, Christ Je-sus lives to-day! He walks with me and
He lives, He lives,

talks with me a-long life's nar-row way. He lives, He lives, sal-
He lives, He lives,

Favorite song of Evangelist Bud Lyles.

He Lives

va-tion to im - part! You ask me how I know He lives? He lives within my heart.

When I See My Savior

32

MAUD FRAZER

ROBERT HARKNESS

1. When I see my Sav - iour, hang-ing on Cal - va - ry,
2. I can see the blood-drops, red 'neath His thorn - y crown,
3. "Why hast thou for - sak - en?" list to that sad, sad moan!

Bear - ing there for sin - ners bit - ter-est ag - o - ny,
From the cru - el nail-wounds now they are fall - ing down;
Oh, His heart was bro - ken, suf - fer-ing there a - lone:

Grat - i - tude o'er-whelms me, makes mine eyes grow dim,
Lord, when I would wan - der from Thy love a - way,
Bro - ken then that mor - tals ne'er need cry in vain

All my ran-somed be - ing cap - tive is to Him.
Let me see those blood-drops shed for me that day.
For God's love and com - fort, in the hour of pain.

Christ Arose!

ROBERT LOWRY

ROBERT LOWRY

1. Low in the grave He lay— Je-sus my Sav-ior! Wait-ing the com-ing day—
2. Vain-ly they watch His bed—Je-sus my Sav-ior! Vain-ly they seal the dead—
3. Death cannot keep his prey—Je-sus my Sav-ior! He tore the bars a-way—

REFRAIN *Fasier*

Je - sus my Lord! Up from the grave He a - rose,(He a-rose,)With a

might-y tri-umph o'er His foes; (He a-rose!)He a-rose a Vic-tor from the

dark do-main, And He lives for-ev-er with His saints to reign. He a-

rit.

rose! He a-rose! Hal - le - lu-jah! Christ a - rose!
He a-rose! He a-rose!

CHARLES WESLEY   ARR. FROM "LYRA DAVIDICA"

1. Christ the Lord is ris'n to-day, Al - - le - lu - ia!
2. Lives a - gain our glo - rious King: Al - - le - lu - ia!
3. Love's re - deem - ing work is done, Al - - le - lu - ia!
4. Soar we now, where Christ has led, Al - - le - lu - ia!

Sons of men and an - gels say: Al - - le - lu - ia!
Where, O death, is now thy sting? Al - - le - lu - ia!
Fought the fight, the bat - tle won; Al - - le - lu - ia!
Fol - l'wing our ex - alt - ed Head; Al - - le - lu - ia!

Raise your joys and tri - umphs high, Al - - le - lu - ia!
Dy - ing once, He all doth save: Al - - le - lu - ia!
Death in vain for - bids Him rise; Al - - le - lu - ia!
Made like Him, like Him we rise; Al - - le - lu - ia!

Sing, ye heav'ns, and earth re - ply. Al - - le - lu - ia!
Where thy vic - to - ry, O grave? Al - - le - lu - ia!
Christ has o - pened Par - a - dise. Al - - le - lu - ia!
Ours the cross, the grave, the skies. Al - - le - lu - ia!

35   I Know That My Redeemer Liveth

Jessie B. Pounds   James H. Fillmore

1. I know that my Redeemer liv-eth, And on the earth a-gain shall stand;
2. I know His promise never fail-eth, The word He speaks, it can-not die;
3. I know my mansion He prepareth, That where He is there I may be;

1. And on the earth again shall stand;

I know e-ter-nal life He giv-eth, That grace and pow'r are in His hand.
Tho' cruel death my flesh assaileth, Yet I shall see .... Him by and by.
O wondrous tho't, for me He careth, And He at last.... will come for me.

That grace and pow'r are in His hand.

CHORUS

I know, I know........ that Je-sus liv-eth, And on the
I know, I know

earth...... a-gain shall stand; I know, I know......
And on the earth   I know, I know

that life He giv-eth, That grace and pow'r...... are in His hand.
That grace and pow'r

He Lives on High

Words by
B. B. McKinney

Copyright 1921. Renewal 1949
Broadman Press, owner.
Used by Permission

Arr. by B. B. McKinney
From Hawaiin Folk Song

1. Christ the Sav-iour came from heaven's glo - ry, To re-deem the
2. He a-rose from death and all its sor - row, To dwell in that
3. Wea-ry soul, to Je-sus come con-fess - ing, Re-demp-tion from

lost from sin and shame; On His brow He wore the thorn-crown
land of joy and love; He is com-ing back some glad to-
sin He of-fers thee; Look to Je - sus and re-ceive a

go - ry, And up-on Cal-va-ry He took my blame.
mor - row, And He'll take all His chil-dren home a - bove.
bless - ing, There is life, there is joy and vic - to - ry.

Chorus

He lives on high, He lives on high, Tri-um-phant o - ver sin and all its

stain; He lives on high, He lives on high, Some day He's com-ing a - gain.

Hallelujah, We Shall Rise

J. E. T.

1. In the res-ur-rec-tion morn-ing, When the trump of God shall sound,
2. In the res-ur-rec-tion morn-ing, What a meet-ing it will be,
3. In the res-ur-rec-tion morn-ing, Bless-ed tho't it is to me,
4. In the res-ur-rec-tion morn-ing, We shall meet Him in the air,

We shall rise, we shall rise! Then the saints will come re-joic-ing
When our fa-thers and our moth-ers,
Hal-le-lu-jah! I shall see my bless-ed Sav-iour,
And be car-ried up to glo-ry,

FINE.

And no tears will e'er be found, We shall rise, we shall rise.
And our loved ones we shall see,
Who so free-ly died for me,
To our home so bright and fair, Hal-le-lu-jah! in that morning we shall rise.

CHORUS

Hal-le-lu-jah! A-men! We shall rise!
We shall rise! we shall rise! Hal-le-lu-jah!

D. S.

In the res-ur-rec-tion morning, When death's prison bars are brok-en,

WILLIAM O. CUSHING

IRA D. SANKEY

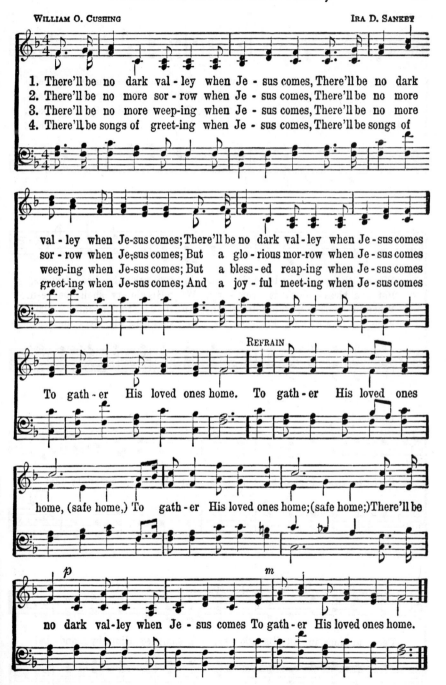

1. There'll be no dark val-ley when Je - sus comes, There'll be no dark
2. There'll be no more sor - row when Je - sus comes, There'll be no more
3. There'll be no more weep-ing when Je - sus comes, There'll be no more
4. There'll be songs of greet-ing when Je - sus comes, There'll be songs of

val - ley when Je-sus comes; There'll be no dark val - ley when Je - sus comes
sor - row when Je-sus comes; But a glo - rious mor-row when Je - sus comes
weep-ing when Je-sus comes; But a bless - ed reap-ing when Je - sus comes
greet-ing when Je-sus comes; And a joy - ful meet-ing when Je - sus comes

REFRAIN

To gath - er His loved ones home. To gath - er His loved ones

home, (safe home,) To gath - er His loved ones home; (safe home;) There'll be

p *m*

no dark val - ley when Je - sus comes To gath - er His loved ones home.

39 Face to Face

Carrie E. Breck

Grant C. Tullar

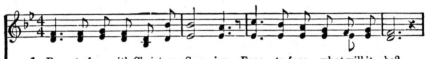

1. Face to face with Christ, my Sav - ior, Face to face—what will it be?
2. On - ly faint - ly now I see Him, With the dark-ling veil be-tween,
3. What re-joic - ing in His pres - ence, When are ban-ished grief and pain;
4. Face to face! O bliss - ful mo - ment! Face to face—to see and know;

When with rap-ture I be - hold Him, Je - sus Christ who died for me.
But a bless - ed day is com - ing, When His glo - ry shall be seen.
When the crook-ed ways are straightened, And the dark things shall be plain.
Face to face with my Re-deem - er, Je - sus Christ who loves me so.

CHORUS

Face to face I shall be - hold Him, Far be-yond the star - ry sky;

Face to face in all His glo - ry, I shall see Him by and by!

Sweet By and By

40

Sanford F. Bennett

Joseph P. Webster

1. There's a land that is fair-er than day, And by faith we can
see it a-far; For the Fa-ther waits o-ver the way, To pre-
pare us a dwell-ing-place there.

2. We shall sing on that beau-ti-ful shore The mel-o-di-ous
songs of the blest, And our spir-its shall sor-row no more, Not a
sigh for the bless-ing of rest.

3. To our boun-ti-ful Fa-ther a-bove, We will of-fer our
trib-ute of praise, For the glo-ri-ous gift of His love, And the
bless-ings that hal-low our days.

Chorus

In the sweet by and by, We shall meet on that beau-ti-ful shore; In the sweet by and by, We shall meet on that beau-ti-ful shore.

41 No Disappointment in Heaven

F. M. L.

F. M. Lehman

1. There's no dis-ap-point-ment in heav-en, No wear-i - ness, sor-row or pain;
2. We'll nev-er pay rent for our man-sion, The tax-es will nev-er come due;
3. There'll never be crepe on the door-knob, No fu-ner - al train in the sky;

No hearts that are bleeding and bro-ken, No song with a mi - nor re-frain;
Our garments will never grow threadbare, But al - ways be fade-less and new;
No graves on the hill-sides of glo - ry, For there we shall nev-er more die;

The clouds of our earth-ly ho - ri - zon Will nev - er ap-pear in the sky,
We'll nev-er be hun-gry nor thirst-y, Nor lan-guish in pov - er - ty there,
The old will be young there for-ev-er, Transformed in a mo-ment of time;

For all will be sun-shine and gladness, With nev-er a sob nor a sigh.
For all the rich bounties of heav-en His sanc - ti - fied children will share.
Im - mor - tal we'll stand in His like-ness, The stars and the sun to out-shine.

CHORUS.

I'm bound for that beau-ti - ful ci - ty My Lord has pre-pared for His own;

No Disappointment in Heaven

where all the re-deemed of all a - ges Sing "glo-ry" a-round the white throne;

Some-times I grow homesick for heaven, And the glo-ries I there shall be-hold;

Rit.

What a joy that will be when my Savior I see, In that beautiful ci-ty of gold.

Peace, Perfect Peace 42

EDWARD H. BICKERSTETH

Alt. from GEORGE T. CALDBECK
by CHARLES J. VINCENT

1. Peace, per - fect peace, in this dark world of sin?
2. Peace, per - fect peace, with sor - rows surg - ing round?
3. Peace, per - fect peace, our fu - ture all un - known?
4. Peace, per - fect peace, death shad - ow-ing us and ours?
5. It is e - nough: earth's strug - gles soon shall cease,

The blood of Je - sus whis - pers peace with - in.
On Je - sus' bos - om naught but calm is found.
Je - sus we know, and He is on the throne.
Je - sus has van-quished death and all its powers.
And, Je - sus, call us to heaven's per - fect peace. A - MEN.

43 My Latest Sun Is Sinking Fast

J. HASCALL

WM. B. BRADBURY

1. My lat-est sun is sink-ing fast, My race is near-ly run;
2. I know I'm nearing the ho-ly ranks Of friends and kin-dred dear,
3. I've al-most gained my heaven-ly home, My spir-it loud-ly sings;
4. O bear my long-ing heart to Him, Who bled and died for me:

My strong-est tri-als now are past, My tri-umph is be-gun.
For I brush the dews on Jor-dan's banks, The cross-ing must be near.
Thy ho-ly ones, be-hold, they come! I hear the noise of wings.
Whose blood now cleans-es from all sin, And gives me vic-to-ry.

f CHORUS

O come, an-gel band, Come and a-round me stand; O bear me a-

way on your snow-y wings To my im-mor-tal home; O

bear me a-way on your snow-y wings To my im-mor-tal home.

When I Can Read My Title Clear

Isaac Watts

J. C. Lowry

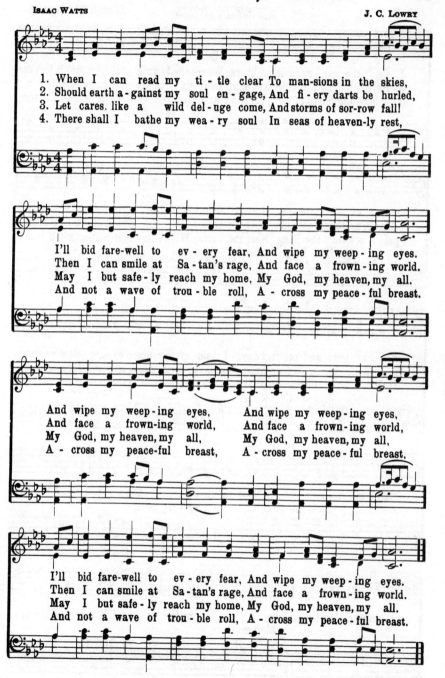

1. When I can read my ti - tle clear To man-sions in the skies,
2. Should earth a - gainst my soul en - gage, And fi - ery darts be hurled,
3. Let cares, like a wild del - uge come, And storms of sor-row fall!
4. There shall I bathe my wea - ry soul In seas of heaven-ly rest,

I'll bid fare-well to ev - ery fear, And wipe my weep - ing eyes.
Then I can smile at Sa - tan's rage, And face a frown - ing world.
May I but safe - ly reach my home, My God, my heaven, my all.
And not a wave of trou - ble roll, A - cross my peace - ful breast.

And wipe my weep - ing eyes, And wipe my weep - ing eyes,
And face a frown - ing world, And face a frown - ing world,
My God, my heaven, my all, My God, my heaven, my all,
A - cross my peace-ful breast, A - cross my peace - ful breast,

I'll bid fare-well to ev - ery fear, And wipe my weep - ing eyes.
Then I can smile at Sa - tan's rage, And face a frown - ing world.
May I but safe - ly reach my home, My God, my heaven, my all.
And not a wave of trou - ble roll, A - cross my peace - ful breast.

45 Meet Me There

H. E. Blair.

Wm. J. Kirkpatrick.

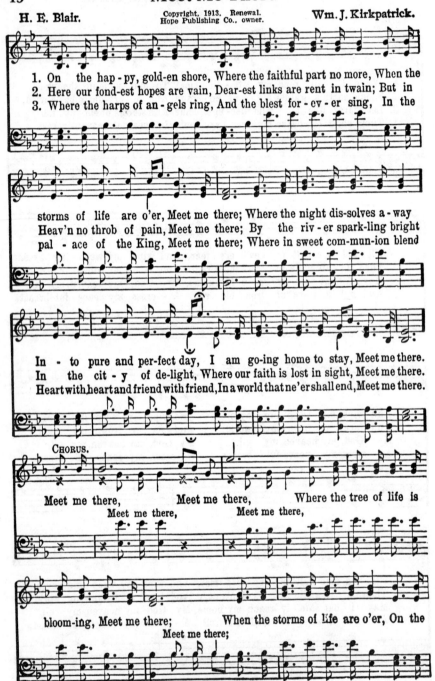

1. On the hap-py, gold-en shore, Where the faithful part no more, When the
2. Here our fond-est hopes are vain, Dear-est links are rent in twain; But in
3. Where the harps of an-gels ring, And the blest for-ev-er sing, In the

storms of life are o'er, Meet me there; Where the night dis-solves a-way
Heav'n no throb of pain, Meet me there; By the riv-er spark-ling bright
pal-ace of the King, Meet me there; Where in sweet com-mun-ion blend

In-to pure and per-fect day, I am go-ing home to stay, Meet me there.
In the cit-y of de-light, Where our faith is lost in sight, Meet me there.
Heart with heart and friend with friend, In a world that ne'er shall end, Meet me there.

CHORUS.

Meet me there, Meet me there, Where the tree of life is
Meet me there, Meet me there,

bloom-ing, Meet me there; When the storms of life are o'er, On the
Meet me there;

Meet Me There

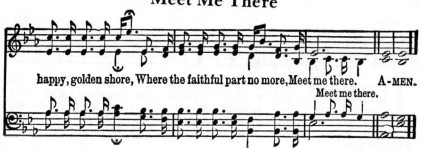

happy, golden shore, Where the faithful part no more, Meet me there. A-MEN.

Meet me there.

We'll Work Till Jesus Comes

ELIZABETH MILLS

WILLIAM MILLER

1. O land of rest, for thee I sigh! When will the mo-ment come When
2. To Je-sus Christ I fled for rest; He bade me cease to roam, And
3. I sought at once my Sav-iour's side, No more my steps shall roam; With

CHORUS.

I shall lay my ar-mor by, And dwell in peace at home? We'll work till
lean for suc-cor on His breast Till He con-duct me home.
Him I'll brave death's chilling tide, And reach my heavenly home. We'll work

Je-sus comes, We'll work till Je-sus comes; And we'll be gath-ered home.

We'll work

We're Marching to Zion

Isaac Watts

Robert Lowry

Spirited

1. Come, we that love the Lord, And let our joys be known, Join
2. Let those re - fuse to sing Who nev - er knew our God; But
3. The hill of Zi - on yields A thou - sand sa - cred sweets Be -
4. Then let our songs a - bound, And ev - 'ry tear be dry; We're

in a song with sweet ac - cord, Join in a song with sweet ac-cord, And
chil-dren of the heav'n-ly King, But chil-dren of the heav'n-ly King, May
fore we reach the heav'n-ly fields, Be - fore we reach the heav'n-ly fields, Or
marching thro' Immanuel's ground, We're marching thro' Immanuel's ground, To

thus sur - - round the throne, And thus sur-round the throne.
speak their joys a - broad, May speak their joys a - broad.
walk the gold - en streets, Or walk the gold - en streets.
fair - - er worlds on high, To fair - er worlds on high.

thus sur-round the throne, And thus sur - round the throne.

CHORUS

We're march - ing to Zi - on, Beau-ti - ful, beau-ti - ful Zi - on; We're
We're march-ing on to Zi - on,

march-ing up-ward to Zi - on, The beau-ti - ful cit - y of God.
Zi - on, Zi - on,

The Sands of Time

48

ANNE ROSS COUSIN

CHRETIEN URHAN
ARR. BY EDWARD F. RIMBAULT

1. The sands of time are sink-ing, The dawn of heav-en breaks;
2. O Christ! He is the foun-tain, The deep, sweet well of love!
3. Oh, I am my Be-lov-ed's, And my Be-lov-ed's mine!
4. The Bride eyes not her gar-ment, But her dear Bridegroom's face;

The sum-mer morn I've sighed for, The fair, sweet morn a-wakes:
The streams on earth I've tast-ed, More deep I'll drink a-bove:
He brings a poor vile sin-ner In-to His "house of wine."
I will not gaze at glo-ry, But on my King of grace.

Dark, dark hath been the mid-night, But day-spring is at hand,
There, to an o-cean ful-ness, His mer-cy doth ex-pand,
I stand up-on His mer-it, I know no oth-er stand,
Not at the crown He giv-eth, But on His pierc-ed hand,

And glo-ry, glo-ry dwell-eth In Im-man-uel's land.
And glo-ry, glo-ry dwell-eth In Im-man-uel's land.
Not e'en where glo-ry dwell-eth In Im-mau-uel's land.
The Lamb is all the glo-ry Of Im-man-uel's land. A-MEN.

The Pearly White City

49

A. F. I.

Arthur F. Ingler.

Moderato.

1. There's a ho - ly and beau-ti - ful cit - y, Whose builder and rul-er is God;
2. No sin is al-lowed in that cit - y, And nothing de - fil - ing or mean;
3. No heartaches are known in that cit - y, No tears ev - er moist-en the eye;
4. My loved ones are gath-er - ing yon-der, My friends, too, are passing a-way;

John saw it de-scend-ing from heav-en, When Pat-mos, in ex - ile, he trod;
No pain and no sick-ness can en - ter, No crape on the door-knob is seen;
There's no dis-ap-point-ment in heav - en, No en - vy and strife in the sky;
And soon I shall join their bright number, And dwell in e - ter-ni-ty's day;

Its high, massive wall is of jas - per, The cit - y it - self is pure gold;
Earth's sorrows and cares are forgot- ten, No tempt-er is there to an-noy;
The saints are all sanc-ti - fied whol-ly, They live in sweet har-mo - ny there;
They're safe now in glo - ry with Je - sus, Their tri-als and bat-tles are past;

rit. ad lib.

And when my frail tent here is fold-ed, Mine eyes shall its glo - ry be-hold.
No part-ing words ev - er are spo-ken, There's nothing to hurt or de-stroy.
My heart is now set on that cit - y, And some day its bless-ings I'll share.
They o - ver-came sin and the tempter, They've reached that fair city at last.

The Pearly White City

In that bright cit - y, . . pearl - y white cit - y, . . I have a
man - sion, an harp, and a crown; Now I am watch - ing, wait - ing, and
long - ing, For the white cit - y that's soon com - ing down. A - MEN.

I'll Be So Glad

50

Anon.

I'll be so glad when day is done, I'll be so glad when vic - t'ry's won;
There'll be no sor - row in God's to - mor - row, I'll be so glad when Je - sus comes.

51 My Savior First of All

Fanny J. Crosby

John R. Sweney

1. When my life-work is end-ed, and I cross the swell-ing tide, When the
2. Oh, the soul-thrill-ing rap-ture when I view His bless-ed face, And the
3. Oh, the dear ones in glo-ry, how they beck-on me to come, And our
4. Thro' the gates to the cit-y in a robe of spot-less white, He will

bright and glorious morning I shall see; I shall know my Re-deem-er when I
lus-ter of His kind-ly beaming eye; How my full heart will praise Him for the
part-ing at the riv-er I re-call; To the sweet vales of E-den they will
lead me where no tears will ev-er fall; In the glad song of a-ges I shall

reach the oth-er side, And His smile will be the first to wel-come me.
mer-cy, love, and grace, That pre-pare for me a man-sion in the sky.
sing my wel-come home; But I long to meet my Sav-ior first of all.
min-gle with de-light; But I long to meet my Sav-ior first of all.

Chorus

I shall know . . Him, I shall know Him, And redeemed by His side I shall stand,
I shall know Him,

I shall know . . Him, I shall know Him By the print of the nails in His hand.
I shall know Him,

Where We'll Never Grow Old

JAS. C. MOORE (*Dedicated to my Father and Mother*) JAS. C. MOORE

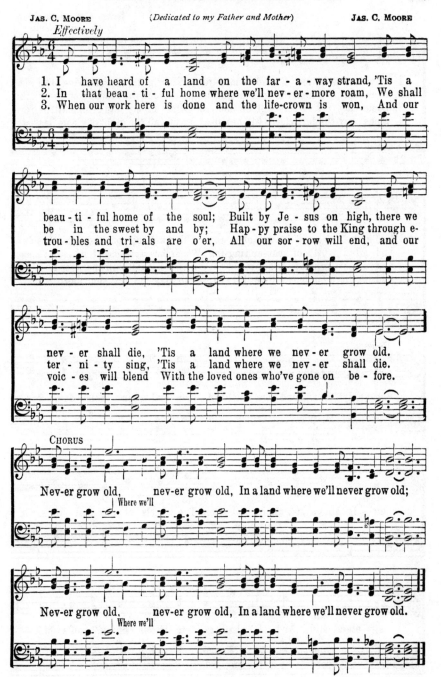

1. I have heard of a land on the far-a-way strand, 'Tis a
2. In that beau-ti-ful home where we'll nev-er-more roam, We shall
3. When our work here is done and the life-crown is won, And our

beau-ti-ful home of the soul; Built by Je-sus on high, there we
be in the sweet by and by; Hap-py praise to the King through e-
trou-bles and tri-als are o'er, All our sor-row will end, and our

nev-er shall die, 'Tis a land where we nev-er grow old.
ter-ni-ty sing, 'Tis a land where we nev-er shall die.
voic-es will blend With the loved ones who've gone on be-fore.

CHORUS

Nev-er grow old, nev-er grow old, In a land where we'll never grow old;
Where we'll

Nev-er grow old, nev-er grow old, In a land where we'll never grow old.
Where we'll

53 Zion's Hill

James A. Crutchfield
Arr. by Haldor Lillenas

J. A. C.

1. There waits for me a glad to-mor-row, Where gates of pearl swing open wide,
2. Some day I'll hear the an-gels sing-ing, Be-yond the shadows of the tomb;
3. Some day my la-bors will be end-ed, And all my wand'rings will be o'er,
4. Some day the dark clouds will be rift-ed, And all the night of gloom be past;

And when I've passed this vale of sor-row, I'll dwell up-on the oth-er side.
And all the bells of heav-en ring-ing, While saints are singing, "Home, sweet home."
And all earth's broken ties be mend-ed, And I shall sigh and weep no more.
And all life's burdens will be lift-ed, The day of rest shall dawn at last.

CHORUS.

Some day be-yond the reach of mor-tal ken, Some day, God on-ly knows just where and when, The wheels of mor-tal life shall all stand still, And I shall go to dwell on Zi-on's hill.

Beulah Land

EDGAR PAGE STITES

JOHN R. SWENEY

1. I've reached the land of corn and wine, And all its rich-es free-ly mine;
2. My Sav-ior comes and walks with me, And sweet com-mun-ion here have we;
3. A sweet per-fume up-on the breeze Is borne from ev-er-ver-nal trees
4. The zeph-yrs seem to float to me Sweet sounds of heav-en's mel-o-dy,

Here shines un-dimmed one bliss-ful day, For all my night has passed a-way.
He gen-tly leads me by His hand, For this is heav-en's bor-der-land.
And flow'rs that nev-er-fad-ing grow, Where streams of life for-ev-er flow.
As an-gels with the white-robed throng Join in the sweet Re-demp-tion song.

CHORUS

O Beu-lah Land, sweet Beu-lah Land! As on thy high-est mount I stand,

I look a-way a-cross the sea, Where man-sions are pre-pared for me,

And view the shin-ing glo-ry-shore— My heav'n, my home for-ev-er-more!

55   When the Roll Is Called Up Yonder

JAMES M. BLACK   JAMES M. BLACK

1. When the trumpet of the Lord shall sound, and time shall be no more, And the
2. On that bright and cloudless morning when the dead in Christ shall rise, And the
3. Let us la-bor for the Mas-ter from the dawn till set-ting sun, Let us

morning breaks, e-ter-nal, bright and fair; When the saved of earth shall gather
glo-ry of His res-ur-rec-tion share; When His cho-sen ones shall gather
talk of all His wondrous love and care; Then when all of life is o-ver,

o-ver on the oth-er shore, And the roll is called up yon-der, I'll be there.
to their home beyond the skies, And the roll is called up yon-der, I'll be there.
and our work on earth is done, And the roll is called up yon-der, I'll be there.

CHORUS.

When the roll . . . . . . is called up yon - - - - der, When the
When the roll is called up yon-der, I'll be there,

roll . . . . is called up yon - - der, When the roll . . . . is called up
When the roll is called up yon-der, I'll be there,   When the roll is called up

When the Roll Is Called Up Yonder

yon - der, When the roll is called up yon - der, I'll be there.

When We All Get to Heaven

ELIZA E. HEWITT   EMILY D. WILSON

1. Sing the won-drous love of Je - sus, Sing His mer-cy and His grace;
2. While we walk the pil - grim pathway, Clouds will o - ver-spread the sky;
3. Let us then be true and faith-ful, Trust-ing, serv-ing ev - 'ry day;
4. On - ward to the prize be - fore us! Soon His beau-ty we'll be - hold;

In the man-sions bright and blessed, He'll pre-pare for us a place.
But when trav'ling days are o - ver, Not a shad-ow, not a sigh.
Just one glimpse of Him in glo - ry Will the toils of life re - pay.
Soon the pearl - y gates will o - pen, We shall tread the streets of gold.

for us a place.

CHORUS

When we all get to heaven, What a day of re-joicing that will be!
When we all   What a day of re-joicing that will be!

When we all see Je-sus, We'll sing and shout the vic-to-ry . . . .
When we all   and shout the vic-to-ry.

57 He the Pearly Gates Will Open

FRED BLOM
TR. BY NATHANIEL CARLSON

ELSIE AHLWEN

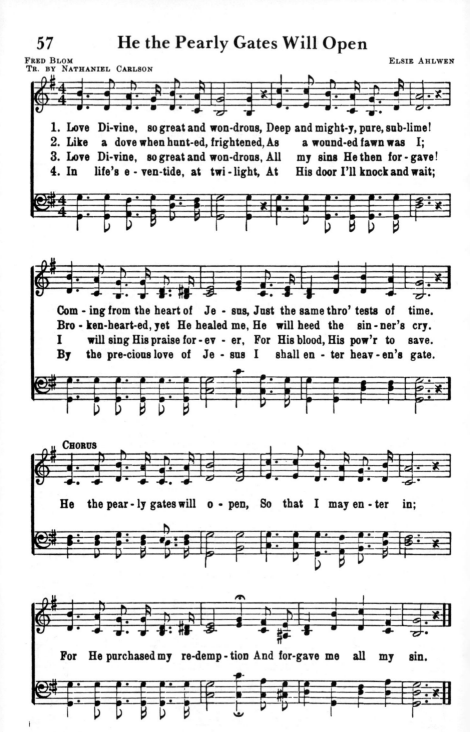

1. Love Di-vine, so great and won-drous, Deep and might-y, pure, sub-lime!
2. Like a dove when hunt-ed, frightened, As a wound-ed fawn was I;
3. Love Di-vine, so great and won-drous, All my sins He then for-gave!
4. In life's e-ven-tide, at twi-light, At His door I'll knock and wait;

Com - ing from the heart of Je - sus, Just the same thro' tests of time.
Bro - ken-heart-ed, yet He healed me, He will heed the sin-ner's cry.
I will sing His praise for-ev-er, For His blood, His pow'r to save.
By the pre-cious love of Je - sus I shall en-ter heav-en's gate.

CHORUS

He the pear-ly gates will o - pen, So that I may en-ter in;

For He purchased my re-demp - tion And for-gave me all my sin.

When the Mists Have Rolled Away

ANNIE HERBERT. Arr.

IRA D. SANKEY

1. When the mists have rolled in splendor From the beau-ty of the hills, And the
2. Oft we tread the path be-fore us With a wea-ry burdened heart; Oft we
3. We shall come with joy and gladness, We shall gather round the throne; Face to

sun-light falls in gladness On the riv - er and the rills, We re - call our
toil a - mid the shadows, And our fields are far a - part; But the Sav-iour's
face with those that love us, We shall know as we are known: And the song of

D. S.—*In the dawn-ing*

Fa-ther's promise In the rain-bow of the spray: We shall know each oth-er
"Come, ye blessed" All our la - bor will re - pay, When we gath-er in the
our re-demp-tion Shall resound thro' endless day When the shadows have de-

of the morn-ing Of that bright and hap - py day, We shall know each oth - er

rit. FINE CHORUS

bet - ter When the mists have rolled a-way. We shall know . . . as we are
morning Where the mists have rolled a-way.
part - ed, And the mists have rolled a-way. We shall know

bet - ter When the mists have rolled a - way.

D. S.

known, ... Nev-er - more . . . . to walk a - lone; . . . .
as we are known, Nev - er-more to walk a - lone;

When They Ring the Golden Bells

Dion De Marbelle

1. There's a land be-yond the riv-er, That we call the sweet for-ev-er, And we
2. We shall know no sin nor sor-row, In that ha-ven of to-mor-row, When our
3. When our days shall know their number, When in death we sweetly slumber, When the

on-ly reach that shore by faith's decree; One by one we'll gain the portals, There to
barque shall sail beyond the sil-ver sea; We shall on-ly know the blessing Of our
King commands the spir-it to be free; Nevermore with anguish la-den, We shall

dwell with the immortals, When they ring the golden bells for you and me.
Father's sweet caressing, When they ring the golden bells for you and me.
reach that love-ly Ai-den, When they ring the golden bells for you and me.

you and me.

CHORUS

Don't you hear the bells now ringing? Don't you hear the an-gels singing? 'Tis the

glo-ry hal-le-lu-jah Ju-bi-lee (Ju-bi-lee). In that far-off sweet for-ev-er, Just be-

When They Ring the Golden Bells

yond the shining river, When they ring the golden bells for you and me.

you and me.

Shall We Gather at the River?   60

ROBERT LOWRY

ROBERT LOWRY

1. Shall we gath-er at the riv - er, Where bright an-gel feet have trod;
2. On the bos-om of the riv - er, Where the Sav-ior-King we own,
3. Ere we reach the shin-ing riv - er, Lay we ev-'ry bur-den down;
4. Soon we'll reach the shin-ing riv - er, Soon our pil-grim-age will cease;

With its crys - tal tide for - ev - er Flow-ing by the throne of God?
We shall meet, and sor-row nev - er,'Neath the glo - ry of the throne.
Grace our spir - its will de - liv - er, And pro - vide a robe and crown.
Soon our hap - py hearts will quiv-er With the mel - o - dy of peace.

CHORUS

Yes, we'll gath-er at the riv - er, The beau-ti-ful, the beau-ti-ful riv - er,

Gath-er with the saints at the riv - er That flows by the throne of God.

61 Just Over in the Glory Land

R. E. Winsett, Dayton, Tenn., owner

Jas. W. Acuff

Emmet S. Dean

1. I've a home pre-pared where the saints a-bide, Just o-ver in the glo-ry land;
2. I am on my way to those mansions fair, Just o-ver in the glo-ry land;
3. What a joy-ful thought that my Lord I'll see, Just o-ver in the glo-ry land;
4. With the blood-washed throng I will shout and sing, Just o-ver in the glo-ry land;

And I long to be by my Sa-vior's side, Just o-ver in the glo-ry land.
There to sing God's praise and His glo-ry share, Just o-ver in the glo-ry land.
And with kindred saved, there for-ev-er be, Just o-ver in the glo-ry land.
Glad ho-san-nas to Christ, the Lord and King, Just o-ver in the glo-ry land.

CHORUS.

Just o-ver in the glo-ry land, I'll join the hap-py
Just o-ver, o-ver I'll join, yes, join

an-gel band, Just o-ver in the glo-ry land; Just o-ver
Just o-ver, o-ver

in the glo-ry land, There with the might-y host I'll stand,
There with, yes, with

Caught Up Together

Words and music by Evangelist John R. Rice

by John R. Rice

1. I sing hal-le-lu-jah that Je-sus is com-ing, And oh, what a rais-ing of
2. We wait for the com ing of Je sus our Sav iour, Ex-pect-ing the rapture, caught
3. We'll rise in-cor-rupt-i-ble when sounds the trum pet; O Grave, where the vic to ry
4. Come up, all ye saints of the past to that meet-ing, From A-bel to Mo-ses, from

life from the dead; The graves burst-ing o-pen to give up God's chil-dren, Those
up in the clouds; The world has its sor-rows, we'll leave them so glad-ly, We'll
long you have known? All changed then the liv-ing, and all go to-geth-er, And
Dav-id to Paul; Come up, all ye mar-tyrs, soul win-ners, Christ lov-ers, All

bod-ies long mold-ered in grave's dust-y bed.
wipe all our tears when the trum-pet calls loud. Caught up to greet Him to-geth-er,
oh, what a gath-'ring to Christ of His own.
un-der the blood of our Sav-iour, come all.

to-geth-er, Caught up with Je-sus and nev-er to part; Changed in a mo-ment to

be with my Sav-iour, Caught up to-geth-er and nev-er to part.

63 O That Will Be Glory

Charles H. Gabriel

Charles H. Gabriel

1. When all my la-bors and tri-als are o'er, And I am safe on that
2. When, by the gift of His in-fi-nite grace, I am ac-cord-ed in
3. Friends will be there I have loved long a-go; Joy like a riv-er a-

beau-ti-ful shore, Just to be near the dear Lord I a-dore,
Heav-en a place, Just to be there and to look on His face,
round me will flow; Yet, just a smile from my Sav-ior, I know,

rit.

Will thro' the a-ges be glo-ry for me. . . .

Chorus. *Faster*

O that will be
O . . . . . . that will

glo-ry for me, Glo-ry for me, glo-ry for me; When by His grace
be glo-ry for me, Glo-ry for me, glo-ry for me; . . . . . .

rit.

I shall look on His face, That will be glo-ry, be glo-ry for me.

Saved by Grace

FANNY J. CROSBY

GEORGE C. STEBBINS
Alt. by SEYMOUR SWETS

1. Some day the sil - ver cord will break, And I no more as now shall sing;
2. Some day my earth - ly house will fall, I can-not tell how soon 'twill be;
3. Some day, when fades the gold-en sun Be-neath the ro - sy-tint-ed west,
4. Some day: till then I'll watch and wait, My lamp all trimmed and burning bright,

But oh, the joy when I shall wake With-in the pal - ace of the King!
But this I know—my All in All Has now a place in heav'n for me.
My blessed Lord will say, "Well done!" And I shall en - ter in - to rest.
That when my Sav - ior opes the gate, My soul to Him may take its flight.

REFRAIN

And I shall see Him face to face, And tell the sto-ry—Saved by grace;
shall see to face,

And I shall see Him face to face, And tell the sto-ry—Saved by grace.
shall see to face,

rit.

65   We'll Never Say Good-bye

Words and music by Evangelist John R. Rice

John R. Rice

1. We say good-bye in part-ing With loved ones here be-low; We
   al-ways hope to meet a-gain, As on our way we go. But oft our
   hearts are griev-ing For those we nev-er meet. We'll say good-
   bye in sor-row Till we meet at Je-sus' feet.

2. Our chil-dren leave the home nest For school or wed-ding bells; Or
   coun-try's call or mis-sion field May take them far as well. Now wed-ding
   let-ters bind our fel-low-ship; We miss them, though we try
   bells are hap-py, And God's way al-ways right. And ab-sent
   days are end-ed When we meet them in the air.

3. We greet and part with dear ones; We say hel-lo, good-bye; And
   al-ways near us, And fol-low them with prayer. But part-ing
   ones, we'll greet them In the ci-ty al-ways bright.

4. Oh hap-py, glad home com-ing With Je-sus in the sky: For
   some-times He seems far a-way, Though al-ways if we try, We find Him
   near to help us, His Spir-it dwells with-in. But on-ly
   per-fect un-ion When we Heav-en en-ter in.

We'll nev-er say good-bye in Glo-ry, In the morn-ing, o-ver yon-der; We'll nev-er say good-bye in Glo-ry; We'll nev-er say good-bye up there.

Remembering in Heaven

Words and music by Evangelist John R. Rice

John R. Rice

1. Should I, up in Hea - ven, Re - mem - ber the heart - ache, All the
2. Or if, on the gold streets I think of earth treas - ures, Of the
3. Should I, in the Glo - ry Re - mem - ber a loved one, One who
4. Oh, then, spread the mes - sage, the work He has giv - en, Nev - er

pain and the cross, All the shame and the loss, The re-proach of the
things I had bought, Of the fame dear - ly sought; I'd smile in my
walked by my side, But is lost and out-side; If I nev - er had
mind the world's praise, Nor po - ses - sions men crave. But oh! for the

Sav - iour I'd borne in earth's con-flicts; In Hea - ven I'd laugh at the
man - sion, my gem - stud - ded man-sion In Hea - ven I'd smile, "They are
begged him to trust in the Sav-iour, In Hea - ven I'd sit down and
Sav - iour, bring souls in - to Hea - ven, And joy through E - ter - ni - ty's

Chorus:

naught!" Je - sus' blood paid my ran - som, and I'm bound for Hea-
cost!
Day!

ven. But what will I think when re - mem - b'ring in Hea - ven?

67   What a Day That Will Be

Words and Music by
Jim Hill

1. There is com-ing a day when no heart-aches shall come,
2. There'll be no sor-row there, no more bur-dens to bear,

No more clouds in the sky, no more tears to dim the eye;
No more sick-ness, no pain, no more part-ing o-ver there;

All is peace for-ev-er-more on that hap-py gold-en shore,
And for-ev-er I will be with the One who died for me,

CHORUS

What a day, glo-ri-ous day that will be. WHAT A DAY

What a Day That Will Be

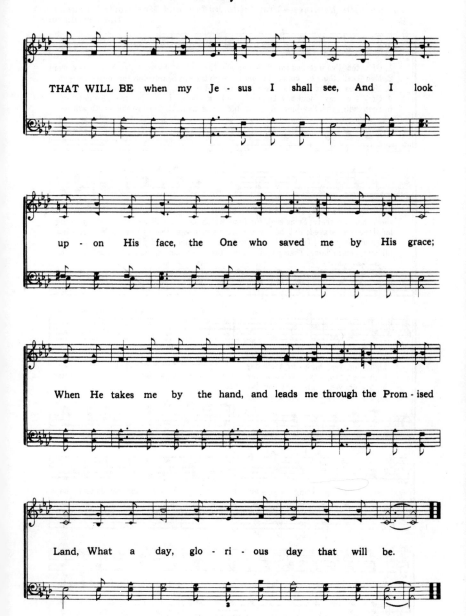

THAT WILL BE when my Je - sus I shall see, And I look up - on His face, the One who saved me by His grace; When He takes me by the hand, and leads me through the Prom - ised Land, What a day, glo - ri - ous day that will be.

68   I'm Going Higher

(To two little heroines—Mrs. Lillie Buffum and Mrs. Golden Young)

H. B.   Herbert Buffum

1. Of - ten I've watched the clouds up in the sky, Al-ways I've heard they were
2. Men sail the o - cean, or soar through the air, Scarce can the nat - 'ral eye
3. Mos - es went up in a mountain and prayed, Glo - ry came down while a-
4. Of - ten my soul has been lift - ed a - bove, Lost in the o - cean of
5. Soon will the Sav-iour ap-pear, bless His name! Some day this earth will be

ma - ny miles high; Then as they sailed out of sight far a - way, I said, "I'm
see them up there; Some seek for fame which so soon will de-cay, I'm go - ing
lone there he stayed; But he came back, he just went there to pray, I'm go - ing
God's might-y love; Though I am high - er than once, still I say, "I'm go - ing
all wrapped in flame; Then as I see the fire mounting so high, I'm go - ing

go - ing far high - er some day."
high - er, yes, high - er some day.
high - er, yes, high - er some day.
high - er, yes, high - er some day.'
high - er, be - yond the blue sky.

CHORUS

I'm go - ing high - er, yes, high-er some
day, I'm go - ing high - er to stay; Ov - er the clouds and be -
yond the blue sky, Go - ing where none ev - er sick - en or die, Loved ones to

I'm Going Higher

meet in the "Sweet by and by"; I'm go - ing high-er some day............
high - er some day.

On Jordan's Stormy Banks

SAMUEL STENNETT

AMERICAN FOLK HYMN
ARR. BY RIGDON M. McINTOSH

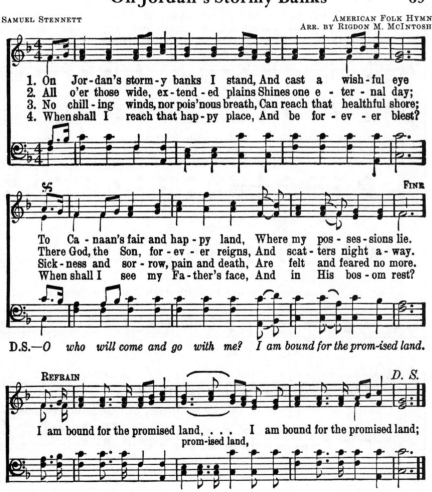

1. On Jor-dan's storm-y banks I stand, And cast a wish-ful eye
2. All o'er those wide, ex-tend-ed plains Shines one e - ter - nal day;
3. No chill-ing winds, nor pois'nous breath, Can reach that healthful shore;
4. When shall I reach that hap-py place, And be for - ev - er blest?

To Ca-naan's fair and hap-py land, Where my pos - ses-sions lie.
There God, the Son, for - ev - er reigns, And scat-ters night a - way.
Sick-ness and sor-row, pain and death, Are felt and feared no more.
When shall I see my Fa-ther's face, And in His bos - om rest?

D.S.—*O who will come and go with me? I am bound for the prom-ised land.*

REFRAIN

D. S.

I am bound for the promised land, . . . I am bound for the promised land;
prom-ised land,

When We See Christ

ESTHER KERR RUSTHOI

ESTHER KERR RUSTHOI

1. Oft - times the day seems long, our tri - als hard to bear, We're tempt-ed
2. Some-times the sky looks dark with not a ray of light, We're tossed and
3. Life's day will soon be o'er, all storms for-ev - er past, We'll cross the

to com-plain, to mur-mur and de - spair; But Christ will soon ap-pear
driv-en on, no hu-man help in sight; But there is one in heav'n
great di - vide to glo - ry, safe at last; We'll share the joys of heav'n—

to catch His Bride a - way, All tears for-ev - er o - ver in
who knows our deep-est care, Let Je - sus solve your prob-lem— just
a harp, a home, a crown, The tempt-er will be ban-ished, we'll

CHORUS

God's e - ter-nal day.
go to Him in pray'r. It will be worth it all when we see Je - sus,
lay our bur-den down.

Life's trials will seem so small when we see Christ; One glimpse of His dear face

When We See Christ

all sor-row will e - rase, So brave-ly run the race till we see Christ.

When He Cometh   71

WILLIAM O. CUSHING   GEORGE F. ROOT

1. When He com - eth, when He com - eth To make up His jew - els,
2. He will gath - er, He will gath - er The gems for His king-dom,
3. Lit - tle chil - dren, lit - tle chil - dren Who love their Re - deem - er

All His jew - els, pre-cious jew - els, His loved and His own:
All the pure ones, all the bright ones, His loved and His own:
Are the jew - els, pre-cious jew - els, His loved and His own:

REFRAIN

Like the stars of the morn - ing, His bright crown a - dorn - ing,

They shall shine in their beau - ty— Bright gems for His crown.

72 Jesus Is Coming Again

JOHN W. PETERSON

JOHN W. PETERSON

1. Mar-vel-ous mes-sage we bring, Glo-ri-ous car-ol we sing,
2. For-est and flow-er ex - claim, Moun-tain and mead-ow the same,
3. Stand-ing be-fore Him at last, Tri - al and trou-ble all past,

Won-der - ful word of the King— Je-sus is com-ing a - gain! (a-gain!)
All earth and heav-en pro - claim— Je-sus is com-ing a - gain! (a-gain!)
Crowns at His feet we will cast— Je-sus is com-ing a - gain! (a-gain!)

CHORUS

Com - ing a - gain, Com - ing a - gain;

May - be morn - ing, may-be noon, May - be eve-ning and may-be soon!

Com - ing a - gain, Com - ing a - gain;

Jesus Is Coming Again

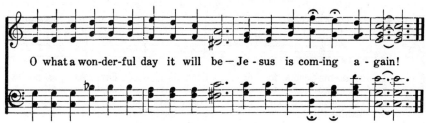

O what a won-der-ful day it will be — Je - sus is com-ing a - gain!

There's a Great Day Coming

73

W. L. T.

Will L. Thompson

1. There's a great day coming, A great day coming, There's a great day coming by and
2. There's a bright day coming, A bright day coming, There's a bright day coming by and
3. There's a sad day coming, A sad day coming, There's a sad day coming by and

by; When the saints and the sin-ners shall be part-ed right and left, Are you
by; But its brightness shall on-ly come to them that love the Lord, Are you
by; When the sin-ner shall hear his doom, "De-part, I know ye not," Are you

CHORUS

read-y for that day to come? Are you read-y? Are you read-y? Are you read-y

for the judgment day? Are you read-y? Are you read-y for the judgment day?

Is It the Crowning Day?

GEORGE WALKER WHITCOMB   CHARLES H. MARSH

1. Je - sus may come to - day,   Glad day! Glad day! And I would
2. I may go home to - day,   Glad day! Glad day! Seem-eth I
3. Why should I anx-ious be?   Glad day! Glad day! Lights ap - pear
4. Faithful I'll be to - day,   Glad day! Glad day! And I will

see   my   Friend;   Dan-gers and trou - bles would   end   If
hear their   song;   Hail to the ra - di - ant   throng!   If
on the   shore,   Storms will af - fright nev - er - more,   For
free - ly   tell   Why I should love Him so   well,   For

CHORUS

Je - sus should come to - day.
I should go home to - day.   Glad day! Glad day! Is it the crowning
He is "at hand" to - day.
He is my all to - day.

day? I'll live for to - day, nor anx - ious be, Je - sus, my Lord, I

rit.

soon shall see; Glad   day! Glad day! Is it the crown-ing day?

Some Bright Morning

75

Charlotte G. Homer

Chas. H. Gabriel

1. Be not a-wea-ry, for la-bor will cease Some glad morn-ing;
2. Wea-ri-some bur-dens will all be laid down, Some glad morn-ing;
3. La-bor well done shall re-ceive its re-ward, Some glad morn-ing;
4. O what a time of re-joic-ing will come, Some glad morn-ing;
5. There with the loved ones who've gone on be-fore, Some glad morn-ing;

Tur-moil will change in-to in-fi-nite peace, Some bright morn-ing.
Then shall our cross be exchanged for a crown, Some bright morn-ing.
Thou who art faith-ful shall be with the Lord, Some bright morn-ing.
When all the ransomed are gathered at home, Some bright morn-ing.
We shall sing praise to the Lamb ev-er-more, Some bright morn-ing.

CHORUS

Some bright morn-ing, Some glad morn-ing, When the sun is shin-ing in th' e-ter-nal sky; .... Some bright morn-ing, Some glad morn-ing, We shall see the Lord of Har-vest, By and by.

Copyright 1926 by Homer A. Rodeheaver. ©Renewed 1954, The Rodeheaver Co., Owner.
All Rights Reserved. Used by Permission.

76 Some Golden Daybreak

CARL A. BLACKMORE

CARL A. BLACKMORE

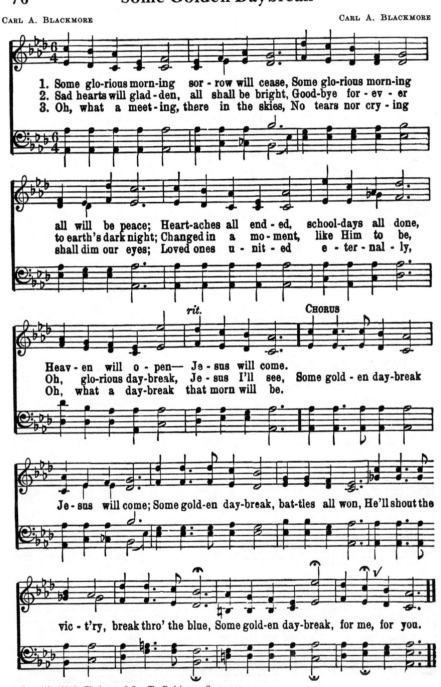

1. Some glo-rious morn-ing sor-row will cease, Some glo-rious morn-ing
2. Sad hearts will glad-den, all shall be bright, Good-bye for-ev-er
3. Oh, what a meet-ing, there in the skies, No tears nor cry-ing

all will be peace; Heart-aches all end-ed, school-days all done,
to earth's dark night; Changed in a mo-ment, like Him to be,
shall dim our eyes; Loved ones u-nit-ed e-ter-nal-ly,

rit. **CHORUS**

Heav-en will o-pen— Je-sus will come.
Oh, glo-rious day-break, Je-sus I'll see, Some gold-en day-break
Oh, what a day-break that morn will be.

Je-sus will come; Some gold-en day-break, bat-tles all won, He'll shout the

vic-t'ry, break thro' the blue, Some gold-en day-break, for me, for you.

Christ Returneth

H. L. TURNER

JAMES McGRANAHAN

1. It may be at morn, when the day is a - wak-ing, When sunlight thro'
2. It may be at mid - day, it may be at twi-light, It may be, per-
3. While its hosts cry Hosanna, from heaven de-scend-ing, With glo - ri - fied
4. Oh, joy! oh, de-light! should we go with-out dy - ing, No sick-ness, no

dark - ness and shad-ow is break-ing, That Je - sus will come in the
chance, that the black-ness of mid-night Will burst in - to light in the
saints and the an - gels at - tend-ing, With grace on His brow, like a
sad - ness, no dread and no cry-ing, Caught up thro' the clouds with our

full - ness of glo - ry, To re - ceive from the world "His own."
blaze of His glo - ry, When Je - sus re - ceives "His own."
ha - lo of glo - ry, Will Je - sus re - ceive "His own."
Lord in - to glo - ry, When Je - sus re - ceives "His own."

CHORUS

O Lord Je - sus, how long, how long Ere we shout the glad song, Christ re-

rit.

turn-eth! Hal - le - lu - jah! hal - le - lu - jah! A - men, Hal - le - lu - jah! A - men.

What if It Were Today?

LEILA N. MORRIS   LEILA N. MORRIS

1. Je - sus is com-ing to earth a - gain, What if it were to - day?
2. Sa - tan's do - min-ion will then be o'er, O that it were to - day!
3. Faith-ful and true would He find us here If He should come to - day?

Com-ing in pow - er and love to reign, What if it were to - day?
Sor - row and sigh-ing shall be no more, O that it were to - day!
Watching in glad-ness and not in fear, If He should come to - day?

Com-ing to claim His cho - sen Bride, All the re-deemed and pu - ri - fied,
Then shall the dead in Christ a - rise, Caught up to meet Him in the skies,
Signs of His com - ing mul - ti - ply, Morning light breaks in east-ern sky,

rit.   *a tempo*

O - ver this whole earth scat - tered wide, What if it were to - day?
When shall these glo - ries meet our eyes? What if it were to - day?
Watch, for the time is draw - ing nigh, What if it were to - day?

CHORUS

Glo - ry, glo - ry! Joy to my heart 'twill bring;.. Glo - ry, glo - ry!
Joy to my heart 'twill bring;

What if It Were Today?

When we shall crown Him King;... Glo - ry, glo - ry! Haste to pre-pare the
When we shall crown Him King; Haste to pre-

ritard.

way;.... Glo - ry, glo - ry! Je - sus will come some day.
pare the way;

Behold, He Comes! 79

E. S. M.

ELEANOR S. MURRAY

* Deliberately but joyfully

Be-hold, He comes! Be-hold, He comes! Be-hold, He comes! Be-hold, He comes! And

ev-'ry eye shall see Him! Friend, will you be read-y when Je - sus comes?

*Divide group into 4 sections. Each section sings the first phrase, sustaining the word "comes" until the four parts swell to a climax.

Will Jesus Find Us Watching?

FANNY J. CROSBY

W. H. DOANE

1. When Je - sus comes to re - ward His serv-ants, Wheth-er it be
2. If, at the dawn of the ear - ly morn-ing, He shall call us
3. Have we been true to the trust He left us? Do we seek to
4. Bless - ed are those whom the Lord finds watch-ing, In His glo - ry

noon or night, Faith - ful to Him will He find us watch-ing,
one by one, When to the Lord we re - store our tal - ents,
do our best? If in our hearts there is naught con-demns us,
they shall share; If He shall come at the dawn or mid-night,

rit.

With our lamps all trimmed and bright?
Will He an - swer thee—"Well done"?
We shall have a glo - rious rest.
Will He find us watch - ing there?

CHORUS

Oh, can we say we are read - y, broth - er? Read - y for the soul's bright home? Say, will He find you and me still watch-ing, Wait-ing, wait-ing when the Lord shall come?

Jesus Is Coming

81

Words and music by Evangelist John R. Rice

John R. Rice

1. Come, dear Lord Je-sus, for long we've been watch-ing; God's chil-dren are home-
2. Mid-night ap-proach-es, wise vir-gins are read-y; With oil in our lamp,
3. Night when we sleep He may take one and leave one, Or day those we work
4. Glad re-sur-rec-tion, O happ-y re-un-ion When we shall be chang'd

sick for Heav-en our home. Come then, Lord Je-sus, come quick-ly and take
may our wicks be trimm'd too. "Ho! comes the Bride-groom, go ye out to meet
with be left when we're gone. Wit-ness to-day then, and turn men to Je-
in a mo-ment of time; Meet all our loved ones, re-deemed of all a-

Chorus:

us; The wed-ding feast waits when the Bride-groom shall come.
Him!" Oh, glad blest an-nounce-ment we hope to hear soon. Je-sus is com-ing
sus, Soon pass-es the sea-son for win-ning our own.
ges. And, oh, what glad greet-ings for mine and for thine!

is com-ing, is com-ing! It may be to-mor-row, It may be to-day. May be the

trum-pet sound, may be the an-gel shout, Then "come up high-er," the Sav-iour will say!

82　When Jesus Comes to Reign

JRR

John R. Rice

1. Sor-row and sigh-ing shall flee a-way, When Je-sus comes to reign. Eyes of the blind will be o-pened then; Tongue of the dumb shall sing.
2. Rap-tured with Christ, then a hon-ey-moon With Him in glo-ry-land. With Him to earth, when the an-gels bring Is-rael to Ho-ly land.
3. Lame men shall leap as an hart, for then All sick-ness gone, all sore. Des-erts will bloom and the thorns, and briars Shall curse the earth no more!
4. King-doms shall fall, and old Sa-tan's rule Shall end with all its tears. Right-eous-ness fill all the earth, and peace Reign for a thou-sand years.
5. We pray, dear Lord, may Thy King-dom come, On earth Thy will be done. But we have now all Thy peace and joy And in our hearts Thy throne.

Chorus

Sor-row and sigh-ing shall flee a-way! (They shall)
Flee a-way that glo-ry day! (And the) Gar-den of E-den re-

When Jesus Comes to Reign

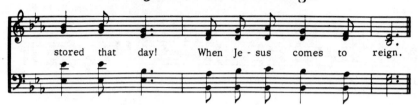

stored that day! When Je-sus comes to reign.

We Shall Shine As the Stars   83

J. W. V.   J. W. Van DeVenter

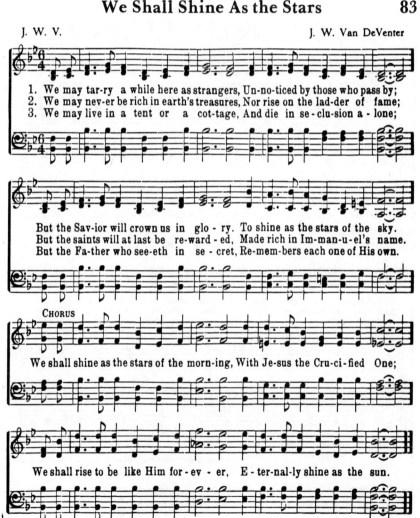

1. We may tar-ry a while here as strangers, Un-no-ticed by those who pass by;
2. We may nev-er be rich in earth's treasures, Nor rise on the lad-der of fame;
3. We may live in a tent or a cot-tage, And die in se-clu-sion a-lone;

But the Sav-ior will crown us in glo-ry, To shine as the stars of the sky.
But the saints will at last be re-ward-ed, Made rich in Im-man-u-el's name.
But the Fa-ther who see-eth in se-cret, Re-mem-bers each one of His own.

CHORUS

We shall shine as the stars of the morn-ing, With Je-sus the Cru-ci-fied One;

We shall rise to be like Him for-ev-er, E-ter-nal-ly shine as the sun.

84 Coming Today?

JRR

John R. Rice.

Introduction

1. Com - ing to-day? To-
2. Saints from the North, South,
3. Then will the King come
4. Then will our wrongs be

day? Yes, Je-sus may come to-day.   Watch for the Lord's re - turn - ing,
East, West Come to the wed-ding grand; There with the shin - ing Bride-groom
lead - ing Ar - mies of Heav-en strong, On a white horse re - turn - ing
right - ed; Then will be dried our tears! Then all our sins be con-quered;

Watch as we work and pray. Oh, what a grand a - wak'-ning
Saved ones from ev' - ry land. How we'll re - joice and sing then
To sit on Da - vid's throne. Bring-ing His saints to serve Him
Still will be all our fears. Eyes of the blind be o - pened,

When shall a -rise the dead, And what a blest re - un - ion
And our re-wards re - ceive, And ev - er be with Je - sus
And to en - joy His peace; O - ver the whole world reign-ing,
Ears of the deaf shall hear, Sor - row and sigh - ing end - ed

CHORUS: (Unison)

When He comes, as He said!
Him on whom we be - lieve.   When He comes, Hail, ____ Hail, ____
Mak -ing all wars to cease.
Through-out the end - less years.

Coming Today?

Hail _____ Him! _____ Je - sus may come to - day. _____

Then what a shout ___ of tri - umph, _____ Up and with Him ___ a -

way. _____ Rend-ing the sky ___ wide, _____ high, ___ all, _____

All the re-deemed we'll see, _____ So we will go ___ to

Heav - en, _____ Ev - er with Christ ___ to be!

85 In the Garden

C. AUSTIN MILES
C. AUSTIN MILES

1. I come to the gar-den a-lone, While the dew is still on the
2. He speaks,and the sound of His voice Is so sweet the birds hush their
3. I'd stay in the gar-den with Him Tho' the night a-round me be

ros - es, And the voice I hear, Fall-ing on my ear, The
sing - ing, And the mel - o - dy That He gave to me, With-
fall - ing, But He bids me go; Thro' the voice of woe His

Son of God dis - clos - es.
in my heart is ring - ing. And He walks with me, and He
voice to me is call - ing.

talks with me, And He tells me I am His own; And the

joy we share as we tar - ry there, None oth - er has ev - er known.

How Can I Be Lonely?

H. L.

Haldor Lillenas

Legato

1. One is walk-ing with me o - ver life's un - e - ven way, Con-stant-ly sup-
2. Days may bring their burdens and their tri-als as I go, But my Lord is
3. In the hour of sad be-reave-ment or of bit - ter loss, I can find sup-
4. In life's ros - y morn-ing when the skies a-bove are clear, In its noon-tide

port - ing me each mo-ment of the day; How can I be lone - ly when such
near and helps to make them lighter grow. Life may have its cross-es, or its
port and con - so - la - tion at the cross; Want or woe or suf-f'ring all seem
hours with man-y cares and problems near, Or when eve-ning shad-ows fall at

REFRAIN

fel-low-ship is mine, With my blessed Lord di-vine!
loss-es, or in-crease, Je-sus meets them all with peace. How can I be lone-ly
glo - ri-fied when He Dai-ly walks and talks with me.
clos-ing of my day Je - sus will be there al-way.

When I've Je - sus on - ly To be my com-pan-ion and un-fail-ing guide:

rit.

Why should I be wea-ry, Or my path seem dreary, When He's walking by my side.

Just When I Need Him Most

Rev. Wm. Poole

Chas. H. Gabriel

1. Just when I need Him, Je-sus is near, Just when I fal - ter,
2. Just when I need Him, Je-sus is true, Nev - er for-sak - ing
3. Just when I need Him, Je-sus is strong, Bear-ing my bur - dens
4. Just when I need Him, He is my all, An - swer-ing when up -

just when I fear; Read - y to help me, read - y to cheer,
all the way thro'; Giv - ing for bur - dens pleas-ures a - new,
all the day long; For all my sor - row giv - ing a song,
on Him I call; Ten - der - ly watch - ing lest I should fall,

CHORUS.

Just when I need Him most. Just when I need Him most,

Just when I need Him most; Je - sus is near to

com - fort and cheer, Just when I need Him most. A - MEN.

Favorite song of
Dr. Lee Roberson.

Some Time We'll Understand

Maxwell N. Cornelius

James McGranahan

1. Not now, but in the com-ing years, It may be in the bet-ter land,
2. We'll catch the broken thread a-gain, And fin-ish what we here be-gan;
3. We'll know why clouds instead of sun Were o-ver many a cherished plan;
4. God knows the way, He holds the key, He guides us with un-err-ing hand;

We'll read the meaning of our tears, And there, some time, we'll understand.
Heav'n will the mys-ter-ies ex-plain, And then, ah, then, we'll understand.
Why song has ceased when scarce begun; 'Tis there, some time, we'll understand.
Some time with tearless eyes we'll see; Yes, there, up there, we'll understand.

CHORUS. *A little faster*

Then trust in God thro' all the days; Fear not, for He doth hold thy hand;
doth hold thy hand;

A tempo *cres.* *ad lib.*

Though dark thy way, still sing and praise, Some time, some time, we'll understand.

89   God Will Take Care of You

CIVILLA D. MARTIN   W. STILLMAN MARTIN

1. Be not dis - mayed what-e'er be - tide, God will take care of you;
2. Thro' days of toil when heart doth fail, God will take care of you;
3. All you may need He will pro - vide, God will take care of you;
4. No mat - ter what may be the test, God will take care of you;

Be - neath His wings of love a - bide, God will take care of you.
When dan-gers fierce your path as - sail, God will take care of you.
Noth - ing you ask will be de - nied, God will take care of you.
Lean, wear - y one, up - on His breast, God will take care of you.

CHORUS

God will take care of you, Thro' ev - 'ry day, O'er all the way;

He will take care of you, God will take care of you.
take care of you.

Frank E. Graeff

J. Lincoln Hall

1. Does Je-sus care when my heart is pained Too deep-ly for mirth and song;
2. Does Je-sus care when my way is dark With a name-less dread and fear?
3. Does Je-sus care when I've tried and failed To re-sist some temp-ta-tion strong;
4. Does Je-sus care when I've said "good-by" To the dear-est on earth to me,

As the burdens press, and the cares distress, And the way grows wea-ry and long?
As the daylight fades into deep night shades, Does He care e-nough to be near?
When for my deep grief I find no re-lief, Tho' my tears flow all the night long?
And my sad heart aches till it nearly breaks—Is it aught to Him? Does He see?

CHORUS

O yes, He cares; I know He cares, His heart is touched with my grief;

ad lib.　　　　　　　　　　*rit.*

When the days are wea-ry, the long nights dreary, I know my Sav-ior cares.

He cares.

91

Jesus, Savior, Pilot Me

EDWARD HOPPER

JOHN E. GOULD

1. Je - sus, Sav - ior, pi - lot me O - ver life's tem - pes-tuous sea;
2. As a moth - er stills her child, Thou canst hush the o - cean wild;
3. When at last I near the shore, And the fear - ful break-ers roar

Un-known waves be - fore me roll, Hid - ing rock and treacherous shoal;
Boisterous waves o - bey Thy will When Thou say'st to them "Be still!"
'Twixt me and the peace-ful rest, Then, while lean-ing on Thy breast,

Chart and com - pass came from Thee: Je - sus, Sav - ior, pi - lot me.
Won-drous Sov-'reign of the sea, Je - sus, Sav - ior, pi - lot me.
May I hear Thee say to me, "Fear not, I will pi - lot thee."

92

I Need Thee Every Hour

ANNIE S. HAWKS

ROBERT LOWRY

1. I need Thee ev-'ry hour, Most gra - cious Lord; No ten - der voice like
2. I need Thee ev-'ry hour, Stay Thou near by; Temp-ta-tions lose their
3. I need Thee ev-'ry hour, In joy or pain; Come quick-ly and a-
4. I need Thee ev-'ry hour, Most Ho - ly One; O make me Thine in-

I Need Thee Every Hour

CHORUS

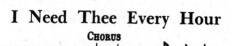
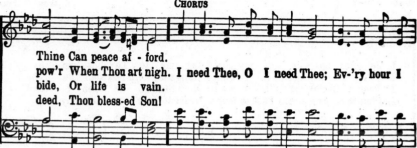

Thine Can peace af - ford.
pow'r When Thou art nigh. I need Thee, O I need Thee; Ev-'ry hour I
bide, Or life is vain.
deed, Thou bless-ed Son!

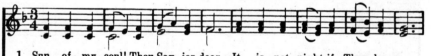

need Thee! O bless me now, my Sav - ior, I come to Thee!

Sun of My Soul   93

JOHN KEBLE   ADAPTED FROM "KATHOLISCHES GESANGBUCH"

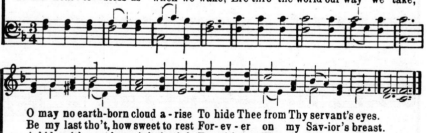

1. Sun of my soul! Thou Sav-ior dear, It is not night if Thou be near;
2. When the soft dews of kind-ly sleep My wea-ry eye-lids gen-tly steep,
3. A - bide with me from morn till eve, For with-out Thee I can-not live;
4. Be near to bless us when we wake, Ere thro' the world our way we take;

O may no earth-born cloud a - rise To hide Thee from Thy servant's eyes.
Be my last tho't, how sweet to rest For-ev - er on my Sav-ior's breast.
A-bide with me when night is nigh, For with-out Thee I dare not die.
Till, in the o - cean of Thy love, We lose our-selves in heav'n a-bove. A-MEN.

94   Jesus, Lover of My Soul

CHARLES WESLEY

SIMEON B. MARSH

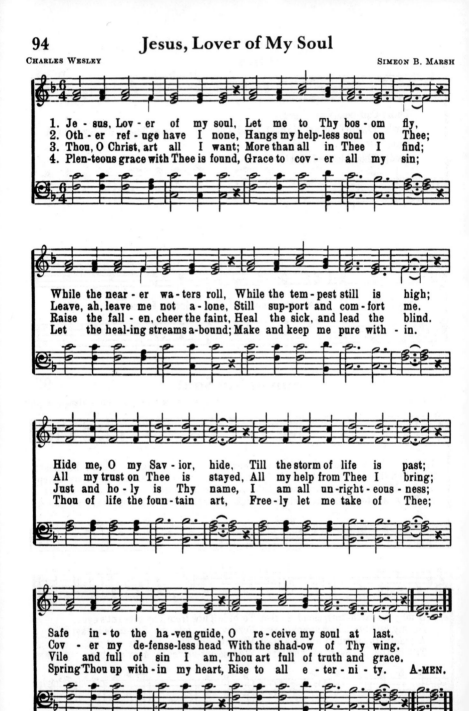

1. Je - sus, Lov - er of my soul, Let me to Thy bos - om fly,
2. Oth - er ref - uge have I none, Hangs my help-less soul on Thee;
3. Thou, O Christ, art all I want; More than all in Thee I find;
4. Plen-teous grace with Thee is found, Grace to cov - er all my sin;

While the near - er wa - ters roll, While the tem - pest still is high;
Leave, ah, leave me not a - lone, Still sup-port and com - fort me.
Raise the fall - en, cheer the faint, Heal the sick, and lead the blind.
Let the heal-ing streams a-bound; Make and keep me pure with - in.

Hide me, O my Sav - ior, hide, Till the storm of life is past;
All my trust on Thee is stayed, All my help from Thee I bring;
Just and ho - ly is Thy name, I am all un-right - eous - ness;
Thou of life the foun - tain art, Free - ly let me take of Thee;

Safe in - to the ha - ven guide, O re - ceive my soul at last.
Cov - er my de-fense-less head With the shad-ow of Thy wing.
Vile and full of sin I am, Thou art full of truth and grace.
Spring Thou up with - in my heart, Rise to all e - ter - ni - ty. A-MEN.

Hiding in Thee

WM O. CUSHING

IRA D. SANKEY

1. O safe to the Rock that is high-er than I, My soul in its
2. In the calm of the noon-tide, in sor-row's lone hour, In times when temp-
3. How oft in the con-flict, when pressed by the foe, I have fled to my

con-flicts and sor-rows would fly; So sin-ful, so wea-ry, Thine,
ta-tion casts o'er me its pow'r; In the tem-pests of life, on its
Ref-uge and breathed out my woe; How oft-en, when tri-als like

Thine would I be; Thou blest "Rock of A-ges," I'm hid-ing in Thee.
wide, heaving sea, Thou blest "Rock of A-ges," I'm hid-ing in Thee.
sea-bil-lows roll, Have I hid-den in Thee, O Thou Rock of my soul.

CHORUS

Hid-ing in Thee, Hiding in Thee, Thou blest "Rock of Ages," I'm hid-ing in Thee.

Abide With Me

Henry F. Lyte

William H. Monk

1. A - bide with me: fast falls the e - ven - tide; The dark - ness
2. Swift to its close ebbs out life's lit - tle day; Earth's joys grow
3. I need Thy pres - ence ev - 'ry pass - ing hour: What but Thy
4. Hold Thou Thy cross be - fore my clos - ing eyes; Shine thro' the

deep - ens; Lord, with me a - bide: When oth - er help - ers fail, and
dim, its glo - ries pass a - way; Change and de - cay in all a -
grace can foil the tempter's pow'r? Who like Thy - self my guide and
gloom, and point me to the skies: Heav'n's morning breaks, and earth's vain

com - forts flee, Help of the help-less, O a - bide with me!
round I see; O Thou who chang-est not, a - bide with me!
stay can be? Thro' cloud and sun-shine, O a - bide with me!
shad - ows flee: In life, in death, O Lord, a - bide with me! A-MEN.

97   Art Thou Weary, Art Thou Languid?

John M. Neale
Based on an Early Greek Hymn

Henry W. Baker

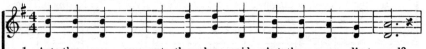

1. Art thou wea - ry, art thou lan - guid, Art thou sore dis-tressed?
2. Hath He marks to lead me to Him, If He be my guide?
3. Is there di - a - dem, as Mon-arch, That His brow a - dorns?
4. If I ask Him to re - ceive me, Will He say me nay?
5. Find-ing, fol-l'wing, keep - ing, strug-gling, Is He sure to bless?

Art Thou Weary, Art Thou Languid?

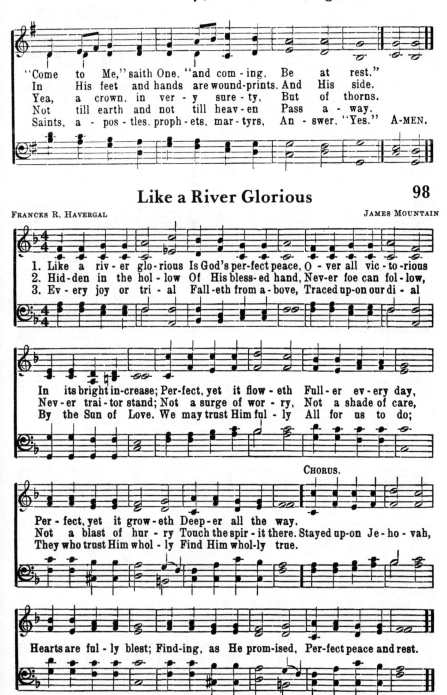

"Come to Me," saith One, "and com-ing, Be at rest."
In His feet and hands are wound-prints, And His side.
Yea, a crown, in ver-y sure-ty, But of thorns.
Not till earth and not till heav-en Pass a-way.
Saints, a-pos-tles, proph-ets, mar-tyrs, An-swer, "Yes." A-MEN.

Like a River Glorious

98

FRANCES R. HAVERGAL

JAMES MOUNTAIN

1. Like a riv-er glo-rious Is God's per-fect peace, O-ver all vic-to-rious
2. Hid-den in the hol-low Of His bless-ed hand, Nev-er foe can fol-low,
3. Ev-ery joy or tri-al Fall-eth from a-bove, Traced up-on our di-al

In its bright in-crease; Per-fect, yet it flow-eth Full-er ev-ery day,
Nev-er trai-tor stand; Not a surge of wor-ry, Not a shade of care,
By the Sun of Love. We may trust Him ful-ly All for us to do;

CHORUS.

Per-fect, yet it grow-eth Deep-er all the way.
Not a blast of hur-ry Touch the spir-it there. Stayed up-on Je-ho-vah,
They who trust Him whol-ly Find Him whol-ly true.

Hearts are ful-ly blest; Find-ing, as He prom-ised, Per-fect peace and rest.

99 Stand by Me

C. A. T.

C. A. TINDLEY
Arr. by F. A. CLARK

1. When the storms of life are rag-ing, Stand by me (stand by me); When the
2. In the midst of trib - u - la - tions, In the
3. In the midst of faults and fail-ures, In the
4. In the midst of per - se - cu - tion, In the
5. When I'm grow-ing old and fee - ble, (by me); When I'm

storms of life are rag-ing, Stand by me; .... When the
midst of trib - u - la-tions, When the
midst of faults and fail - ures, When I
midst of per - se - cu - tion, When my
grow - ing old and fee - ble, stand by me; When my

world is toss - ing me Like a ship up - on the sea;
hosts of hell as - sail, And my strength be - gins to fail,
do the best I can, And my friends mis - un - der-stand,
foes in bat - tle ar - ray Un - der - take to stop my way,
life be - comes a bur - den, And I'm near - ing chill - y Jor - dan,

Thou who rul - est wind and wa - ter, Stand by me (stand by me).
Thou who nev - er lost a bat - tle,
Thou who know-est all a - bout me,
Thou who saved Paul and Si - las,
O Thou "Lil - y of the Val - ley," (by me).

The Lord Is My Shepherd

James Montgomery

Thomas Koschat

1. The Lord is my Shep-herd, no want shall I know; I feed in green pas-tures, safe-fold-ed I rest; He lead-eth my soul where the still wa-ters flow, Re-stores me when wan-dering, re-deems when op-pressed; Re-stores me when wan-dering, re-deems when op-pressed.

2. Thro' the val-ley and shad-ow of death though I stray, Since Thou art my Guard-ian, no e-vil I fear; Thy rod shall de-fend me, Thy staff be my stay; No harm can be-fall, with my Com-fort-er near; No harm can be-fall, with my Com-fort-er near.

3. In the midst of af-flic-tion my ta-ble is spread; With blessings un-meas-ured my cup run-neth o'er; With per-fume and oil Thou a-noint-est my head; O what shall I ask of Thy prov-i-dence more? O what shall I ask of Thy prov-i-dence more?

4. Let good-ness and mer-cy, my boun-ti-ful God, Still fol-low my steps till I meet Thee a-bove: I seek by the path which my fore-fa-thers trod, Thro' the land of their so-journ, Thy king-dom of love; Thro' the land of their so-journ, Thy king-dom of love.

101 God Leads Us Along

G. A. Young

G. A. Young

1. In shad-y, green pas-tures, so rich and so sweet. God leads His dear
2. Sometimes on the mount where the sun shines so bright, God leads His dear
3. Tho' sor-rows be-fall us, and Sa-tan op-pose, God leads His dear
4. A-way from the mire, and a-way from the clay, God leads His dear

chil-dren a-long; Where the wa-ter's cold flow bathes the wea-ry one's feet,
chil-dren a-long; Some-times in the val-ley, in dark-est of night,
chil-dren a-long; Through grace we can con-quer, de-feat all our foes,
chil-dren a-long; A-way up in glo-ry, e-ter-ni-ty's day,

CHORUS

God leads His dear chil-dren a-long. Some thro' the waters, some thro' the flood,

Some thro' the fire, but all thro' the blood; Some thro' great sor-row, but

rit.

God gives a song, In the night sea-son and all the day long.

W. C. Martin

Edmund S. Lorenz

1. The name of Je - sus is so sweet, I love its mu - sic to re - peat; It makes my joys full and com-plete, The pre - cious name of Je - sus.
2. I love the name of Him whose heart Knows all my griefs and bears a part; Who bids all anx - ious fears de - part— I love the pre - cious name
3. That name I fond - ly love to hear, It nev - er fails my heart to cheer, Its mu - sic dries the fall - ing tear; Ex - alt the
4. No word of man can ev - er tell How sweet the name I love so well; Oh, let its prais - es ev - er swell, Oh, praise the The

CHORUS

"Je - sus," oh, how sweet the name! "Je - sus," ev - 'ry day the same; "Je - sus," let all saints pro - claim Its wor - thy praise for - ev - er.

Its wor - thy praise

103 Come, Ye Disconsolate

THOMAS MOORE
ALT. BY THOMAS HASTINGS

SAMUEL WEBBE

1. Come, ye dis-con-so-late, wher-e'er ye lan-guish; Come to the
2. Joy of the des-o-late, light of the stray-ing, Hope of the
3. Here see the bread of life; see wa-ters flow-ing Forth from the

mer-cy-seat, fer-vent-ly kneel; Here bring your wound-ed hearts,
pen-i-tent, fade-less and pure, Here speaks the Com-fort-er,
throne of God, pure from a-bove; Come to the feast of love;

here tell your an-guish; Earth has no sor-row that Heav'n can-not heal.
ten-der-ly say-ing, "Earth has no sor-row that Heav'n can-not cure."
come, ev-er know-ing Earth has no sor-row but Heav'n can re-move. A-MEN.

Favorite hymn of Dr. Bob Jones, Jr.

104 Jesus! Jesus! Jesus!

Llanthony Abbey Hymns

Anon.

Slowly

1. Je-sus! Je-sus! Je-sus! Sing a-loud the Name;
2. Je-sus! Name of cleans-ing, Wash-ing all our stains;
3. Je-sus! Name of bold-ness,— Mak-ing cow-ards brave;
4. Je-sus! Name of vic-t'ry, Stretch-ing far a-way,
5. Je-sus, be our joy-note In this vale of tears;

Jesus! Jesus! Jesus!

Till it soft - ly, slow - ly, Sets all hearts a - flame.
Je - sus! Name of heal - ing, Balm for all our pains.
Name! that in the bat - tle, Cer - tain - ly must save.
Right a - cross earth's war-fields, To the plains of day.
Till we reach the home - land. And th' e - ter - nal years!

Jesus Never Fails 105

A. A. Luther

A. A. Luther

1. Earth-ly friends may prove untrue, Doubts and fears as-sail; One still loves and
2. Tho' the sky be dark and drear, Fierce and strong the gale, Just re-mem-ber
3. In life's dark and bit-ter hour Love will still pre-vail; Trust His ev-er-

CHORUS

cares for you: One who will not fail.

He is near, And He will not fail. Je - sus nev - er fails,

last - ing pow'r, Je - sus will not fail.

Je-sus nev-er fails; Heav'n and earth may pass away But Jesus nev-er fails.

He Hideth My Soul

FANNY J. CROSBY   WILLIAM J. KIRKPATRICK

Allegretto

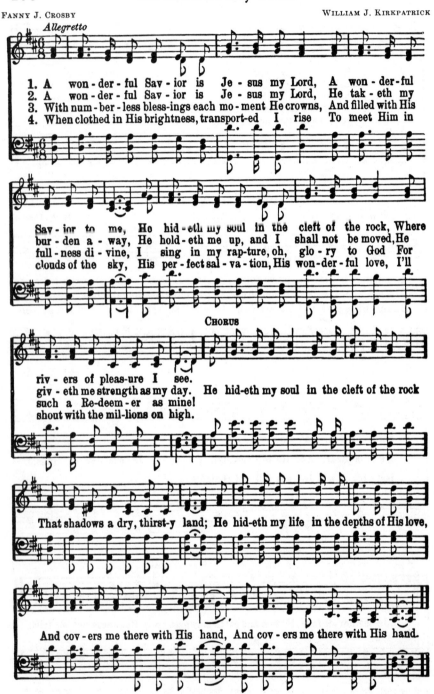

1. A won-der-ful Sav-ior is Je-sus my Lord, A won-der-ful
2. A won-der-ful Sav-ior is Je-sus my Lord, He tak-eth my
3. With num-ber-less bless-ings each mo-ment He crowns, And filled with His
4. When clothed in His brightness, transport-ed I rise To meet Him in

Sav-ior to me, He hid-eth my soul in the cleft of the rock, Where
bur-den a-way, He hold-eth me up, and I shall not be moved, He
full-ness di-vine, I sing in my rap-ture, oh, glo-ry to God For
clouds of the sky, His per-fect sal-va-tion, His won-der-ful love, I'll

riv-ers of pleas-ure I see.
giv-eth me strength as my day.
such a Re-deem-er as mine!
shout with the mil-lions on high.

CHORUS

He hid-eth my soul in the cleft of the rock

That shadows a dry, thirst-y land; He hid-eth my life in the depths of His love,

And cov-ers me there with His hand, And cov-ers me there with His hand.

Day by Day

LINA SANDELL BERG
Trans. by Andrew L. Skoog

OSCAR AHNFELT

1. Day by day and with each pass-ing mo-ment, Strength I find to
2. Ev - 'ry day the Lord Him-self is near me With a spe - cial
3. Help me then in ev - 'ry trib - u - la - tion So to trust Thy

meet my tri - als here; Trust-ing in my Fa-ther's wise be - stow-ment,
mer - cy for each hour; All my cares He fain would bear, and cheer me,
prom - is - es, O Lord, That I lose not faith's sweet con-so - la - tion

I've no cause for wor - ry or for fear. He whose heart is kind be -
He whose name is Coun-sel-lor and Pow'r. The pro - tec - tion of His
Of - fered me with-in Thy ho - ly word. Help me, Lord, when toil and

yond all meas-ure Gives un - to each day what He deems best— Lov - ing -
child and treas-ure Is a charge that on Him-self He laid; "As thy
trou - ble meet-ing, E'er to take, as from a fa-ther's hand, One by

ly, its part of pain and pleas-ure, Min-gling toil with peace and rest.
days, thy strength shall be in meas-ure," This the pledge to me He made.
one, the days, the mo-ments fleet-ing, Till I reach the prom-ised land.

108 Under His Wings

WILLIAM O. CUSHING

IRA D. SANKEY

1. Un - der His wings I am safe - ly a - bid - ing; Tho' the night
2. Un - der His wings, what a ref - uge in sor - row! How the heart
3. Un - der His wings, O what pre - cious en - joy - ment! There will I

deep - ens and tem - pests are wild, Still I can trust Him; I
yearn - ing - ly turns to His rest! Oft - en when earth has no
hide till life's tri - als are o'er; Shel - tered, pro - tect - ed, no

know He will keep me; He has re - deemed me, and I am His child.
balm for my heal - ing, There I find com - fort, and there I am blest.
e - vil can harm me; Rest - ing in Je - sus I'm safe ev - er - more.

CHORUS

Un - der His wings, un - der His wings, Who from His love can sev - er?

Un - der His wings my soul shall a - bide, Safe - ly a - bide for - ev - er.

Lean on His Arms

Edgar Lewis

L. E. Jones

1. Just lean up-on the arms of Je - sus, He'll help you a - long,
2. Just lean up-on the arms of Je - sus, He'll bright-en the way,
3. Just lean up-on the arms of Je - sus, O bring ev - 'ry care,
4. Just lean up-on the arms of Je - sus, Then leave all to Him,

help you a - long; If you will trust His love un - fail - ing, He'll
bright-en the way; Just fol - low glad-ly where He lead - eth, His
bring ev - 'ry care! The bur - den that has seemed so heav - y, Take
leave all to Him; His heart is full of love and mer - cy, His

CHORUS

fill your heart with song.
gen - tle voice o - bey.   Lean on His arms,   trust-ing in His love;
to the Lord in pray'r.   Lean up-on His arms, ful-ly   trust-ing in His love;
eyes are nev - er dim.

Lean on His arms,   all His mer - cies prove; Lean on His
Lean up - on His arms.   and all His mer - cies prove;   Lean up - on His

arms,   look-ing home a-bove, Just lean on the Sav - ior's arms!
arms,   ev - er

All That Thrills My Soul

THORO HARRIS

1. Who can cheer the heart like Je - sus, By His pres-ence all di - vine?
2. Love of Christ so free - ly giv - en, Grace of God be - yond de - gree,
3. What a won - der - ful re - demp - tion! Nev - er can a mor - tal know
4. Ev - 'ry need His hand sup - ply - ing, Ev - 'ry good in Him I see;
5. By the crys - tal flow - ing riv - er With the ran - somed I will sing,

True and ten - der, pure and pre - cious, O how blest to call Him mine!
Mer - cy high - er than the heav - en, Deep - er than the deep - est sea.
How my sin, tho' red like crim - son, Can be whit - er than the snow.
On His strength di - vine re - ly - ing, He is all in all to me.
And for - ev - er and for - ev - er Praise and glo - ri - fy the King.

REFRAIN

All that thrills my soul is Je - sus, He is more than life to me (to me);

And the fair - est of ten thou - sand In my bless - ed Lord I see.

111   ## Praise the Savior

THOS. KELLY   German

1. Praise the Sav - ior, ye who know Him! Who can tell how much we owe Him?
2. Je - sus is the name that charms us; He for con - flict fits and arms us;
3. Trust in Him, ye saints, for - ev - er; He is faith - ful, changing nev - er;
4. Keep us, Lord, O keep us cleav - ing To Thy - self and still be - liev - ing;
5. Then we shall be where we would be, Then we shall be what we should be;

Praise the Savior

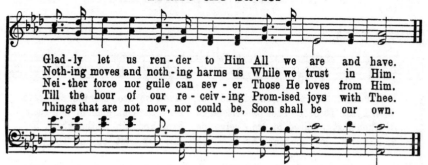

Glad-ly let us ren-der to Him All we are and have.
Noth-ing moves and noth-ing harms us While we trust in Him.
Nei-ther force nor guile can sev-er Those He loves from Him.
Till the hour of our re-ceiv-ing Prom-ised joys with Thee.
Things that are not now, nor could be, Soon shall be our own.

Near to the Heart of God

CLELAND B. McAFEE

CLELAND B. McAFEE

1. There is a place of qui-et rest, Near to the heart of God,
2. There is a place of com-fort sweet, Near to the heart of God,
3. There is a place of full re-lease, Near to the heart of God,

A place where sin can-not mo-lest, Near to the heart of God.
A place where we our Sav-ior meet, Near to the heart of God.
A place where all is joy and peace, Near to the heart of God.

REFRAIN

O Je-sus, blest Re-deem-er, Sent from the heart of God,

Hold us, who wait be-fore Thee, Near to the heart of God.

Savior, Like a Shepherd Lead Us

"Hymns for the Young"
Asc. to Dorothy A. Thrupp

William B. Bradbury

1. Sav - ior, like a shep-herd lead us, Much we need Thy ten-der care;
2. We are Thine; do Thou be - friend us, Be the Guardian of our way;
3. Thou hast promised to re - ceive us, Poor and sin-ful though we be;
4. Ear - ly let us seek Thy fa - vor; Ear - ly let us do Thy will;

In Thy pleas-ant pas-tures feed us, For our use Thy folds pre-pare:
Keep Thy flock, from sin de - fend us, Seek us when we go a-stray:
Thou hast mer - cy to re - lieve us, Grace to cleanse, and pow'r to free:
Bless - ed Lord and on - ly Sav - ior, With Thy love our bos-oms fill:

Bless-ed Je - sus, Bless-ed Je - sus, Thou hast bought us, Thine we are;
Bless-ed Je - sus, Bless-ed Je - sus, Hear, O hear us when we pray;
Bless-ed Je - sus, Bless-ed Je - sus, Ear - ly let us turn to Thee;
Bless-ed Je - sus, Bless-ed Je - sus, Thou hast loved us, love us still;

Bless-ed Je - sus, Bless-ed Je - sus, Thou hast bought us, Thine we are.
Bless-ed Je - sus, Bless-ed Je - sus, Hear, O hear us when we pray.
Bless-ed Je - sus, Bless-ed Je - sus, Ear - ly let us turn to Thee.
Bless-ed Je - sus, Bless-ed Je - sus, Thou hast loved us, love us still.

All the Way My Savior Leads Me

FANNY J. CROSBY

ROBERT LOWRY

1. All the way my Sav-ior leads me; What have I to ask be-side?
2. All the way my Sav-ior leads me, Cheers each wind-ing path I tread,
3. All the way my Sav-ior leads me; Oh, the full-ness of His love!

Can I doubt His ten-der mer-cy, Who thro' life has been my Guide?
Gives me grace for ev-'ry tri-al, Feeds me with the liv-ing bread.
Per-fect rest to me is prom-ised In my Fa-ther's house a-bove.

Heav'n-ly peace, di-vin-est com-fort, Here by faith in Him to dwell!
Though my wea-ry steps may fal-ter, And my soul a-thirst may be,
When my spir-it, clothed im-mor-tal, Wings its flight to realms of day,

For I know, whate'er be-fall me, Je-sus do-eth all things well; well.
Gushing from the Rock be-fore me, Lo! a spring of joy I see; see.
This my song thro' end-less a-ges: Je-sus led me all the way; way.

115 He Leadeth Me

JOSEPH H. GILMORE

W·LLIAM B. BRADBURY

1. He lead-eth, me O bless-ed tho't! O words with heav'nly comfort fraught!
2. Sometimes 'mid scenes of deepest gloom, Sometimes where Eden's bowers bloom,
3. Lord, I would clasp Thy hand in mine, Nor ev-er mur-mur nor re-pine,
4. And when my task on earth is done, When, by Thy grace, the vic-t'ry's won,

What-e'er I do, wher-e'er I be, Still 'tis God's hand that lead-eth me.
By wa-ters still, o'er trou-bled sea,—Still 'tis His hand that lead-eth me!
Con-tent, what-ev-er lot I see, Since 'tis my God that lead-eth me!
E'en death's cold wave I will not flee, Since God thro' Jor-dan lead-eth me.

REFRAIN

{He lead-eth me, He lead-eth me! By His own hand He leadeth me!
{His faithful foll'wer I would be, For by His hand He(*Omit*.....)leadeth me.

116 The Great Physician

WM. HUNTER

J. H. STOCKTON

FINE.

1.{The great Phy-si-cian now is near, The sym-pa-thiz-ing Je-sus;}
{He speaks the droop-ing heart to cheer, Oh, hear the voice of Je-sus. }

2.{Your man-y sins are all for-giv'n, Oh, hear the voice of Je-sus;}
{Go on your way in peace to heav'n, And wear a crown with Je-sus. }

3.{All glo-ry to the dy-ing Lamb! I now be-lieve in Je-sus;}
{I love the bless-ed Sav-ior's name, I love the name of Je-sus. }

4.{And when to that bright world a-bove We rise to be with Je-sus,}
{We'll sing a-round the throne of love, His name, the name of Je-sus. }

D. S.—*Sweet-est car-ol ev-er sung,* ⌐ *Je-sus, bless-ed Je-sus.*

The Great Physician

D.S.

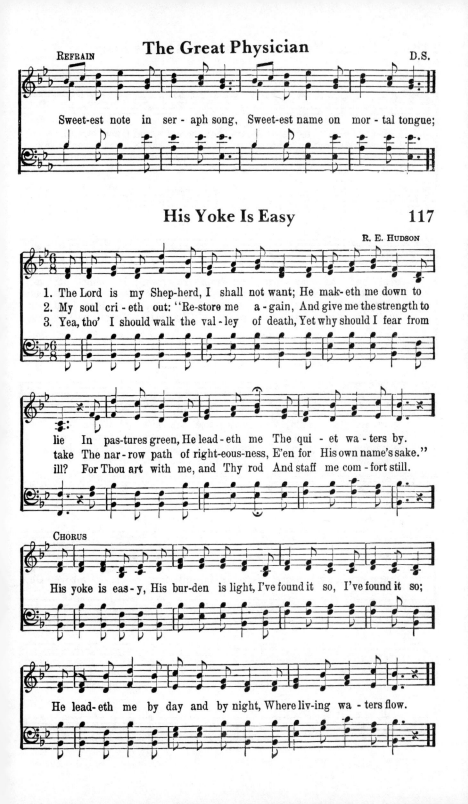

Sweet-est note in ser - aph song, Sweet-est name on mor - tal tongue;

His Yoke Is Easy 117

R. E. HUDSON

1. The Lord is my Shep-herd, I shall not want; He mak-eth me down to
2. My soul cri - eth out: "Re-store me a - gain, And give me the strength to
3. Yea, tho' I should walk the val - ley of death, Yet why should I fear from

lie In pas-tures green, He lead-eth me The qui - et wa-ters by.
take The nar-row path of right-eous-ness, E'en for His own name's sake."
ill? For Thou art with me, and Thy rod And staff me com - fort still.

CHORUS

His yoke is eas-y, His bur-den is light, I've found it so, I've found it so;

He lead-eth me by day and by night, Where liv-ing wa - ters flow.

Sweet Peace, the Gift of God's Love

P. P. B.

P. P. BILHORN

1. There comes to my heart one sweet strain (sweet strain), A
2. Through Christ on the cross peace was made (was made), My
3. When Jesus as Lord I had crowned (had crowned), My
4. In Jesus for peace I abide (abide), And

glad and a joyous refrain (refrain); I sing it a-
debt by His death was all paid (all paid); No other foun-
heart with this peace did abound (abound); In Him the rich
as I keep close to His side (His side), There's nothing but

gain and again, Sweet peace, the gift of God's love.
dation is laid For peace, the gift of God's love.
blessing I found, Sweet peace, the gift of God's love.
peace doth betide, Sweet peace, the gift of God's love.

CHORUS

Peace, peace, sweet peace! Wonderful gift from above (above)! Oh,

cres.

wonderful, wonderful peace! Sweet peace, the gift of God's love!

W. D. CORNELL, ALT.

W. G. COOPER

1. Far a-way in the depths of my spir-it to-night Rolls a
2. What a treas-ure I have in this won-der-ful peace, Bur-ied
3. I am rest-ing to-night in this won-der-ful peace, Rest-ing
4. And me-thinks when I rise to that Cit-y of peace, Where the
5. Ah! soul, are you here with-out com-fort or rest, March-ing

mel-o-dy sweet-er than psalm; In ce-les-tial-like strains it un-
deep in the heart of my soul; So se-cure that no pow-er can
sweet-ly in Je-sus' con-trol; For I'm kept from all dan-ger by
Au-thor of peace I shall see, That one strain of the song which the
down the rough pathway of time? Make Je-sus your friend ere the

ceas-ing-ly falls O'er my soul like an in-fi-nite calm.
mine it a-way, While the years of e-ter-ni-ty roll.
night and by day, And His glo-ry is flood-ing my soul.
ran-somed will sing, In that heav-en-ly king-dom shall be:
shad-ows grow dark; Oh, ac-cept this sweet peace so sub-lime.

CHORUS

Peace! peace! won-der-ful peace, Com-ing down from the Fa-ther a-bove; Sweep

o-ver my spir-it for-ev-er, I pray, In fath-om-less bil-lows of love.

120 No One Ever Cared for Me Like Jesus

C. F. W.

C. F. WEIGLE

1. I would love to tell you what I think of Je-sus Since I found in Him a
2. All my life was full of sin when Jesus found me, All my heart was full of
3. Ev-'ry day He comes to me with new as-surance, More and more I un-der-

friend so strong and true; I would tell you how He changed my life completely,
mis-er-y and woe; Je-sus plac'd His strong and loving arms a-bout me,
stand His words of love; But I'll nev-er know just why He came to save me,

CHORUS

He did something that no oth-er friend could do.
And He led me in the way I ought to go. } No one ev-er cared for
Till some day I see His bless-ed face a-bove,

me like Je-sus, There's no oth-er friend so kind as He; No one

else could take the sin and darkness from me, O how much He cared for me.

The Cross Is Not Greater

B. B.

BALLINGTON BOOTH

1. The cross that He gave may be heav-y,   But it ne'er out-weighs His grace;
2. The thorns in my path are not sharp-er   Than composed His crown for me;
3. The light of His love shineth bright-er,   As it falls on paths of woe;
4. His will I have joy in ful-fill-ing,   As I'm walk-ing in His sight;

The storm that I feared may surround me,   But it ne'er excludes His face.
The cup that I drink not more bit-ter   Than He drank in Geth-sem-a-ne.
The toil of my work grow-eth light-er,   As I stoop to raise the low.
My all to the blood I am bring-ing,   It a-lone can keep me right.

CHORUS

The cross is not great-er than His grace, The storm can-not hide His bless-ed face; I am sat-is-fied to know That with Je-sus here be-low, I can con-quer ev-ery foe.

122 The Christian's Good-Night

Sarah Doudney

Ira D. Sankey

1. Sleep on, be - lov - ed, sleep, and take thy rest; Lay down thy head up - on thy Sav-ior's
2. Calm is thy slum - ber as an infant's sleep; But thou shalt wake no more to toil and
3. Un - til e - ter - nal glo - ry lights the skies, Un - til the dead in Je - sus shall a -
4. On - ly "Good-night," be - lov - ed—not "Farewell!" A lit - tle while, and all His saints shall
5. Un - til we meet a - gain before His throne, Clothed in the spot - less robe He gives His

breast; We love thee well, but Je - sus loves thee best—Good-night! Good-night! Good-night!
weep: Thine is a per - fect rest, secure and deep—Good-night! Good-night! Good-night!
rise, And He shall come, but not in low - ly guise—Good-night! Good-night! Good-night!
dwell In hal-lowed un - ion in - di - vis - i - ble—Good-night! Good-night! Good-night!
own, Un - til we know e - ven as we are known—Good-night! Good-night! Good-night!

123 O God, Our Help

Isaac Watts

William Croft

1. O God, our help in a - ges past, Our hope for years to come,
2. Un - der the shad - ow of Thy throne Thy saints have dwelt se - cure;
3. Be - fore the hills in or - der stood, Or earth re - ceived her frame,
4. A thou - sand a - ges in Thy sight Are like an eve - ning gone,
5. O God, our help in a - ges past, Our hope for years to come;

Our shel - ter from the storm - y blast, And our e - ter - nal home!
Suf - fi - cient is Thine arm a - lone, And our de - fense is sure.
From ev - er - last - ing Thou art God, To end - less years the same.
Short as the watch that ends the night Be - fore the ris - ing sun.
Be Thou our guide while life shall last, And our e - ter - nal home.

Safe in the Arms of Jesus

Fanny J. Crosby

William H. Doane

1. Safe in the arms of Je - sus, Safe on His gen-tle breast, There by His
2. Safe in the arms of Je - sus, Safe from cor-rod-ing care, Safe from the
3. Je - sus, my heart's dear ref - uge, Je - sus has died for me; Firm on the

love o'er - shad - ed, Sweet-ly my soul shall rest. Hark! 'tis the voice of
world's temp-ta - tions, Sin can-not harm me there. Free from the blight of
Rock of A - ges, Ev - er my trust shall be. Here let me wait with

an - gels, Borne in a song to me,.. O - ver the fields of glo - ry,
sor - row, Free from my doubts and fears; On - ly a few more tri - als,
pa - tience, Wait till the night is o'er; Wait till I see the morn - ing

Chorus

O - ver the jas - per sea.......
On - ly a few more tears!..... Safe in the arms of Je - sus, Safe on His
Break on the gold - en shore.....

gen - tle breast, There by His love o'er - shad- ed, Sweetly my soul shall rest.

125 Be Still, My Soul

FROM PSALM 46
KATHARINA VON SCHLEGEL
TR. BY JANE L. BORTHWICK

JEAN SIBELIUS

1. Be still, my soul: the Lord is on thy side; Bear pa-tient-ly the
2. Be still, my soul: thy God doth un-der-take To guide the fu-ture
3. Be still, my soul: the hour is hast-'ning on When we shall be for-

cross of grief or pain; Leave to thy God to or-der and pro-vide;
as He has the past. Thy hope, thy con-fi-dence let noth-ing shake;
ev-er with the Lord, When dis-ap-point-ment, grief, and fear are gone,

In ev-ery change He faith-ful will re-main. Be still, my soul: thy
All now mys-te-rious shall be bright at last. Be still, my soul: the
Sor-row for-got, love's pur-est joys re-stored. Be still, my soul: when

best, thy heav'n-ly Friend Thro' thorn-y ways leads to a joy-ful end.
waves and winds still know His voice who ruled them while He dwelt be-low.
change and tears are past. All safe and bless-ed we shall meet at last. A-MEN.

The Rock That Is Higher Than I

Erastus Johnson

William G. Fischer

1. O some-times the shadows are deep, And rough seems the path to the goal,
2. O sometimes how long seems the day, And sometimes how wea-ry my feet;
3. O near to the Rock let me keep, If bless-ings or sor-rows pre-vail;

And sorrows, sometimes how they sweep Like tempests down o - ver the soul!
But toil - ing in life's dust-y way, The Rock's blessed shadow, how sweet!
Or climb-ing the mountain way steep, Or walk-ing the shad-ow-y vale.

REFRAIN

O then to the Rock let me fly,
let me fly,
To the

Rock that is high - er than I;
is high - er than I;
O then to the

Rock let me fly,
let me fly,
To the Rock that is high - er than I!

127 Jesus, Blessed Jesus

Chas. H. Gabriel

Chas. H. Gabriel

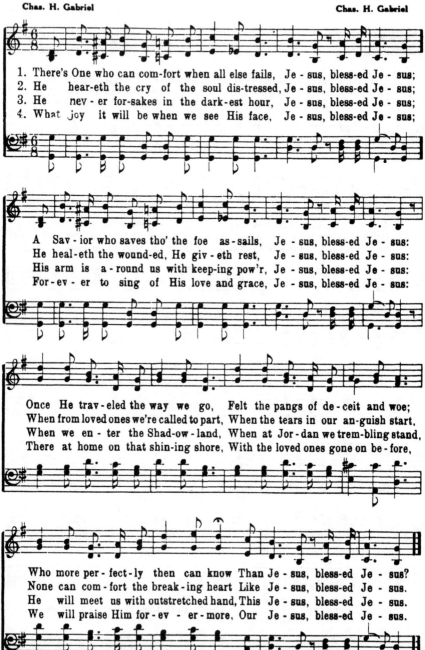

1. There's One who can com-fort when all else fails, Je - sus, bless-ed Je - sus;
2. He hear-eth the cry of the soul dis-tressed, Je - sus, bless-ed Je - sus;
3. He nev - er for-sakes in the dark-est hour, Je - sus, bless-ed Je - sus;
4. What joy it will be when we see His face, Je - sus, bless-ed Je - sus;

A Sav - ior who saves tho' the foe as-sails, Je - sus, bless-ed Je - sus:
He heal-eth the wound-ed, He giv-eth rest, Je - sus, bless-ed Je - sus:
His arm is a - round us with keep-ing pow'r, Je - sus, bless-ed Je - sus:
For-ev - er to sing of His love and grace, Je - sus, bless-ed Je - sus:

Once He trav-eled the way we go, Felt the pangs of de-ceit and woe;
When from loved ones we're called to part, When the tears in our an-guish start,
When we en - ter the Shad-ow - land, When at Jor - dan we trem-bling stand,
There at home on that shin-ing shore, With the loved ones gone on be - fore,

Who more per - fect-ly then can know Than Je - sus, bless-ed Je - sus?
None can com - fort the break-ing heart Like Je - sus, bless-ed Je - sus.
He will meet us with outstretched hand, This Je - sus, bless-ed Je - sus.
We will praise Him for-ev - er-more, Our Je - sus, bless-ed Je - sus.

'Til the Storm Passes By

Words and Music by
Mosie Lister

1. In the dark of the mid-night have I oft hid my face, while the storm howls a-bove me,
2. Man-y times sa-tan whis-pered, "There is no need to try, for there's no end of sor-row,
3. When the long night has end-ed and the storms come no more, let me stand in Thy pres-ence,

and there's no hid-ing place; 'Mid the crash of the thun-der, Pre-cious Lord, hear my cry,
there's no hope by and by;" But I know Thou art with me, and to-mor-row I'll rise
on that bright peace-ful shore; In that land where the temp-est nev-er comes, Lord, may I

CHORUS

keep me safe 'til the storm pass-es by.
where the storms nev-er dark-en the skies. 'Til the storm pass-es o-ver, 'Til the
dwell with Thee when the storm pass-es by.

thun-der sounds no more, 'Til the clouds roll for-ev-er from the sky; Hold me fast,

let me stand in the hol-low of Thy hand, Keep me safe 'til the storm pass-es by.

Favorite song of Dr. David A. Cavin and Dr. John Rawlings.

129 Each Step I Take

W. Elmo Mercer   W. Elmo Mercer

1. Each step I take my Sa-viour goes be-fore me, And with His loving hand
2. At times I feel my faith be-gin to wa-ver, When up a-head I see
3. I trust in God, no mat-ter come what may, For life e - ter - nal

He leads the way. And with each breath I whis-per "I a-dore Thee," Oh, what
a chas-m wide. It's then I turn and look up to my Sav-iour, I am
is in His hand. He holds the key that o-pens up the way, That will

rit. **Chorus**

joy to walk with Him each day......
strong when He is by my side...... Each step I take I know that He will
lead me to the promised land......

guide me; To higher ground He ev-er leads me on. Un-til some day the last

rit.

step will be tak-en, Each step I take just leads me clos-er home.

JESSIE H. BROWN and Mrs. C. M. ALEXANDER

D. B. TOWNER

1. An - y-where with Je - sus I can safe-ly go; An - y-where He
2. An - y-where with Je - sus I am not a - lone; Oth - er friends may
3. An - y-where with Je - sus o - ver land and sea, Tell - ing souls in
4. An - y-where with Je - sus I can go to sleep, When the dark-'ning

leads me in this world be - low; An - y-where with-out Him dear-est
fail me, He is still my own; Tho' His hand may lead me o - ver
dark-ness of sal - va - tion free; Read - y as He sum-mons me to
shad-ows round a - bout me creep; Know-ing I shall wak - en nev - er

joys would fade; An - y-where with Je - sus I am not a - fraid.
drear - y ways, An - y-where with Je - sus is a house of praise.
go or stay, An - y-where with Je - sus when He points the way.
more to roam, An - y-where with Je - sus will be home, sweet home.

CHORUS

An - y-where! an - y-where! Fear I can-not know;

An - y-where with Je - sus I can safe - ly go.

131 'Tis So Sweet to Trust in Jesus

LOUISA M. R. STEAD

WILLIAM J. KIRKPATRICK

1. 'Tis so sweet to trust in Je-sus, Just to take Him at His Word;
2. O how sweet to trust in Je-sus, Just to trust His cleans-ing blood;
3. Yes,'tis sweet to trust in Je-sus, Just from sin and self to cease;
4. I'm so glad I learned to trust Thee, Pre-cious Je-sus, Sav-ior, Friend;

Just to rest up-on His prom-ise; Just to know,"Thus saith the Lord."
Just in sim-ple faith to plunge me 'Neath the heal-ing, cleans-ing flood!
Just from Je-sus sim-ply tak-ing Life and rest, and joy and peace.
And I know that Thou art with me, Wilt be with me to the end.

CHORUS

Je-sus, Je-sus, how I trust Him! How I've proved Him o'er and o'er!

Je-sus, Je-sus, pre-cious Je-sus! O for grace to trust Him more!

132 The Old-Time Religion

CHO.—'Tis the old-time re-lig-ion, 'Tis the old-time re-lig-ion,
1. It was good for our moth-ers, It was good for our moth-ers,
2. It has saved our.. fa-thers, It has saved our.. fa-thers,
3. Makes me love ev-'ry-bod-y, Makes me love ev-'ry-bod-y,
4. It will do when I am dy-ing, It will do when I am dy-ing,
5. It will take us all to heav-en, It will take us all to heav-en,

The Old-Time Religion

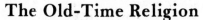

'Tis the old-time re-lig-ion, And it's good e-nough for me.
It was good for our moth-ers, And it's good e-nough for me.
It has saved our . . fa-thers, And it's good e-nough for me.
Makes me love ev-'ry-bod-y, And it's good e-nough for me.
It will do when I am dy-ing, And it's good e-nough for me.
It will take us all to heav-en, And it's good e-nough for me.

Rock of Ages

133

AUGUSTUS M. TOPLADY

THOMAS HASTINGS

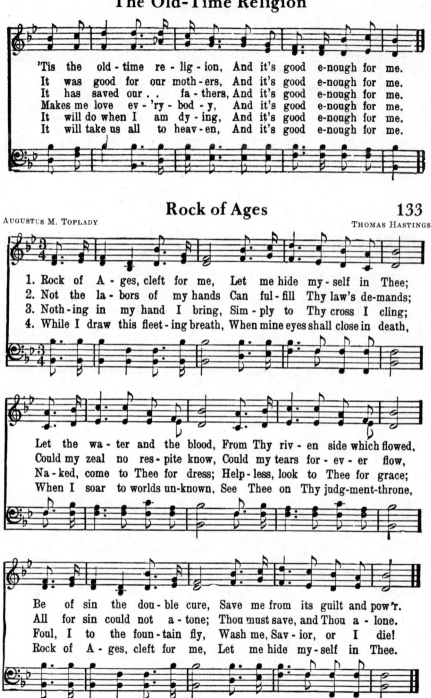

1. Rock of A-ges, cleft for me, Let me hide my-self in Thee;
2. Not the la-bors of my hands Can ful-fill Thy law's de-mands;
3. Noth-ing in my hand I bring, Sim-ply to Thy cross I cling;
4. While I draw this fleet-ing breath, When mine eyes shall close in death,

Let the wa-ter and the blood, From Thy riv-en side which flowed,
Could my zeal no res-pite know, Could my tears for-ev-er flow,
Na-ked, come to Thee for dress; Help-less, look to Thee for grace;
When I soar to worlds un-known, See Thee on Thy judg-ment-throne,

Be of sin the dou-ble cure, Save me from its guilt and pow'r.
All for sin could not a-tone; Thou must save, and Thou a-lone.
Foul, I to the foun-tain fly, Wash me, Sav-ior, or I die!
Rock of A-ges, cleft for me, Let me hide my-self in Thee.

134   I Do Believe

C. Wesley.

Unknown.

1. Fa - ther, I stretch my hands to Thee, No oth - er help I know;
2. What did Thine on - ly Son en - dure, Be - fore I drew my breath;
3. O Je - sus, could I this be - lieve, I now should feel Thy pow'r;
4. Au - thor of faith, to Thee I lift My wea - ry, long - ing eyes;

CHO.—I do be - lieve, I now be - lieve, That Je - sus died for me;

If Thou with-draw Thy-self from me, Ah! whith-er shall I go?
What pain, what la - bor to se - cure My soul from end - less death!
And all my wants Thou wouldst relieve, In this ac-cept - ed hour.
Oh, let me now re - ceive that gift; My soul with-out it dies.

And thro' His blood, His pre-cious blood, I shall from sin be free. A-MEN.

135   Christ Is All I Need

UNKNOWN

1. Christ is all I need, Christ is all I need, All, all, I need.
2. He was cru - ci - fied, For Me He died, On Cal - va - ry.

Christ Is All I Need

Christ is all I need, Christ is all I need, All, all I need.
That He loved me so, This is why I know Christ is all I need.

I Know I Am Saved

136

B. L.

BUD LYLES

I know I am saved, For Christ set me free, He

ran - somed my poor soul On the cross of Cal - va - ry. And now I can

sing, For Christ is my King, I'll see His face in Glo - ry bye and bye.—

Yesterday, Today, Forever

A. B. SIMPSON   J. H. BURKE

1. O how sweet the glo-rious mes-sage, Sim-ple faith may claim;
2. He who par-doned err-ing Pe-ter, Nev-er need'st thou fear;
3. He who 'mid the rag-ing bil-lows, Walked up-on the sea;
4. As of old He walked to Em-maus, With them to a-bide;

Yes-ter-day, to-day, for-ev-er, Je-sus is the same.
He that came to faith-less Tho-mas, All thy doubt will clear.
Still can hush our wild-est tem-pest, As on Gal-i-lee.
So thro' all life's way He walk-eth, Ev-er near our side.

Still He loves to save the sin-ful, Heal the sick and lame;
He who let the loved dis-ci-ple On His bos-om rest,
He who wept and prayed in an-guish, In Geth-sem-a-ne,
Soon a-gain shall we be-hold Him, Has-ten, Lord, the day!

Cheer the mourn-er, still the tem-pest, Glo-ry to His name!
Bids thee still, with love as ten-der, Lean up-on His breast.
Drinks with us each cup of trem-bling, In our ag-o-ny.
But 'twill still be "this same Je-sus," As He went a-way.

CHORUS

Yes-ter-day, to-day, for-ev-er, Je-sus is the same, All may change, but

Yesterday, To-day, Forever

Je - sus nev-er! Glo-ry to His name, Glo-ry to His name,

Glo-ry to His name, All may change, but Jesus nev-er! Glo-ry to His name.

Security   138

LINA SANDELL. (Swedish)
Tr. Composite

Swedish

1. More se - cure is no one ev - er Than the
2. God His own doth tend and nour - ish, In His
3. Nei - ther life nor death can ev - er From the
4. Lit - tle flock, to joy then yield thee! Ja - cob's
5. What He takes or what He gives us Shows the

loved ones of the Sav - ior; Not yon star on high a-
ho - ly courts they flour - ish; Like a fa - ther kind He
Lord His chil - dren sev - er; For His love and deep com-
God will ev - er shield thee; Rest se - cure with this De-
Fa - ther's love so pre - cious; We may trust His pur - pose

bid - ing, Nor the bird in home - nest hid - ing.
spares them, In His lov - ing arms He bears them.
pas - sion Com - forts them in trib - u - la - tion.
fend - er, At His will all foes sur - ren - der.
whol - ly— 'Tis His chil - dren's wel - fare sole - ly.

Never Alone!

AUTHOR UNKNOWN

AUTHOR UNKNOWN
ARR. BY FRED JACKY

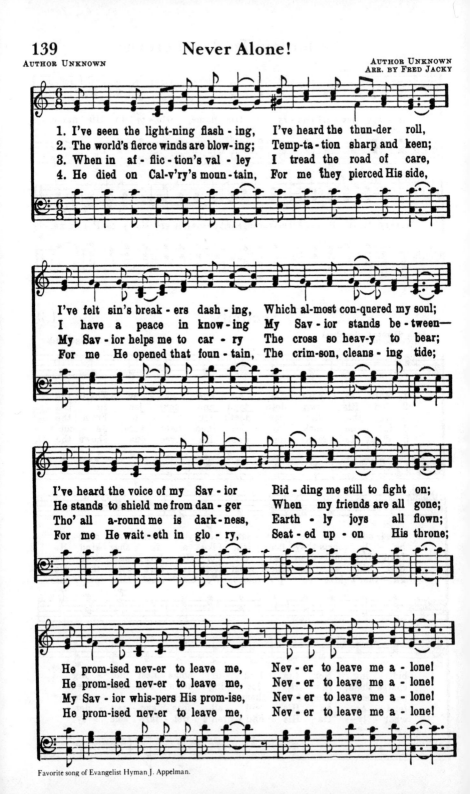

1. I've seen the light-ning flash - ing, I've heard the thun-der roll,
2. The world's fierce winds are blow-ing; Temp-ta-tion sharp and keen;
3. When in af - flic - tion's val - ley I tread the road of care,
4. He died on Cal-v'ry's moun-tain, For me they pierced His side,

I've felt sin's break - ers dash - ing, Which al-most con-quered my soul;
I have a peace in know - ing My Sav - ior stands be - tween—
My Sav - ior helps me to car - ry The cross so heav-y to bear;
For me He opened that foun - tain, The crim-son, cleans - ing tide;

I've heard the voice of my Sav - ior Bid - ding me still to fight on;
He stands to shield me from dan - ger When my friends are all gone;
Tho' all a-round me is dark - ness, Earth - ly joys all flown;
For me He wait - eth in glo - ry, Seat - ed up - on His throne;

He prom-ised nev-er to leave me, Nev - er to leave me a - lone!
He prom-ised nev-er to leave me, Nev - er to leave me a - lone!
My Sav - ior whis-pers His prom-ise, Nev - er to leave me a - lone!
He prom-ised nev-er to leave me, Nev - er to leave me a - lone!

Favorite song of Evangelist Hyman J. Appelman.

Never Alone!

CHORUS

No, nev-er a - lone,.......... No, nev-er a - lone, ... He prom-ised nev-er to
No, nev-er a - lone, No. no, nev-er a - lone,

leave me, He'll claim me for His own. No, nev-er a - lone,...... No, nev-er a-
No, nev-er a - lone, No, no,

lone,...... He prom-ised nev - er to leave me, Nev - er to leave me a - lone.
nev-er a - lone,

Blest Be the Tie That Binds 140

JOHN FAWCETT

HANS G. NÄGELI
ARR. BY LOWELL MASON

1. Blest be the tie that binds Our hearts in Chris-tian love; The
2. Be - fore our Fa-ther's throne, We pour our ar - dent prayers; Our
3. We share our mu - tual woes, Our mu - tual bur - dens bear; And
4. When we a - sun - der part, It gives us in - ward pain; But

fel - low - ship of kin - dred minds Is like to that a - bove.
fears, our hopes, our aims are one, Our com-forts and our cares.
oft - en for each oth - er flows The sym - pa - thiz-ing tear.
we shall still be joined in heart, And hope to meet a - gain. A - MEN.

141   I Am His, and He Is Mine

George W. Robinson   James Mountain

1. Loved with ev-er-last-ing love, Led by grace that love to know;
2. Heav'n a-bove is soft-er blue, Earth a-round is sweet-er green!
3. Things that once were wild a-larms Can-not now dis-turb my rest;
4. His for-ev-er, on-ly His; Who the Lord and me shall part?

Spir-it, breath-ing from a-bove, Thou hast taught me it is so!
Some-thing lives in ev-'ry hue Christ-less eyes have nev-er seen:
Closed in ev-er-last-ing arms, Pil-lowed on the lov-ing breast.
Ah, with what a rest of bliss Christ can fill the lov-ing heart!

Oh, this full and per-fect peace! Oh, this trans-port all di-vine!
Birds with glad-der songs o'er-flow, Flow'rs with deep-er beau-ties shine,
Oh, to lie for-ev-er here, Doubt and care and self re-sign,
Heav'n and earth may fade and flee, First-born light in gloom de-cline,

In a love which can-not cease, I am His and He is mine.
Since I know, as now I know, I am His and He is mine.
While He whis-pers in my ear— I am His and He is mine.
But while God and I shall be, I am His and He is mine.

Trusting Jesus

EDGAR P. STITES

IRA D. SANKEY

1. Sim - ply trust - ing ev - 'ry day, Trust - ing through a storm - y way;
2. Bright-ly doth His Spir - it shine In - to this poor heart of mine;
3. Sing-ing if my way is clear; Pray - ing if the path be drear;
4. Trust-ing Him while life shall last, Trust - ing Him till earth be past;

E - ven when my faith is small, Trust-ing Je - sus, that is all.
While He leads I can - not fall; Trust-ing Je - sus, that is all.
If in dan - ger, for Him call; Trust-ing Je - sus, that is all.
Till with - in the jas - per wall: Trust-ing Je - sus, that is all.

CHORUS

Trust - ing as the mo - ments fly, Trust - ing as the days go by;

Trust - ing Him what - e'er be - fall, Trust - ing Je - sus, that is all.

143 My Faith Has Found a Resting Place

LIDIE H. EDMUNDS

ARR. BY WILLIAM J. KIRKPATRICK

1. My faith has found a rest-ing place, Not in de-vice nor creed;
2. E - nough for me that Je-sus saves, This ends my fear and doubt;
3. My heart is lean-ing on the Word, The writ-ten Word of God,
4. My great Phy - si-cian heals the sick, The lost He came to save;

I trust the Ev - er - liv-ing One, His wounds for me shall plead.
A sin-ful soul I come to Him, He'll nev-er cast me out.
Sal - va-tion by my Sav iou's name, Sal - va-tion thro' His blood.
For me His pre-cious blood He shed, For me His life He gave.

CHORUS

I need no oth-er ar-gu-ment, I need no oth-er plea,

It is e-nough that Je-sus died, And that He died for me.

144 I Am Trusting Thee, Lord Jesus

FRANCES R. HAVERGAL

ETHELBERT W. BULLINGER

1. I am trust-ing Thee, Lord Je - sus! Trust-ing on - ly Thee!
2. I am trust-ing Thee, Lord Je - sus! At Thy feet I bow,
3. I am trust-ing Thee to guide me: Thou a - lone shalt lead,
4. I am trust-ing Thee, Lord Je - sus! Nev - er let me fall!

I Am Trusting Thee, Lord Jesus

Trust-ing Thee for full sal - va - tion, Great and free.
For Thy grace and ten - der mer - cy, Trust - ing now!
Ev - 'ry day and hour sup - ply - ing All my need.
I am trust - ing Thee for - ev - er, And for all.

Arise, My Soul, Arise!   145

CHARLES WESLEY

Harm. by J. W. P., and
Daniel B. Towner

1. A - rise, my soul, a - rise! Shake off thy guilt - y fears;
2. He ev - er lives a - bove, For me to in - ter - cede;
3. Five bleed - ing wounds He bears, Re - ceived on Cal - va - ry;
4. The Fa - ther hears Him pray, His dear a - noint - ed one;
5. My God is rec - on - ciled, His par - d'ning voice I hear;

The bleed - ing Sac - ri - fice In my be - half ap-pears:
His all - re - deem - ing love, His pre - cious blood to plead:
They pour ef - fec - tual prayers, They strong-ly plead for me:
He can - not turn a - way The pres - ence of His Son:
He owns me for His child, I can no long - er fear:

Be - fore the throne my Sure - ty stands— My name is writ - ten
His blood a - toned for all our race, And sprin-kles now the
"For - give him, O for - give," they cry, "Nor let that ran - somed
His Spir - it an - swers to the blood, And tells me I am
With con - fi - dence I now draw nigh, And "Fa - ther, Ab - ba,

on His hands, My name is writ - ten on His hands.
throne of grace, And sprin - kles now the throne of grace.
sin - ner die! Nor let that ran - somed sin - ner die!"
born of God, And tells me I am born of God.
Fa - ther!"cry, And "Fa - ther, Ab - ba, Fa - ther" cry.

My Anchor Holds

W. C. Martin, alt.

Daniel B. Towner

1. Tho' the an - gry sur - ges roll On my tem - pest-driv - en soul,
2. Might-y tides a - bout me sweep, Per - ils lurk with - in the deep,
3. I can feel the an - chor fast As I meet each sud - den blast,
4. Troub-les al - most 'whelm the soul; Griefs like bil - lows o'er me roll;

I am peace - ful, for I know, Wild - ly though the winds may blow,
An - gry clouds o'er-shade the sky, And the tem - pest ris - es high;
And the ca - ble, though un - seen, Bears the heav - y strain be - tween;
Tempters seek to lure a - stray; Storms ob - scure the light of day:

I've an an - chor safe and sure, That can ev - er-more en - dure.
Still I stand the tem-pest's shock, For my an - chor grips the Rock.
Thro' the storm I safe - ly ride, Till the turn - ing of the tide.
But in Christ I can be bold, I've an an - chor that shall hold.

Chorus

And it holds, my an - chor holds; Blow your wild - est, then, O
And it holds, ... my an - chor holds; Blow your wild - - - est,

gale, On my bark so small and frail: By His grace I shall not
then, O gale,

My Anchor Holds

fail, For my an - chor holds, my an - chor holds.
For my an - chor holds, it firm - ly holds,

Leaning on the Everlasting Arms 147

ELISHA A. HOFFMAN

ANTHONY J. SHOWALTER

1. What a fel-low-ship, what a joy di-vine, Leaning on the ev-er-last-ing arms;
2. Oh, how sweet to walk in this pilgrim way, Leaning on the ev-er-last-ing arms;
3. What have I to dread, what have I to fear, Leaning on the ev-er-last-ing arms?

What a bless-ed-ness, what a peace is mine, Leaning on the ev-er-last-ing arms.
Oh, how bright the path grows from day to day, Leaning on the ev-er-last-ing arms.
I have bless-ed peace with my Lord so near, Leaning on the ev-er-last-ing arms.

REFRAIN

Lean - ing, lean - ing, Safe and se-cure from all a-larms;
Lean-ing on Je - sus, lean-ing on Je - sus,

Lean - ing, lean - ing, Lean-ing on the ev-er-last-ing arms.
Lean-ing on Je - sus, lean-ing on Je - sus,

148 Master, the Tempest Is Raging

Mary A. Baker

H. R. Palmer

1. Mas-ter, the tem-pest is rag-ing! The bil-lows are toss-ing high!
2. Mas-ter, with an-guish of spir-it I bow in my grief to-day;
3. Mas-ter, the ter-ror is o-ver, The el-e-ments sweet-ly rest;

The sky is o'er-shadowed with blackness, No shel-ter or help is nigh:
The depths of my sad heart are trou-bled; O wak-en and save, I pray!
Earth's sun in the calm lake is mir-rored, And heav-en's with-in my breast.

"Car-est Thou not that we per-ish?" How canst Thou lie a-sleep,
Tor-rents of sin and of an-guish Sweep o'er my sink-ing soul!
Lin-ger, O bless-ed Re-deem-er, Leave me a-lone no more;

When each moment so mad-ly is threatening A grave in the an-gry deep?
And I per-ish! I per-ish, dear Mas-ter; O has-ten, and take con-trol!
And with joy I shall make the blest har-bor, And rest on the bliss-ful shore.

Master, the Tempest Is Raging

149 In Times Like These

Ruth Caye Jones

1. In times like these you need a Sav-iour, In times like these you need an an-chor; [D.S.] Be ver-y sure (Be ver-y sure), Be ver-y sure (Be ver-y sure), Your an-chor holds and grips the Sol-id Rock!

2. In times like these you need the Bi-ble, In times like these, oh, be not i-dle; [D.S.] Be ver-y sure (Be ver-y sure), Be ver-y sure (Be ver-y sure), Your an-chor holds and grips the Sol-id Rock!

3. In times like these I have a Sav-iour, In times like these, I have an an-chor; [D.S.] I'm ver-y sure (I'm ver-y sure), I'm ver-y sure (I'm ver-y sure), My an-chor holds and grips the Sol-id Rock!

FINE   REFRAIN

This Rock is Je-sus,

D. S.

Yes, He's the One, This Rock is Je-sus,— The on-ly One;

A Shelter in the Time of Storm

Words arranged

IRA D. SANKEY

1. The Lord's our Rock, in Him we hide, A shel-ter in the time of storm;
2. A shade by day, de-fense by night, A shel-ter in the time of storm;
3. The rag-ing storms may round us beat, A shel-ter in the time of storm;
4. O Rock di-vine, O Ref-uge dear, A shel-ter in the time of storm;

Se-cure what-ev-er ill be-tide, A shel-ter in the time of storm.
No fears a-larm, no foes af-fright, A shel-ter in the time of storm.
We'll nev-er leave our safe re-treat, A shel-ter in the time of storm.
Be Thou our help-er ev-er near, A shel-ter in the time of storm.

CHORUS

Oh, Je-sus is a Rock in a wea-ry land, A wea-ry land, a wea-ry land;

Oh, Je-sus is a Rock in a wea-ry land, A shel-ter in the time of storm.

The Haven of Rest

Henry L. Gilmour   George D. Moore

1. My soul in sad ex - ile was out on life's sea, So
2. I yield - ed my - self to His ten - der em - brace, And
3. The song of my soul, since the Lord made me whole, Has
4. How pre - cious the thought that we all may re - cline, Like
5. Oh, come to the Sav - ior, He pa - tient - ly waits To

bur-dened with sin and dis - trest, Till I heard a sweet voice say-ing,
faith tak - ing hold of the Word, My fet-ters fell off, and I
been the old sto - ry so blest, Of Je - sus, who'll save who-so-
John the be - lov - ed and blest, On Je - sus' strong arm, where no
save by His pow - er di - vine; Come, an - chor your soul in the

D. S.—The tem - pest may sweep o'er the

Fine.

"Make me your choice;" And I en-tered the "Ha - ven of Rest!"
an - chored my soul; The "Ha - ven of Rest" is my Lord.
ev - er will have A home in the "Ha - ven of Rest!"
tem - pest can harm,— Se - cure in the "Ha - ven of Rest!"
"Ha - ven of Rest," And say, "My Be - lov - ed is mine."

wild, storm-y deep, In Je - sus I'm safe ev - er - more.

Chorus   D. S.

I've anchored my soul in the "Ha-ven of Rest," I'll sail the wide seas no more;

I Know Whom I Have Believed

DANIEL W. WHITTLE   JAMES McGRANAHAN

Moderato

1. I know not why God's won-drous grace To me He hath made known,
2. I know not how this sav-ing faith To me He did im-part,
3. I know not how the Spir-it moves, Con-vinc-ing men of sin,
4. I know not what of good or ill May be re-served for me,
5. I know not when my Lord may come, At night or noon-day fair,

Nor why un-wor-thy—Christ in love Re-deemed me for His own.
Nor how be-liev-ing in His Word Wrought peace within my heart.
Re-veal-ing Je-sus thro' the Word, Cre-at-ing faith in Him.
Of wea-ry ways or gold-en days, Be-fore His face I see.
Nor if I walk the vale with Him, Or "meet Him in the air."

CHORUS

But "I know whom I have be-liev-ed, and am per-suad-ed that He is

a-ble To keep that which I've committed Un-to Him a-gainst that day."

Favorite song of Dr. Dwight Gustafson.

153 Hold to God's Unchanging Hand

Jennie Wilson

F. L. Eiland

1. Time is filled with swift tran-si-tion, Naught of earth unmoved can stand,
2. Trust in Him who will not leave you, What-so-ev-er years may bring,
3. Cov-et not this world's vain riches, That so rap-id-ly de-cay,
4. When your jour-ney is com-plet-ed, If to God, you have been true,

Build your hopes on things e-ter-nal, Hold to God's un-chang-ing hand!
If by earth-ly friends for-sak-en, Still, more close-ly to Him cling!
Seek to gain the heav'n-ly treas-ures, They will nev-er pass a-way.
Fair, and bright the home in glo-ry, Your en-rap-tured soul will view.

REFRAIN

Hold to God's unchanging hand! Hold to God's unchanging hand!
Hold to His hand, Hold to His hand,

rit. *Repeat refrain softly*

Build your hopes on things e-ter-nal, Hold to God's unchanging hand!

How Firm a Foundation

AUTHOR UNKNOWN

154

EARLY AMERICAN MELODY

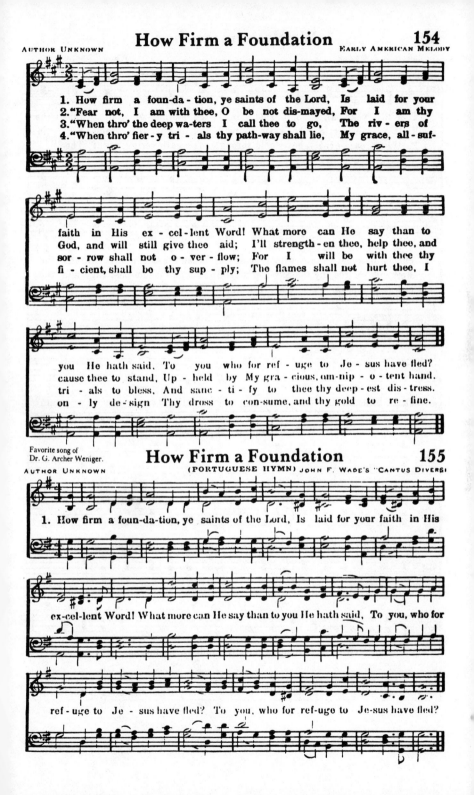

1. How firm a foun-da - tion, ye saints of the Lord, Is laid for your
2. "Fear not, I am with thee, O be not dis-mayed, For I am thy
3. "When thro' the deep wa-ters I call thee to go, The riv - ers of
4. "When thro' fier - y tri - als thy path-way shall lie, My grace, all - suf-

faith in His ex - cel - lent Word! What more can He say than to
God, and will still give thee aid; I'll strength - en thee, help thee, and
sor - row shall not o - ver - flow; For I will be with thee thy
fi - cient, shall be thy sup - ply; The flames shall not hurt thee, I

you He hath said, To you who for ref - uge to Je - sus have fled?
cause thee to stand, Up - held by My gra - cious, om-nip - o - tent hand.
tri - als to bless, And sanc - ti - fy to thee thy deep - est dis - tress.
on - ly de - sign Thy dross to con-sume, and thy gold to re - fine.

Favorite song of
Dr. G. Archer Weniger.

How Firm a Foundation

155

AUTHOR UNKNOWN

(PORTUGUESE HYMN) JOHN F. WADE'S "CANTUS DIVERSI"

1. How firm a foun-da-tion, ye saints of the Lord, Is laid for your faith in His

ex-cel-lent Word! What more can He say than to you He hath said, To you, who for

ref - uge to Je - sus have fled? To you, who for ref-uge to Je-sus have fled?

156 We Have an Anchor

Priscilla J. Owens

Wm. J. Kirkpatrick

1. Will your an-chor hold in the storms of life, When the clouds un-fold their wings of strife? When the strong tides lift, and the ca-bles strain, Will your an-chor drift, or firm re-main?

2. It is safe-ly moored, 'twill the storm with-stand. For 'tis well se-cured by the Sav-iour's hand; Though the tem-pest rage and the wild winds blow, Not an an-gry wave shall our bark o'er-flow.

3. When our eyes be-hold through the gath-ering night The cit-y of gold, our har-bor bright, We shall an-chor fast by the heaven-ly shore, With the storms all past for-ev-er-more.

REFRAIN

We have an an-chor that keeps the soul Steadfast and sure while the bil-lows roll, Fastened to the Rock which cannot move, Grounded firm and deep in the Saviour's love.

Blessed Assurance

FANNY J. CROSBY

PHOEBE P. KNAPP

1. Bless-ed as-sur-ance, Je-sus is mine! Oh, what a fore-taste of
2. Per-fect sub-mis-sion, per-fect de-light, Vis-ions of rap-ture now
3. Per-fect sub-mis-sion, all is at rest, I in my Sav-ior am

glo-ry di-vine! Heir of sal-va-tion, pur-chase of God,
burst on my sight; An-gels de-scend-ing, bring from a-bove
hap-py and blest; Watching and wait-ing, look-ing a-bove,

CHORUS

Born of His Spir-it, washed in His blood.
Ech-oes of mer-cy, whis-pers of love. This is my sto-ry, this is my
Filled with His goodness, lost in His love.

song, Prais-ing my Sav-ior all the day long; This is my sto-ry,

this is my song, Prais-ing my Sav-ior all the day long.

Favorite song of Dr. Jack Hyles and singer Jerome Hines.

158 Precious Promise

NATHANIEL NILES

P. P. BLISS

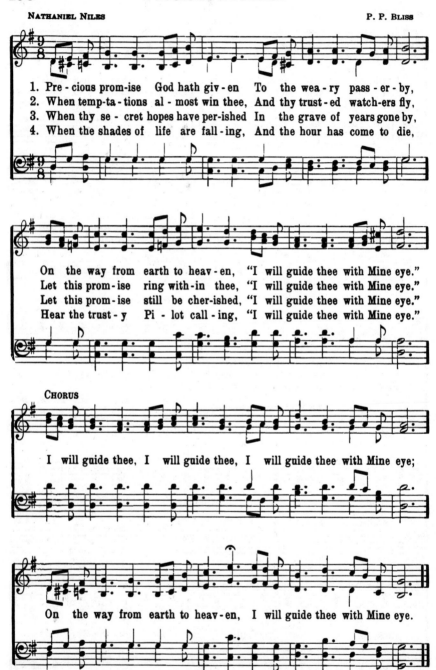

1. Pre - cious prom-ise God hath giv - en To the wea - ry pass - er - by,
2. When temp-ta - tions al - most win thee, And thy trust - ed watch-ers fly,
3. When thy se - cret hopes have per-ished In the grave of years gone by,
4. When the shades of life are fall - ing, And the hour has come to die,

On the way from earth to heav - en, "I will guide thee with Mine eye."
Let this prom - ise ring with - in thee, "I will guide thee with Mine eye."
Let this prom - ise still be cher-ished, "I will guide thee with Mine eye."
Hear the trust - y Pi - lot call - ing, "I will guide thee with Mine eye."

CHORUS

I will guide thee, I will guide thee, I will guide thee with Mine eye;

On the way from earth to heav - en, I will guide thee with Mine eye.

It Is Well With My Soul

H. G. SPAFFORD

P. P. BLISS

1. When peace, like a riv-er, at-tend-eth my way, When sor-rows like
2. Though Sa-tan should buf-fet, tho' tri-als should come, Let this blest as-
3. My sin—oh, the bliss of this glo-ri-ous tho't—My sin—not in
4. And, Lord, haste the day when the faith shall be sight, The clouds be rolled

sea-bil-lows roll; What-ev-er my lot, Thou hast taught me to say,
sur-ance con-trol, That Christ has re-gard-ed my help-less es-tate,
part, but the whole—Is nailed to the cross and I bear it no more,
back as a scroll, The trump shall re-sound and the Lord shall de-scend,

It is well, it is well with my soul.
And hath shed His own blood for my soul.
Praise the Lord, praise the Lord, O my soul!
"E-ven so"—it is well with my soul.

CHORUS

It is well . . . . with my
It is well

soul, ... It is well, it is well with my soul.
with my soul,

160 The Solid Rock

EDWARD MOTE

WILLIAM B. BRADBURY

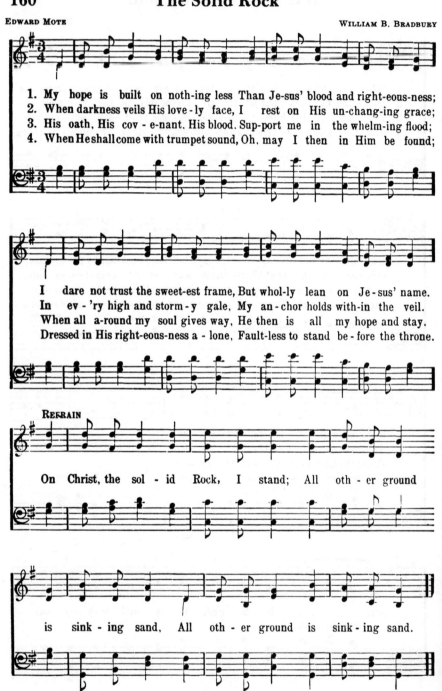

1. My hope is built on noth-ing less Than Je-sus' blood and right-eous-ness;
2. When darkness veils His love-ly face, I rest on His un-chang-ing grace;
3. His oath, His cov-e-nant, His blood. Sup-port me in the whelm-ing flood;
4. When He shall come with trumpet sound, Oh, may I then in Him be found;

I dare not trust the sweet-est frame, But whol-ly lean on Je-sus' name.
In ev-'ry high and storm-y gale, My an-chor holds with-in the veil.
When all a-round my soul gives way, He then is all my hope and stay.
Dressed in His right-eous-ness a-lone, Fault-less to stand be-fore the throne.

REFRAIN

On Christ, the sol-id Rock, I stand; All oth-er ground

is sink-ing sand, All oth-er ground is sink-ing sand.

Favorite song of Dr. Curtis Hutson.

A Mighty Fortress Is Our God

161

MARTIN LUTHER
TR. BY FREDERICK H. HEDGE

MARTIN LUTHER

1. A might-y for-tress is our God, A bul-wark nev-er fail - ing;
2. Did we in our own strength confide, Our striv-ing would be los - ing;
3. And tho' this world, with dev-ils filled, Should threaten to un-do us;
4. That word a-bove all earthly pow'rs—No thanks to them—a-bid - eth:

Our help - er He, a - mid the flood Of mor-tal ills pre-vail - ing.
Were not the right Man on our side, The Man of God's own choos - ing.
We will not fear, for God hath willed His truth to tri-umph through us.
The Spir - it and the gifts are ours Thro' Him who with us sid - eth.

For still our an-cient foe Doth seek to work us woe; His craft and pow'r are
Dost ask who that may be? Christ Je-sus, it is He; Lord Sabaoth is His
The prince of darkness grim—We tremble not for him; His rage we can en-
Let goods and kin-dred go, This mor-tal life al - so; The bod-y they may

great, And, armed with cru-el hate, On earth is not his e - qual.
name, From age to age the same, And He must win the bat - tle.
dure, For lo! his doom is sure, One lit - tle word shall fell him.
kill: God's truth a - bid - eth still, His king-dom is for - ev - er.

162   Blessed Be the Name

W. H. CLARK
REFRAIN, RALPH E. HUDSON

RALPH E. HUDSON
ARR. BY WILLIAM J. KIRKPATRICK

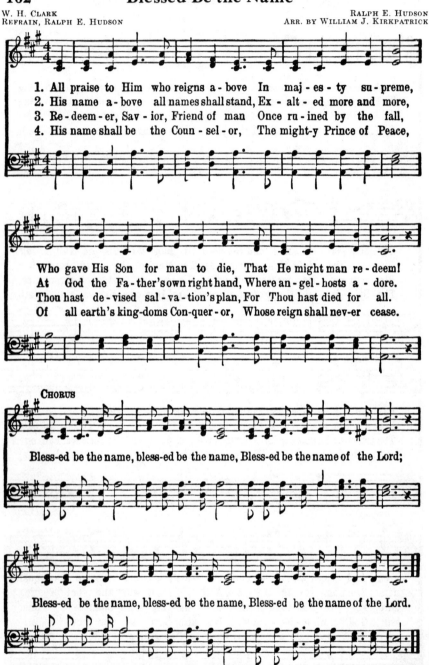

1. All praise to Him who reigns a-bove In maj-es-ty su-preme,
2. His name a-bove all names shall stand, Ex-alt-ed more and more,
3. Re-deem-er, Sav-ior, Friend of man Once ru-ined by the fall,
4. His name shall be the Coun-sel-or, The might-y Prince of Peace,

Who gave His Son for man to die, That He might man re-deem!
At God the Fa-ther's own right hand, Where an-gel-hosts a-dore.
Thou hast de-vised sal-va-tion's plan, For Thou hast died for all.
Of all earth's king-doms Con-quer-or, Whose reign shall nev-er cease.

CHORUS

Bless-ed be the name, bless-ed be the name, Bless-ed be the name of the Lord;

Bless-ed be the name, bless-ed be the name, Bless-ed be the name of the Lord.

LELA LONG

LELA LONG

1. There have been names that I have loved to hear, But nev-er has there
2. There is no name in earth or heav'n a-bove, That we should give such
3. And some day I shall see Him face to face To thank and praise Him

been a name so dear To this heart of mine, as the name divine, The
hon-or and such love As the blessed name, let us all acclaim, That
for His wondrous grace, Which He gave to me, when He made me free, The

pre-cious, precious name of Je-sus.
wondrous, glorious name of Je-sus.
bless-ed Son of God called Je-sus.

CHORUS.

Je-sus is the sweetest name I

know, And He's just the same as His love-ly name, And that's the reason

rall.

why I love Him so; Oh, Je-sus is the sweet-est name I know.

164 His Loving-Kindness

SAMUEL MEDLEY

WILLIAM CALDWELL

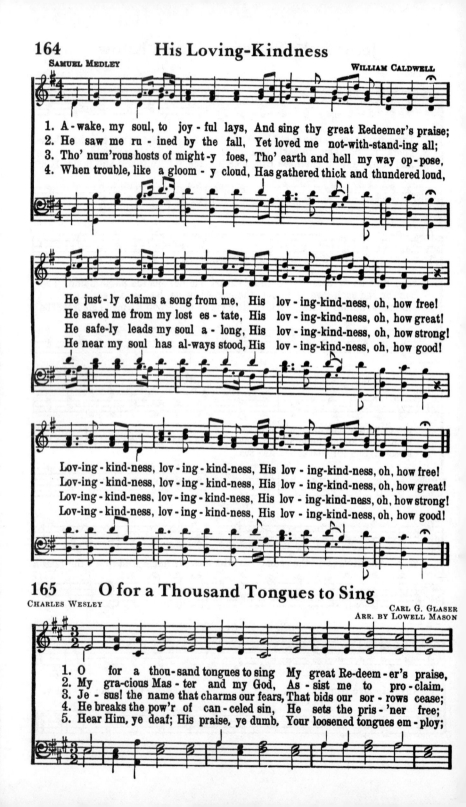

1. A-wake, my soul, to joy-ful lays, And sing thy great Redeemer's praise;
2. He saw me ru-ined by the fall, Yet loved me not-with-stand-ing all;
3. Tho' num'rous hosts of might-y foes, Tho' earth and hell my way op-pose,
4. When trouble, like a gloom-y cloud, Has gathered thick and thundered loud,

He just-ly claims a song from me, His lov-ing-kind-ness, oh, how free!
He saved me from my lost es-tate, His lov-ing-kind-ness, oh, how great!
He safe-ly leads my soul a-long, His lov-ing-kind-ness, oh, how strong!
He near my soul has al-ways stood, His lov-ing-kind-ness, oh, how good!

Lov-ing-kind-ness, lov-ing-kind-ness, His lov-ing-kind-ness, oh, how free!
Lov-ing-kind-ness, lov-ing-kind-ness, His lov-ing-kind-ness, oh, how great!
Lov-ing-kind-ness, lov-ing-kind-ness, His lov-ing-kind-ness, oh, how strong!
Lov-ing-kind-ness, lov-ing-kind-ness, His lov-ing-kind-ness, oh, how good!

165 O for a Thousand Tongues to Sing

CHARLES WESLEY

CARL G. GLASER
ARR. BY LOWELL MASON

1. O for a thou-sand tongues to sing My great Re-deem-er's praise,
2. My gra-cious Mas-ter and my God, As-sist me to pro-claim,
3. Je-sus! the name that charms our fears, That bids our sor-rows cease;
4. He breaks the pow'r of can-celed sin, He sets the pris-'ner free;
5. Hear Him, ye deaf; His praise, ye dumb, Your loosened tongues em-ploy;

O for a Thousand Tongues to Sing

The glo-ries of my God and King, The tri-umphs of His grace.
To spread thro' all the earth a-broad, The hon-ors of Thy name.
'Tis mu-sic in the sin-ner's ears, 'Tis life, and health, and peace.
His blood can make the foul-est clean; His blood a-vailed for me.
Ye blind, be-hold your Sav-ior come; And leap, ye lame, for joy.

Favorite song of Dr. Monroe Parker.

Come, Thou Almighty King　166

Anonymous

FELICE DE GIARDINI

1. Come, Thou Al-might-y King, Help us Thy name to sing,
2. Come, Thou In-car-nate Word, Gird on Thy might-y sword,
3. Come, Ho-ly Com-fort-er, Thy sa-cred wit-ness bear
4. To the great One in Three E-ter-nal prais-es be

Help us to praise: Fa-ther, all-glo-ri-ous, O'er all vic-
Our prayer at-tend: Come, and Thy peo-ple bless, And give Thy
In this glad hour: Thou who al-might-y art, Now rule in
Hence ev-er-more. His sov-'reign maj-es-ty May we in

to-ri-ous, Come, and reign o-ver us, An-cient of days.
word suc-cess: Spir-it of ho-li-ness, On us de-scend.
ev-'ry heart, And ne'er from us de-part, Spir-it of pow'r.
glo-ry see, And to e-ter-ni-ty Love and a-dore. A-MEN.

167 O Could I Speak

SAMUEL MEDLEY

WOLFGANG A. MOZART
ARR. BY LOWELL MASON

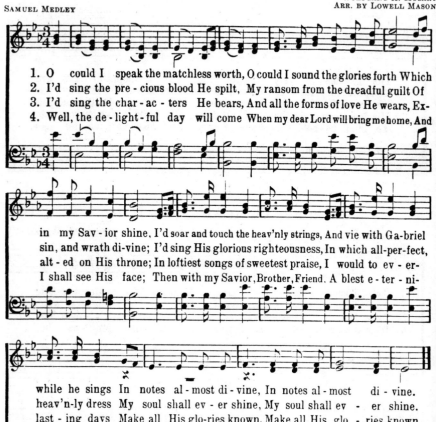

1. O could I speak the matchless worth, O could I sound the glories forth Which
2. I'd sing the pre-cious blood He spilt, My ransom from the dreadful guilt Of
3. I'd sing the char-ac-ters He bears, And all the forms of love He wears, Ex-
4. Well, the de-light-ful day will come When my dear Lord will bring me home, And

in my Sav-ior shine, I'd soar and touch the heav'nly strings, And vie with Ga-briel
sin, and wrath di-vine; I'd sing His glorious righteousness, In which all-per-fect,
alt-ed on His throne; In loftiest songs of sweetest praise, I would to ev-er-
I shall see His face; Then with my Savior, Brother, Friend. A blest e-ter-ni-

while he sings In notes al-most di-vine, In notes al-most di-vine.
heav'n-ly dress My soul shall ev-er shine, My soul shall ev-er shine.
last-ing days Make all His glo-ries known, Make all His glo-ries known.
ty I'll spend, Tri-um-phant in His grace, Tri-um-phant in His grace.

168 When Morning Gilds the Skies

FROM THE GERMAN
TR. BY EDWARD CASWALL

JOSEPH BARNBY

1. When morn-ing gilds the skies, My heart a-wak-ing cries:
2. When sleep her balm de-nies, My si-lent spir-it sighs:
3. Does sad-ness fill my mind, A sol-ace here I find:
4. In heav'n's e-ter-nal bliss The love-liest strain is this:
5. Be this, while life is mine, My can-ti-cle di-vine,

When Morning Gilds the Skies

May Je - sus Christ be praised; A - like at work and prayer . .
May Je - sus Christ be praised; When e - vil thoughts mo - lest, . . .
May Je - sus Christ be praised; Or fades my earth - ly bliss, . .
May Je - sus Christ be praised; The pow'rs of dark - ness fear, . . .
May Je - sus Christ be praised; Be this th' e - ter - nal song, . .

To Je - sus I re - pair: . . May Je - sus Christ be praised.
With this I shield my breast: . May Je - sus Christ be praised.
My com - fort still is this: . . May Je - sus Christ be praised.
When this sweet chant they hear: . May Je - sus Christ be praised.
Thro' all the a - ges on: . . . May Je - sus Christ be praised.

Hallelujah, What a Savior! 169

PHILIP P. BLISS

PHILIP P. BLISS

Moderato *mf*

1. "Man of Sor-rows," what a name For the Son of God who came
2. Bear - ing shame and scoff-ing rude, In my place con-demned He stood;
3. Guilt - y, vile and help-less, we; Spot-less Lamb of God was He;
4. Lift - ed up was He to die, "It is fin-ished," was His cry;
5. When He comes, our glo-rious King, All His ran-somed home to bring,

f *ff*

Ru - ined sin - ners to re-claim! Hal - le - lu - jah! what a Sav - ior!
Sealed my par - don with His blood; Hal - le - lu - jah! what a Sav - ior!
"Full a - tone-ment!" can it be? Hal - le - lu - jah! what a Sav - ior!
Now in heav'n ex - alt - ed high; Hal - le - lu - jah! what a Sav - ior!
Then a - new this song we'll sing: Hal - le - lu - jah! what a Sav - ior!

170   Crown Him With Many Crowns

MATTHEW BRIDGES AND
GODFREY THRING

GEORGE J. ELVEY

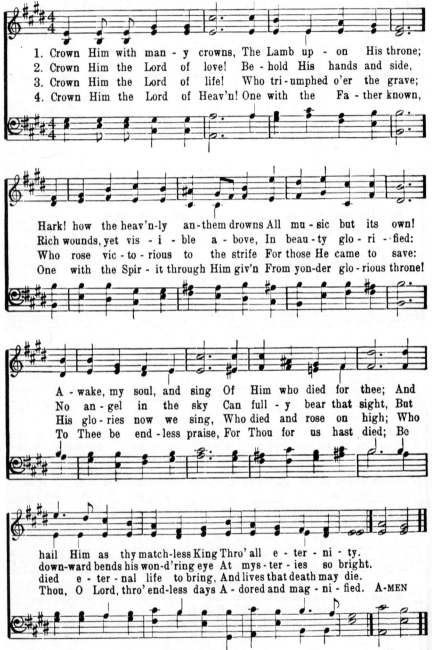

1. Crown Him with man - y crowns, The Lamb up - on His throne;
2. Crown Him the Lord of love! Be - hold His hands and side,
3. Crown Him the Lord of life! Who tri - umphed o'er the grave;
4. Crown Him the Lord of Heav'n! One with the Fa - ther known,

Hark! how the heav'n-ly an-them drowns All mu - sic but its own!
Rich wounds, yet vis - i - ble a - bove, In beau - ty glo - ri - fied:
Who rose vic - to - rious to the strife For those He came to save:
One with the Spir - it through Him giv'n From yon-der glo - rious throne!

A - wake, my soul, and sing Of Him who died for thee; And
No an - gel in the sky Can full - y bear that sight, But
His glo - ries now we sing, Who died and rose on high; Who
To Thee be end - less praise, For Thou for us hast died; Be

hail Him as thy match-less King Thro' all e - ter - ni - ty.
down-ward bends his won-d'ring eye At mys - ter - ies so bright.
died e - ter - nal life to bring, And lives that death may die.
Thou, O Lord, thro' end-less days A - dored and mag - ni - fied. A-MEN

O Worship the King

ROBERT GRANT

ADAPTED FROM J. MICHAEL HAYDN

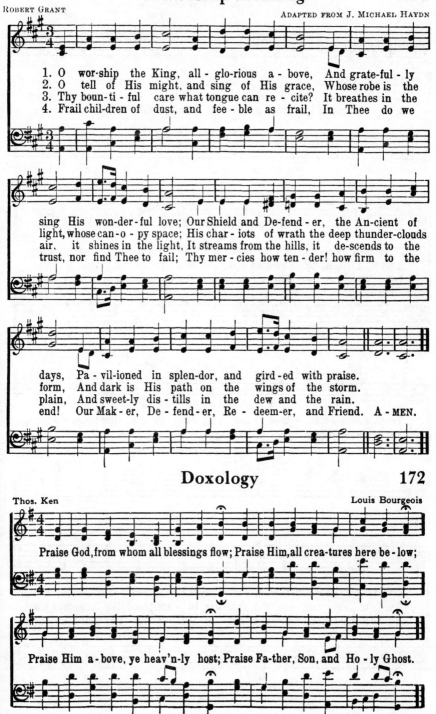

1. O wor-ship the King, all - glo-rious a - bove, And grate-ful - ly
2. O tell of His might, and sing of His grace, Whose robe is the
3. Thy boun-ti - ful care what tongue can re - cite? It breathes in the
4. Frail chil-dren of dust, and fee - ble as frail, In Thee do we

sing His won-der-ful love; Our Shield and De-fend - er, the An-cient of
light, whose can-o - py space; His char - iots of wrath the deep thunder-clouds
air, it shines in the light, It streams from the hills, it de-scends to the
trust, nor find Thee to fail; Thy mer - cies how ten - der! how firm to the

days, Pa - vil-ioned in splen-dor, and gird - ed with praise.
form, And dark is His path on the wings of the storm.
plain, And sweet-ly dis - tills in the dew and the rain.
end! Our Mak - er, De - fend - er, Re - deem-er, and Friend. A - MEN.

Doxology

Thos. Ken

Louis Bourgeois

Praise God, from whom all blessings flow; Praise Him, all crea-tures here be - low;

Praise Him a - bove, ye heav'n-ly host; Praise Fa-ther, Son, and Ho - ly Ghost.

173   Come, Thou Fount

ROBERT ROBINSON   JOHN WYETH

1. Come, Thou Fount of ev - 'ry bless - ing, Tune my heart to sing Thy grace;
2. Here I raise mine Eb - en - e - zer; Hith - er by Thy help I'm come;
3. O   to grace how great a debt - or Dai - ly I'm con-strained to be!

Streams of mer - cy, nev - er ceas - ing, Call for songs of loud-est praise.
And   I hope, by Thy good pleas-ure, Safe - ly to ar - rive at home.
Let   Thy good-ness, like a fet - ter, Bind my wan-d'ring heart to Thee:

Teach me some me - lo-dious son - net, Sung by flam - ing tongues a-bove;
Je - sus sought me when a stran-ger, Wand'ring from the fold of God;
Prone to wan - der, Lord, I feel it, Prone to leave the God I love;

Praise the mount—I'm fixed up - on it—Mount of Thy re-deem-ing love.
He, to res - cue me from dan - ger, In - ter-posed His pre-cious blood.
Here's my heart, O take and seal it; Seal it for Thy courts a - bove.

Great God of Wonders

Samuel Davies

John Newton

1. Great God of won - ders! all Thy ways Are match - less, God - like, and di - vine; But the fair glo - ries of Thy grace More God - like and un - ri - valed shine, More God - like and un - ri - valed shine.

2. In won - der lost, with trem-bling joy We take the par - don of our God; Par - don for crimes of deep - est dye, A par - don bought with Je - sus' blood; A par - don bought with Je - sus' blood:

3. O may this strange, this match-less grace, This God - like mir - a - cle of love, Fill the whole earth with grate-ful praise, And all th'an - gel - ic choirs a - bove, And all th'an - gel - ic choirs a - bove.

Chorus

Who is a par - d'ning God like Thee? Or who has grace so rich and free? Or who has grace so rich and free? A - MEN.

175 To God Be the Glory

FANNY J. CROSBY

WILLIAM H. DOANE

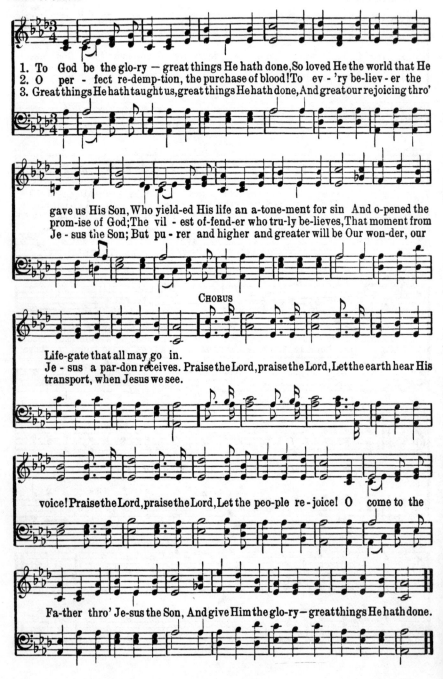

1. To God be the glo-ry — great things He hath done, So loved He the world that He
2. O per - fect re-demp-tion, the purchase of blood! To ev - 'ry be-liev - er the
3. Great things He hath taught us, great things He hath done, And great our rejoicing thro'

gave us His Son, Who yield-ed His life an a-tone-ment for sin And o-pened the
prom-ise of God; The vil - est of-fend-er who tru-ly be-lieves, That moment from
Je - sus the Son; But pu - rer and higher and greater will be Our won-der, our

CHORUS

Life-gate that all may go in.
Je - sus a par-don re-ceives. Praise the Lord, praise the Lord, Let the earth hear His
transport, when Jesus we see.

voice! Praise the Lord, praise the Lord, Let the peo-ple re - joice! O come to the

Fa-ther thro' Je-sus the Son, And give Him the glo-ry — great things He hath done.

Our Great Savior

J. Wilbur Chapman

Rowland W. Prichard
Arr. by Robert Harkness

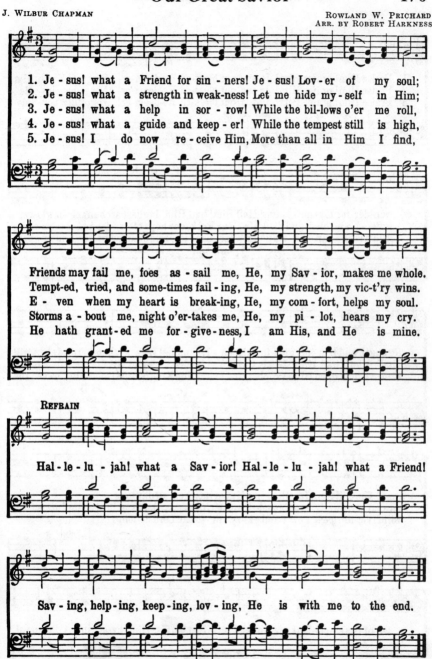

1. Je - sus! what a Friend for sin - ners! Je - sus! Lov - er of my soul;
2. Je - sus! what a strength in weak-ness! Let me hide my - self in Him;
3. Je - sus! what a help in sor - row! While the bil-lows o'er me roll,
4. Je - sus! what a guide and keep - er! While the tempest still is high,
5. Je - sus! I do now re - ceive Him, More than all in Him I find,

Friends may fail me, foes as - sail me, He, my Sav - ior, makes me whole.
Tempt-ed, tried, and some-times fail - ing, He, my strength, my vic-t'ry wins.
E - ven when my heart is break-ing, He, my com - fort, helps my soul.
Storms a - bout me, night o'er-takes me, He, my pi - lot, hears my cry.
He hath grant-ed me for - give-ness, I am His, and He is mine.

Refrain

Hal - le - lu - jah! what a Sav - ior! Hal - le - lu - jah! what a Friend!

Sav - ing, help-ing, keep-ing, lov - ing, He is with me to the end.

Favorite song of Dr. J. R. Faulkner.

177 Praise Him! Praise Him!

FANNY J. CROSBY

CHESTER G. ALLEN

1. Praise Him! praise Him! Je-sus, our bless-ed Re-deem-er! Sing, O Earth, His
2. Praise Him! praise Him! Je-sus, our bless-ed Re-deem-er! For our sins He
3. Praise Him! praise Him! Je-sus, our bless-ed Re-deem-er! Heav'nly por - tals

won-der-ful love pro-claim! Hail Him! hail Him! highest archangels in glo-ry;
suffered, and bled, and died; He our Rock, our hope of e - ter-nal sal-va-tion,
loud with ho-san-nas ring! Je - sus, Sav-ior, reigneth for-ev - er and ev - er;

Strength and hon - or give to His ho - ly name! Like a shep-herd, Je-sus will
Hail Him! hail Him! Je-sus the Cru - ci - fied. Sound His Praises! Je-sus who
Crown Him! crown Him! Prophet, and Priest, and King! Christ is com-ing! o - ver the

REFRAIN

guard His children, In His arms He carries them all day long:
bore our sorrows, Love unbounded, wonderful, deep and strong: Praise Him! praise Him!
world vic-to-rious, Pow'r and glo-ry un - to the Lord be-long:

tell of His ex-cel-lent greatness; Praise Him! praise Him! ev-er in joy-ful song!

I Will Praise Him

Mrs. M. J. Harris

Mrs. M. J. Harris

1. When I saw the cleansing foun-tain O - pen wide for all my sin,
2. Tho' the way seems straight and narrow, All I claimed was swept a - way;
3. Then God's fire up - on the al - tar Of my heart was set a - flame;
4. Bless - ed be the name of Je - sus! I'm so glad He took me in;
5. Glo - ry, glo - ry to the Fa - ther! Glo - ry, glo - ry to the Son!

I o - beyed the Spir - it's woo - ing, When He said, Wilt thou be clean?
My am - bi-tions, plans, and wish-es, At my feet in ash - es lay.
I shall nev - er cease to praise Him, Glo - ry, glo - ry to His name!
He's for-giv - en my trans-gres-sions, He has cleansed my heart from sin.
Glo - ry, glo - ry to the Spir - it! Glo - ry to the Three in One!

Chorus *Faster*

I will praise Him! I will praise Him! Praise the Lamb for sinners slain;

for sin-ners slain;

Give Him glo-ry, all ye peo - ple, For His blood can wash a-way each stain.

179 All Hail the Power of Jesus' Name
(Diadem)

EDWARD PERRONET
ALT. BY JOHN RIPPON

JAMES ELLOR

1. All hail the pow'r of Je - sus' name! Let an - gels pros-trate fall,
2. Ye cho - sen seed of Is - rael's race, Ye ran-somed from the fall,
3. Let ev - 'ry kin - dred, ev - 'ry tribe, On this ter - res-trial ball,
4. O that with yon - der sa - cred throng We at His feet may fall,

Let an - gels pros-trate fall; Bring forth the roy - al di - a - dem,
Ye ran-somed from the fall, Hail Him who saves you by His grace,
On this ter - res-trial ball, To Him all maj - es - ty as - cribe,
We at His feet may fall! We'll join the ev - er - last - ing song,

And crown . . . . Him, Crown Him,
And crown Him, crown Him, crown Him, crown Him, And crown Him Lord of
And crown . . . . Him, Crown Him,
And crown Him, crown Him, crown Him, Crown . . . .

crown Him, crown Him;
all, crown Him; And crown Him Lord of all!
crown . . . . . Him;
. . . . Him; And crown Him Lord of all!

OLIVER HOLDEN

1. All hail the pow'r of Je - sus' name! Let an - gels pros-trate fall:
2. Ye cho - sen seed of Is - rael's race, Ye ran-somed from the fall,
3. Let ev - 'ry kin - dred, ev - 'ry tribe On this ter - res - trial ball,
4. O that with yon - der sa - cred throng We at His feet may fall!

Bring forth the roy - al di - a - dem, And crown Him Lord of all,
Hail Him who saves you by His grace, And crown Him Lord of all,
To Him all maj - es - ty as - cribe, And crown Him Lord of all,
We'll join the ev - er - last - ing song, And crown Him Lord of all,

Bring forth the roy - al di - a - dem, And crown Him Lord of all!
Hail Him who saves you by His grace, And crown Him Lord of all!
To Him all maj - es - ty as - cribe, And crown Him Lord of all!
We'll join the ev - er - last - ing song, And crown Him Lord of all!

[SECOND TUNE] **Miles' Lane** WILLIAM SHRUBSOLE

1. All hail the pow'r of Je - sus' name! Let an - gels pros-trate fall; Bring forth the roy - al

di - a - dem, And crown Him, crown Him, crown Him, Crown Him Lord of all!

181 Love Lifted Me

JAMES ROWE

HOWARD E. SMITH

1. I was sink-ing deep in sin, Far from the peaceful shore, Ver-y deep-ly
2. All my heart to Him I give, Ev-er to Him I'll cling, In His bless-ed
3. Souls in dan-ger, look a-bove, Je-sus com-plete-ly saves; He will lift you

stained with-in, Sink-ing to rise no more; But the Mas-ter of the sea
pres-ence live, Ev-er His prais-es sing. Love so might-y and so true
by His love Out of the an-gry waves. He's the Mas-ter of the sea,

Heard my despairing cry, From the wa-ters lift-ed me, Now safe am I.
Mer-its my soul's best songs; Faith-ful, lov-ing serv-ice, too, To Him be-longs.
Bil-lows His will o-bey; He your Sav-ior wants to be—Be saved to-day.

CHORUS

Love lift-ed me!.... Love lift-ed me!.... When noth-ing
e-ven me! e-ven me!

else could help, Love lift-ed me. Love lift-ed me.

Love Divine, All Loves Excelling 182

Charles Wesley

John Zundel

1. Love di-vine, all loves ex-cel-ling, Joy of heav'n, to earth come down;
2. Breathe, O breathe Thy lov-ing Spir-it In-to ev-'ry troub-led breast!
3. Come, Al-might-y to de-liv-er, Let us all Thy life re-ceive;
4. Fin-ish then Thy new cre-a-tion; Pure and spot-less let us be;

Fix in us Thy hum-ble dwell-ing; All Thy faith-ful mer-cies crown.
Let us all in Thee in-her-it, Let us find that sec-ond rest.
Sud-den-ly re-turn, and nev-er, Nev-er-more Thy tem-ples leave:
Let us see Thy great sal-va-tion Per-fect-ly re-stored in Thee:

Je-sus, Thou art all com-pas-sion, Pure, un-bound-ed love Thou art;
Take a-way our bent to sin-ning, Al-pha and O-me-ga be;
Thee we would be al-ways blessing, Serve Thee as Thy hosts a-bove,
Changed from glo-ry in-to glo-ry, Till in heav'n we take our place,

Vis-it us with Thy sal-va-tion; En-ter ev-'ry trem-bling heart.
End of faith, as its be-gin-ning, Set our hearts at lib-er-ty.
Pray, and praise Thee with-out ceas-ing, Glo-ry in Thy per-fect love.
Till we cast our crowns be-fore Thee, Lost in won-der, love, and praise.

183   My Jesus, I Love Thee

WILLIAM R. FEATHERSTONE   ADONIRAM J. GORDON

1. My Je - sus, I love Thee, I know Thou art mine, For Thee all the
2. I love Thee, be - cause Thou hast first lov - ed me, And pur-chased my
3. I'll love Thee in life, I will love Thee in death, And praise Thee as
4. In man-sions of glo - ry and end-less de-light, I'll ev - er a-

fol - lies of sin I re-sign; My gra-cious Re - deem - er, my
par - don on Cal - va-ry's tree; I love Thee for wear - ing the
long as Thou lend-est me breath; And say when the death - dew lies
dore Thee in heav-en so bright; I'll sing with the glit - ter-ing

Sav - ior art Thou; If ev - er I loved Thee, my Je - sus, 'tis now.
thorns on Thy brow: If ev - er I loved Thee, my Je - sus, 'tis now.
cold on my brow, If ev - er I loved Thee, my Je - sus, 'tis now.
crown on my brow. If ev - er I loved Thee, my Je - sus, 'tis now.

A favorite song of Dr. Alfred B. Smith.

184   I Love Him

English Hymn Book   S. C. FOSTER

1. Gone from my heart the world and all its charm; Gone are my sins and
2. Once I was lost up - on the plains of sin; Once was a slave to
3. Once I was bound, but now I am set free; Once I was blind, but

I Love Him

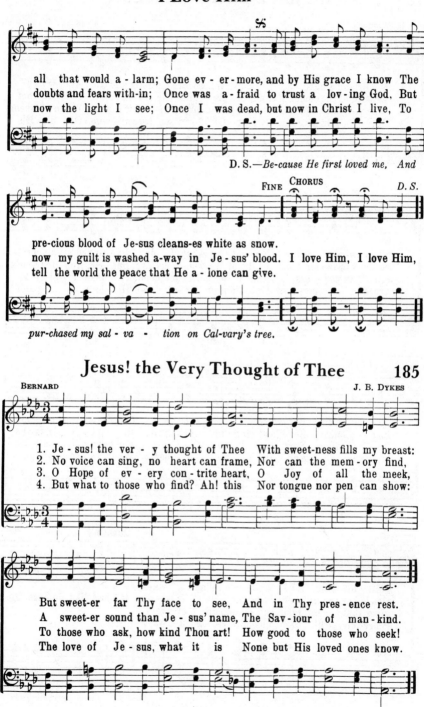

all that would a - larm; Gone ev - er - more, and by His grace I know The
doubts and fears with-in; Once was a - fraid to trust a lov - ing God, But
now the light I see; Once I was dead, but now in Christ I live, To

D. S.—*Be-cause He first loved me, And*

FINE CHORUS D. S.

pre-cious blood of Je-sus cleans-es white as snow.
now my guilt is washed a-way in Je - sus' blood. I love Him, I love Him,
tell the world the peace that He a - lone can give.

pur-chased my sal - va - tion on Cal-vary's tree.

Jesus! the Very Thought of Thee 185

BERNARD
J. B. DYKES

1. Je - sus! the ver - y thought of Thee With sweet-ness fills my breast:
2. No voice can sing, no heart can frame, Nor can the mem - ory find,
3. O Hope of ev - ery con - trite heart, O Joy of all the meek,
4. But what to those who find? Ah! this Nor tongue nor pen can show:

But sweet-er far Thy face to see, And in Thy pres - ence rest.
A sweet-er sound than Je - sus' name, The Sav - iour of man - kind.
To those who ask, how kind Thou art! How good to those who seek!
The love of Je - sus, what it is None but His loved ones know.

It's Just Like His Great Love

Edna H. Worrell

Clarence B. Strouse

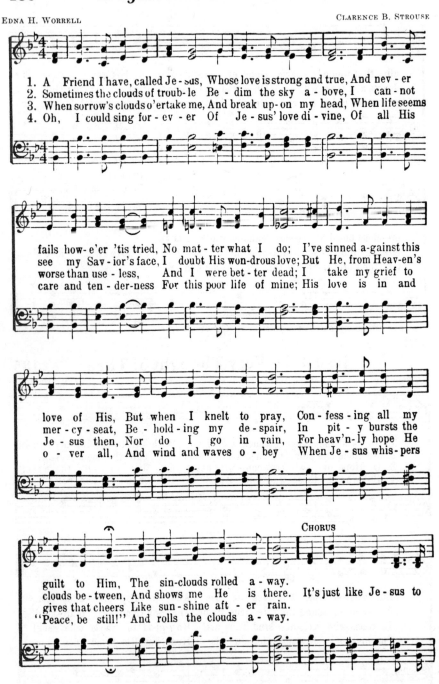

1. A Friend I have, called Je-sus, Whose love is strong and true, And nev-er
2. Sometimes the clouds of troub-le Be-dim the sky a-bove, I can-not
3. When sorrow's clouds o'ertake me, And break up-on my head, When life seems
4. Oh, I could sing for-ev-er Of Je-sus' love di-vine, Of all His

fails how-e'er 'tis tried, No mat-ter what I do; I've sinned a-gainst this
see my Sav-ior's face, I doubt His won-drous love; But He, from Heav-en's
worse than use-less, And I were bet-ter dead; I take my grief to
care and ten-der-ness For this poor life of mine; His love is in and

love of His, But when I knelt to pray, Con-fess-ing all my
mer-cy-seat, Be-hold-ing my de-spair, In pit-y bursts the
Je-sus then, Nor do I go in vain, For heav'n-ly hope He
o-ver all, And wind and waves o-bey When Je-sus whis-pers

guilt to Him, The sin-clouds rolled a-way.
clouds be-tween, And shows me He is there. It's just like Je-sus to
gives that cheers Like sun-shine aft-er rain.
"Peace, be still!" And rolls the clouds a-way.

CHORUS

It's Just Like His Great Love

roll the clouds a-way, It's just like Je-sus to keep me day by day,

It's just like Je-sus all a-long the way, It's just like His great love.

Jesus Loves the Little Children 187

Anonymous

GEO. F. ROOT

Je-sus loves the lit-tle chil-dren, All the chil-dren of the

world; Red and yel-low, black and white, They are

pre-cious in His sight; Je-sus loves the lit-tle chil-dren of the world.

188   The Love of God

FREDERICK M. LEHMAN

FREDERICK M. LEHMAN
ARR. BY CLAUDIA L. MAYS

1. The love of God is great-er far Than tongue or pen can ev - er tell;
2. When hoar-y time shall pass a - way, And earth-ly thrones and king-doms fall;
3. Could we with ink the o - cean fill, And were the skies of parch-ment made,

It goes be-yond the high-est star, And reach-es to the low-est hell;
When men who here re-fuse to pray, On rocks and hills and moun-tains call;
Were ev -'ry stalk on earth a quill, And ev -'ry man a scribe by trade;

The guilt - y pair, bowed down with care, God gave His Son to win;
God's love, so sure, shall still en - dure, All meas-ure - less and strong;
To write the love of God a - bove Would drain the o - cean dry;

His err - ing child He rec - on - ciled, And par-doned from his sin.
Re-deem-ing grace to Ad-am's race – The saints' and an - gels' song.
Nor could the scroll con-tain the whole, Tho' stretched from sky to sky.

CHORUS

Oh love of God, how rich and pure! How meas-ure - less and strong!

The Love of God

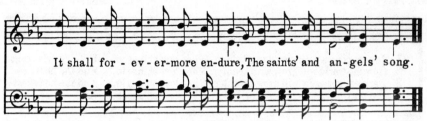

It shall for - ev - er-more en-dure, The saints' and an-gels' song.

Oh, How I Love Jesus

189

FREDERICK WHITFIELD

TRADITIONAL MELODY

1. There is a name I love to hear, I love to sing its worth; It sounds like
2. It   tells me of a Sav-ior's love, Who died to set me free; It tells me
3. It   tells me what my Fa-ther hath In store for ev - 'ry day, And tho' I
4. It   tells of One whose loving heart Can feel my deep-est woe, Who in each

CHORUS

mu - sic in mine ear, The sweetest name on earth.
of His precious blood, The sin-ner's per-fect plea. Oh, how I love Je - sus,
tread a darksome path, Yields sunshine all the way.
sor - row bears a part, That none can bear be-low.

Oh, how I love Je - sus, Oh, how I love Je - sus, Be-cause He first loved me!

190 When Love Shines In

MRS. FRANK A. BRECK

WILLIAM J. KIRKPATRICK

1. Je-sus comes with pow'r to gladden, When love shines in, Ev-'ry life that
2. How the world will grow with beauty, When love shines in, And the heart re-
3. Dark-est sor-row will grow brighter, When love shines in, And the heav-iest
4. We may have un-fad-ing splendor, When love shines in, And a friend-ship

woe can sad-den, When love shines in. Love will teach us how to pray,
joice in du-ty, When love shines in. Tri-als may be sanc-ti-fied,
bur-den light-er, When love shines in. 'Tis the glo-ry that will throw
true and ten-der, When love shines in. When earth vic-t'ries shall be won,

Love will drive the gloom away, Turn our darkness in-to day, When love shines in.
And the soul in peace a-bide, Life will all be glo-ri-fied, When love shines in.
Light to show us where to go; O, the heart shall blessing know, When love shines in.
And our life in Heav'n begun, There will be no need of sun, When love shines in.

CHORUS

When love shines in,...... When love shines in,...
When love shines in,........
When love shines in, When love shines in, When love shines in,....

How the heart is tuned to sing-ing, When love.. shines in;.....
When love shines in;......

When Love Shines In

When love shines in,...... When love shines in,..
When love shines in,........

When love shines in, When love shines in,   When love shines in,...

Joy and peace to oth-ers bring-ing, When love shines in...
When love, when love shines in....

Jesus Loves Me   191

Anna B. Warner   William B. Bradbury

1. Je-sus loves me! this I know, For the Bi-ble tells me so; Lit-tle
2. Je-sus loves me! He who died Heav-en's gate to o-pen wide; He will
3. Je-sus loves me! He will stay Close be-side me all the way; Thou hast

CHORUS

ones to Him be-long, They are weak but He is strong. Yes, Je-sus loves me!
wash a-way my sin, Let His lit-tle child come in.
bled and died for me, I will hence-forth live for Thee.

Yes, Je-sus loves me! Yes, Je-sus loves me! The Bi-ble tells me so.

192 My Savior's Love

CHARLES H. GABRIEL

CHARLES H. GABRIEL

1. I stand a-mazed in the pres-ence Of Je-sus the Naz-a-rene,
2. For me it was in the gar-den He prayed: "Not My will, but Thine;"
3. In pit-y an-gels be-held Him, And came from the world of light
4. He took my sins and my sor-rows, He made them His ver-y own;
5. When with the ransomed in glo-ry His face I at last shall see,

And won-der how He could love me, A sin-ner, condemned, un-clean.
He had no tears for His own griefs, But sweat-drops of blood for mine.
To com-fort Him in the sor-rows He bore for my soul that night.
He bore the bur-den to Cal-v'ry, And suf-fered, and died a-lone.
'Twill be my joy thro' the a-ges To sing of His love for me.

CHORUS.

How mar-vel-ous! how won-der-ful! And my song shall ev-er be:
Oh, how mar-vel-ous! oh, how won-der-ful!

How mar-vel-ous! how won-der-ful Is my Sav-ior's love for me! A-MEN.
Oh, how mar-vel-ous! oh, how won-der-ful

Jesus Loves Even Me

PHILIP P. BLISS

PHILIP P. BLISS

1. I am so glad that our Fa-ther in heav'n Tells of His love in the Book He has giv'n; Won-der-ful things in the Bi-ble I see— This is the dear-est, that Je-sus loves me.

2. Tho I for-get Him and wan-der a-way, Still He doth love me wher-ev-er I stray; Back to His dear lov-ing arms would I flee When I re-mem-ber that Je-sus loves me.

3. O if there's on-ly one song I can sing When in His beau-ty I see the great King, This shall my song in e-ter-ni-ty be: "O what a won-der that Je-sus loves me!"

CHORUS

I am so glad that Je-sus loves me, Je-sus loves me, Je-sus loves me; I am so glad that Je-sus loves me, Je-sus loves e-ven me.

194
Isn't the Love of Jesus
Something Wonderful?

J. W. P.

JOHN W. PETERSON

1. There will nev-er be a sweet-er sto-ry, Sto-ry of the Sav-iour's
2. Bound-less as the u-ni-verse a-round me, Reach-ing to the far-thest
3. Love be-yond our hu-man com-pre-hend-ing, Love of God in Christ—how

love di-vine— Love that bro't Him from the realms of glo-ry Just to
soul a-way— Sav-ing, keep-ing love it was that found me, That is
can it be! This will be my theme and nev-er end-ing, Great re-

save a sin-ful soul like mine.
why my heart can tru-ly say.
deem-ing love of Cal-va-ry.

CHORUS

Is-n't the love of Je-sus some-thing won-der-ful, won-der-ful, (it is) won-der-ful, O is-n't the love of Je-sus some-thing won-der-ful, Won-der-ful it is to me. (to me).

Wonderful Story of Love

J. M. DRIVER

J. M. DRIVER

1. Won-der-ful sto-ry of love; Tell it to me a-gain; Won-der-ful
2. Won-der-ful sto-ry of love; Tho' you are far a-way; Won-der-ful
3. Won-der-ful sto-ry of love; Je-sus pro-vides a rest; Won-der-ful

sto-ry of love; Wake the im-mor-tal strain! An-gels with rapture announce it,
sto-ry of love; Still He doth call to-day; Call-ing from Cal-va-ry's mountain,
sto-ry of love; For all the pure and blest, Rest in those mansions a-bove us,

Shepherds with won-der re-ceive it; Sin-ner, O won't you be-lieve it?
Down from the crys-tal bright foun-tain, E'en from the dawn of cre-a-tion,
With those who've gone on be-fore us, Sing-ing the rap-tur-ous cho-rus,

CHORUS

Won-der-ful sto-ry of love. Won - der - ful! Won - der-
Won-der-ful sto-ry of love; Won-der-ful sto-ry of

full Won - der - ful! Won-der-ful sto-ry of love!
love; Won-der-ful sto-ry of love;

196 Such Love

C. Bishop

Robert Harkness

1. That God should love a sin-ner such as I, Should yearn to change my
2. That Christ should join so free-ly in the scheme, Al-though it meant His
3. That for a wil-ful out-cast such as I, The Father planned, the
4. And now He takes me to His heart—a son, He asks me not to

sor-row in-to bliss, Nor rest till He had planned to bring me nigh,
death on Cal-va-ry, Did ev-er hu-man tongue find no-bler theme
Sav-ior bled and died; Re-demp-tion for a worth-less slave to buy,
fill a servant's place; The "Far-off coun-try" wand'rings all are done,

CHORUS

How won-der-ful is love like this! Such love,..... such
Than love di-vine that ran-somed me? Such love,
Who long had law and grace de-fied. Such love,
Wide o-pen are His arms of grace.

won-drous love, Such love, (Such love), such won-drous love, That God should

love a sin-ner such as I, How won-der-ful is love like this!

I Never Will Cease to Love Him

C. H. G.

Chas. H. Gabriel

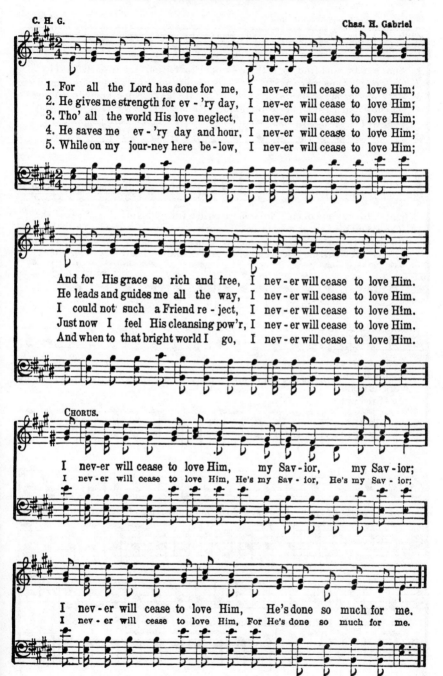

1. For all the Lord has done for me, I nev-er will cease to love Him;
2. He gives me strength for ev-'ry day, I nev-er will cease to love Him;
3. Tho' all the world His love neglect, I nev-er will cease to love Him;
4. He saves me ev-'ry day and hour, I nev-er will cease to love Him;
5. While on my jour-ney here be-low, I nev-er will cease to love Him;

And for His grace so rich and free, I nev-er will cease to love Him.
He leads and guides me all the way, I nev-er will cease to love Him.
I could not such a Friend re-ject, I nev-er will cease to love Him.
Just now I feel His cleansing pow'r, I nev-er will cease to love Him.
And when to that bright world I go, I nev-er will cease to love Him.

Chorus.

I nev-er will cease to love Him, my Sav-ior, my Sav-ior;
I nev-er will cease to love Him, He's my Sav-ior, He's my Sav-ior;

I nev-er will cease to love Him, He's done so much for me.
I nev-er will cease to love Him, For He's done so much for me.

I Love Thee, My Jesus

Words and music by Evangelist John R. Rice

John R. Rice

1. What words can I find to tell Jesus I love Him, Because He first lov'd me; Be-cause of my ran-som He paid with such suff'ring, Up-on the curs-ed tree.

2. Oh, come, let us mag-ni-fy Jesus to-geth-er, For praise be-com-eth Thee; And blessings a-bout me I owe to my Sav-iour, Who all things bought for me.

3. May nev-er my prais-es be slow or be si-lent, Nor e'er my love grow dumb. This sin-ner is saved and my sins all for-giv-en, The Sav-iour's work is done.

4. Oh, how can I love Thee e-nough, dear Redeemer, How e'er re-pay my Friend? I'll spread the glad sound of my praise and my heart love On ev'-ry joy-ful wind.

Chorus:

In the morning, at the noon time, And when come ev'ning shadows I love Thee, my Jesus, I love Thee, my King. In re-joic-ing and in sor-row, In light-ness and bur-den I love Thee, my Saviour and Lord.

Jesus Loves Me

Words and music by Evangelist John R. Rice

John R. Rice

1. Je - sus is such a Sav-iour, Je-sus is such a Friend. Nev - er for-sakes nor
2. Now in His love I glo-ry, Rest and re-joice in Him. Blood-bought and dear to
3. Why should you slight the Saviour? Why turn from Him away? Where will you find for-
4. What can I do for Je-sus? How may I Him re-pay? Oh, to tell all the

leaves me, Nor fails my needs to send. Je-sus who died to save me, Je-sus who
Je - sus, My joy is full with-in. Noth-ing then, I'm per-suad-ed, Can take me
give-ness, Lov-ing care, night and day? No-bo-dy else could save you, No-bo-dy
sto - ry, Of His sal-va-tion's way. Nev - er a theme for sing-ing, Nev - er a

sought for me, Now with His love sur-rounds me, Oh, what a Friend is He!
from His Hand, Nor height nor depth, nor pow-ers, Sa-tan, nor self, nor man.
else could pay Sin's debt for poor, lost sin-ners, He would be yours to - day.
truth for praise As Je-sus' love for sin-ners, I'll sing it all my days.

Je-sus loves me, Yes, Je-sus loves me; For me He died, and the crim-son tide proves

that He loves me, that Je-sus loves me; So sing it a-gain, that Je-sus loves me.

Jesus, I Am Resting

JEAN SOPHIE PIGOTT

J. MOUNTAIN

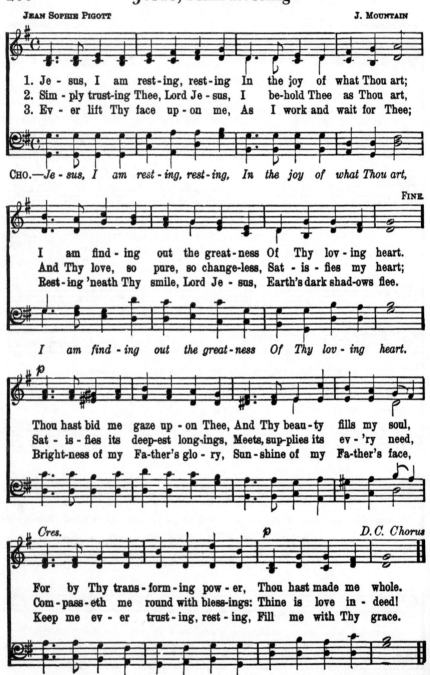

1. Je - sus, I am rest-ing, rest-ing In the joy of what Thou art;
2. Sim - ply trust-ing Thee, Lord Je - sus, I be-hold Thee as Thou art,
3. Ev - er lift Thy face up - on me, As I work and wait for Thee;

CHO.—*Je - sus, I am rest - ing, rest - ing, In the joy of what Thou art,*

FINE.

I am find - ing out the great-ness Of Thy lov - ing heart.
And Thy love, so pure, so change-less, Sat - is - fies my heart;
Rest - ing 'neath Thy smile, Lord Je - sus, Earth's dark shad-ows flee.

I am find - ing out the great-ness Of Thy lov - ing heart.

p

Thou hast bid me gaze up - on Thee, And Thy beau-ty fills my soul,
Sat - is - fies its deep-est long-ings, Meets, sup-plies its ev - 'ry need,
Bright-ness of my Fa-ther's glo - ry, Sun - shine of my Fa-ther's face,

Cres.

p

D.C. *Chorus*

For by Thy trans-form-ing pow - er, Thou hast made me whole.
Com - pass-eth me round with bless-ings: Thine is love in - deed!
Keep me ev - er trust - ing, rest - ing, Fill me with Thy grace.

Wonderful, Wonderful Jesus

ANNA B. RUSSELL   ERNEST O. SELLERS

1. There is nev - er a day so drear - y, There is nev - er a
2. There is nev - er a cross so heav - y, There is nev - er a
3. There is nev - er a care or bur - den, There is nev - er a
4. There is nev - er a guilt - y sin - ner, There is nev - er a

night so long (so long), But the soul that is trust - ing Je - sus Will
weight of woe (of woe), But that Je - sus will help to car - ry Be-
grief or loss (or loss), But that Je - sus in love will light - en When
wan-d'ring one (not one), But that God can in mer - cy par - don Thro'

CHORUS.

some-where find a song (a song).
cause He lov - eth so (loves so). Won - der-ful, won-der - ful Je - sus,
car - ried to the cross (the cross).
Je - sus Christ, His Son (His Son).

In the heart He im-plant-eth a song: .... A song of de-liv-'rance, of

He plant-eth a song,

cour - age, of strength, In the heart He im-plant - eth a song (a song).

202 In My Heart There Rings a Melody

Elton M. Roth

Elton M. Roth

1. I have a song that Je-sus gave me, It was sent from
2. I love the Christ who died on Cal-v'ry, For He washed my
3. 'Twill be my end-less theme in glo-ry, With the an-gels

heav'n a-bove; There nev-er was a sweet-er mel-o-dy, 'Tis a
sins a-way; He put with-in my heart a mel-o-dy, And I
I will sing; 'Twill be a song with glo-rious har-mo-ny, When the

mel-o-dy of love.
know it's there to stay.
courts of heav-en ring.

Chorus

In my heart there rings a mel-o-dy, There

rings a mel-o-dy with heav-en's har-mo-ny; In my heart there

rings a mel-o-dy; There rings a mel-o-dy of love.

He Keeps Me Singing

Luther B. Bridgers   Luther B. Bridgers

1. There's within my heart a mel - o - dy Je - sus whis-pers sweet and low,
2. All   my life was wrecked by sin and strife, Dis-cord filled my heart with pain,
3. Feast-ing on the rich-es of His grace, Resting 'neath His shelt'ring wing,
4. Tho' sometimes He leads thro' waters deep, Tri - als fall a - cross the way,
5. Soon He's com-ing back to wel-come me Far be-yond the star-ry sky;

Fear not, I am with thee, peace, be still, In all of life's ebb and flow.
Je - sus swept across the broken strings, Stirred the slumb'ring chords again.
Al-ways look-ing on His smil-ing face, That is why I shout and sing.
Tho' sometimes the path seems rough and steep, See His footprints all the way.
I shall wing my flight to worlds un-known, I shall reign with Him on high.

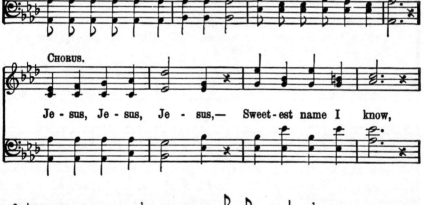

CHORUS.

Je - sus, Je - sus, Je - sus,— Sweet-est name I   know,

Fills my ev - 'ry long - ing, Keeps me sing-ing as I go. A-MEN.

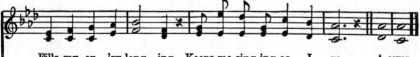

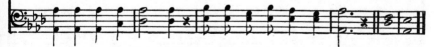

Ring the Bells of Heaven

William O. Cushing

George F. Root

1. Ring the bells of heav-en! there is joy to-day, For a soul re-
2. Ring the bells of heav-en! there is joy to-day, For the wan-d'rer
3. Ring the bells of heav-en! spread the feast to-day, An-gels, swell the

turn-ing from the wild; See! the Fa-ther meets him out up-on the way,
now is rec-on-ciled; Yes, a soul is res-cued from his sin-ful way,
glad tri-um-phant strain! Tell the joy-ful ti-dings, bear it far a-way!

Chorus

Wel-com-ing His wea-ry, wan-d'ring child.
And is born a-new a ran-somed child. Glo-ry! glo-ry! how the
For a pre-cious soul is born a-gain.

an-gels sing; Glo-ry! glo-ry! how the loud harps ring! 'Tis the ran-somed

ar-my, like a might-y sea, Peal-ing forth the an-them of the free.

You May Have the Joy-bells

J. Edward Ruark

William J. Kirkpatrick

1. You may have the joy-bells ring-ing in your heart, And a peace that
2. Love of Je-sus in its full-ness you may know, And this love to
3. You will meet with tri-als as you jour-ney home; Grace suf-fi-cient
4. Let your life speak well of Je-sus ev-'ry day; Own His right to

from you nev-er will de-part; Walk the straight and nar-row way,
those a-round you sweet-ly show; Words of kind-ness al-ways say,
He will give to o-ver-come; Tho' un-seen by mor-tal eye,
ev-'ry serv-ice you can pay; Sin-ners you can help to win

Live for Je-sus ev-'ry day, He will keep the joy-bells ringing in your heart.
Deeds of mer-cy do each day, Then He'll keep the joy-bells ringing in your heart.
He is with you ev-er nigh, And He'll keep the joy-bells ringing in your heart.
If your life is pure and clean, And you keep the joy-bells ringing in your heart.

CHORUS

D. S.—*He will keep the joy-bells ring-ing in your heart.*

Joy - - - bells ring-ing in your heart, Joy - - - - bells
Ring-ing in your heart, You may have the joy-bells

D.S.

ringing in your heart; Take the Sav-ior here below With you ev'rywhere you go;

206   I Will Sing the Wondrous Story

Francis H. Rowley   Peter P. Bilhorn

1. I will sing the won-drous sto - ry Of the Christ who died for me,
2. I was lost, but Je - sus found me, Found the sheep that went a - stray,
3. I was bruised, but Jesus healed me; Faint was I from many a fall;
4. Days of dark-ness still come o'er me, Sor - row's paths I oft - en tread,
5. He will keep me till the riv - er Rolls its wa - ters at my feet;

How He left His home in glo - ry For the cross of Cal - va - ry.
Threw His lov - ing arms a-round me, Drew me back in - to His way.
Sight was gone, and fears possessed me, But He freed me from them all.
But the Sav - ior still is with me; By His hand I'm safe - ly led.
Then He'll bear me safe - ly o - ver, Where the loved ones I shall meet.

CHORUS

Yes, I'll sing .... the won-drous sto - - - ry Of the
Yes, I'll sing   the won-drous sto - ry

Christ .... who died for me, ... Sing it with .... the saints in
Of the Christ   who died for me,   Sing it with

glo - - ry, Gath-ered by ...... the crys-tal sea.........
the saints in glo - ry,   Gath-ered by   the crys-tal sea.

Since Jesus Came Into My Heart

207

Rufus H. McDaniel

Charles H. Gabriel

1. What a won-der-ful change in my life has been wrought Since Je-sus came
2. I have ceased from my wand'ring and go-ing a-stray, Since Je-sus came
3. I'm pos-sessed of a hope that is stead-fast and sure, Since Je-sus came
4. There's a light in the val-ley of death now for me, Since Je-sus came
5. I shall go there to dwell in that Cit-y, I know, Since Je-sus came

in-to my heart! I have light in my soul for which long I had sought,
in-to my heart! And my sins, which were man-y, are all washed a-way,
in-to my heart! And no dark clouds of doubt now my path-way ob-scure,
in-to my heart! And the gates of the Cit-y be-yond I can see,
in-to my heart! And I'm hap-py, so hap-py, as on-ward I go,

CHORUS

Since Je-sus came in-to my heart! Since Je-sus came in-to my
Since Je-sus came in, came

heart, Since Je-sus came in-to my heart, Floods of joy o'er my
in-to my heart, Since Je-sus came in, came in-to my heart,

soul like the sea bil-lows roll, Since Je-sus came in-to my heart.

Oh! Say, But I'm Glad

Rev. Jas. P. Sullivan

Mildred Ellen Sullivan

1. There is a song in my heart to-day, Some-thing I nev-er had;
2. Won-der-ful, mar-vel-ous love He brings, In-to a heart that's sad;
3. We have a fel-low-ship rich and sweet, Tongues can nev-er re-late;
4. Won't you come to Him with all your care, Wea-ry and worn and sad?

Je-sus has tak-en my sins a-way, Oh! say, but I'm glad.
Thro' darkest tun-nels the soul just sings, Oh! say, but I'm glad.
Abid-ing in Him is a re-al treat, Oh! say, but I'm glad.
You too, will sing as His love you share. Oh! say, but I'm glad.

CHORUS

Oh! say, but I'm glad, I'm glad, Oh! say, but I'm glad; (Inst.)

Je-sus has come and my cup's o-ver-run; Oh! say, but I'm glad.

I Will Sing of the Mercies

PSALMS 89:1

Arr. FRANK P. NICKEL

I will sing of the mer-cies of the Lord for-ev-er, I will sing, I will sing; I will sing of the mer-cies

I___ will sing   I will sing

of the Lord for-ev-er, I will sing of the mer-cies of the Lord.

With my mouth will I make known, Thy

with my mouth will I make known

faith-ful-ness, Thy faith-ful-ness; faith-ful-ness to all gen-er-a-tions

Joy Unspeakable

B. E. W.
Lively

B. E. WARREN

1. I have found His grace is   all com-plete, He sup - pli - eth ev - 'ry need;
2. I have found the pleas-ure I once craved, It   is joy and peace with-in;
3. I have found that hope so bright and clear, Liv-ing in the realm of grace;
4. I have found the joy no tongue can tell, How its waves of glo - ry roll!

While I sit and learn at Je - sus' feet, I am free, yes, free in - deed.
What a won-drous bless-ing! I am saved From the aw-ful gulf of sin.
Oh, the Sav-ior's pres-ence is so near, I can see His smil-ing face.
It   is like a great o'er-flow-ing well, Springing up with-in my soul.

CHORUS

It   is joy un-speak-a - ble and full of glo - ry, Full of

glo - ry, full of glo - ry; It   is joy un-speak-a - ble and

full of glo - ry, Oh, the half has nev - er yet been told.

Let the Joy Overflow

211

E. E. HEWITT

S. B. JACKSON

1. There's a clear fountain flowing From the bright throne above, And its waters are
2. Man - y hearts need the story—Are a-thirst for His grace; Go to them with His
3. Be our lives free-ly yield-ed To the Sav-ior's command; By His care ev-er

glow-ing With the sunshine of love; Take the blest con-so - la - tion, Which the
glo - ry Shin-ing out from your face; Tell of Je - sus your Sav - ior! If His
shield-ed And up-held by His hand; In the path-ways of sad-ness, Sweet-est

Lord will be - stow, Take the cup of sal - va-tion—Let the joy o - ver-flow.
mer-cies you know, Show the light of His fa - vor—Let the joy o - ver-flow.
lil - ies may grow; Let us sow seeds of gladness—Let the joy o - ver-flow.

CHORUS

O the joy! . . . . With this wondrous salvation Be our hearts all a - glow;
O the joy!

O the joy! . . . . Let the bless-ing run o-ver, And joy o - ver - flow.
O the joy!

My Redeemer

PHILIP P. BLISS

JAMES McGRANAHAN

1. I will sing of my Re-deem-er, And His won-drous love to me;
2. I will tell the won-drous sto-ry, How my lost es-tate to save,
3. I will praise my dear Re-deem-er, His tri-um-phant pow'r I'll tell,
4. I will sing of my Re-deem-er, And His heav'n-ly love to me;

On the cru-el cross He suf-fered, From the curse to set me free.
In His bound-less love and mer-cy, He the ran-som free-ly gave.
How the vic-to-ry He giv-eth O-ver sin, and death, and hell.
He from death to life hath bro't me, Son of God with Him to be.

CHORUS

Sing, oh, sing ...... of my Re-deem-er,
of my Re-deem-er, Sing, oh, sing of my Re-deem-er,

With His blood .... He pur-chased me, ...
He pur-chased me, With His blood He pur-chased me,

On the cross .... He sealed my par-don,
He sealed my par-don, On the cross He sealed my par-don,

My Redeemer

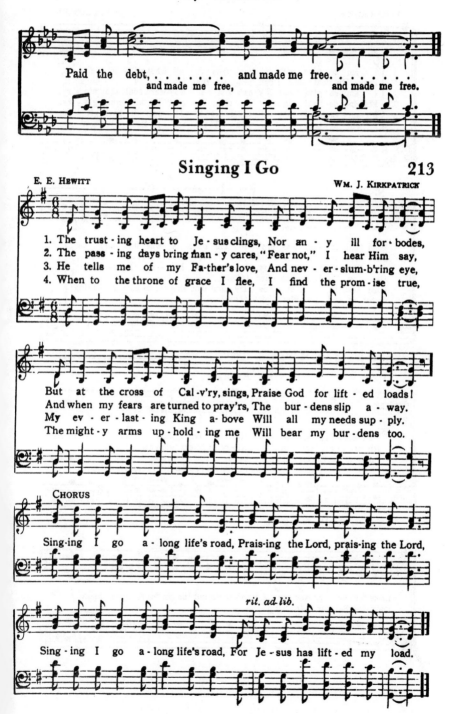

Paid the debt, ... and made me free. . . . .
and made me free, and made me free.

Singing I Go

213

E. E. Hewitt

Wm. J. Kirkpatrick

1. The trust-ing heart to Je-sus clings, Nor an - y ill for-bodes,
2. The pass-ing days bring man-y cares, "Fear not," I hear Him say,
3. He tells me of my Fa-ther's love, And nev-er-slum-b'ring eye,
4. When to the throne of grace I flee, I find the prom-ise true,

But at the cross of Cal-v'ry, sings, Praise God for lift-ed loads!
And when my fears are turned to pray'rs, The bur-dens slip a-way.
My ev-er-last-ing King a-bove Will all my needs sup-ply.
The might-y arms up-hold-ing me Will bear my bur-dens too.

Chorus

Sing-ing I go a - long life's road, Prais-ing the Lord, prais-ing the Lord,

rit. ad lib.

Sing - ing I go a - long life's road, For Je-sus has lift-ed my load.

I Am So Glad

JAMES ROWE.   J. E. THOMAS.

1. { I am so glad sal-va-tion's free to all who will re-ceive it,
     Praise His dear name, I can pro-claim that tru-ly I be-lieve it,

2. { I am so glad that I can tell to way-ward souls the sto-ry,
     Find-ing de-light in serv-ice true, my soul is win-ning glo-ry,

3. { I am so glad that all my heart to Je-sus I have giv-en,
     I will be true un-til with all the hap-py throng in heav-en,

Glad that the news was bro't to me when I was lost and sad;
For I am now His child, (Omit.............................)
Glad that by grace from day to day a help-er I may be;
Glo-ry for Him who gave (Omit............................)
Glad that at ev-en-tide my soul true sheaves to Him may bring;
Sweet-er and no-bler praise (Omit........................)

D.S.—He has re-deemed this soul (Omit...................................)

FINE. REFRAIN.

I know, and I'm so glad. Glo-ry, hon-or, be to His
His life to res-cue me. Glo-ry to Je-sus, glo-ry and hon-or,
I give to Christ, my King. Love Him, Praise Him, Je-sus, the
Love Him and serve Him, Love Him and praise Him,

of mine, and I'm so glad.

name for-ev-er, Nev-er a great-er Friend the sin-ful race has had....
matchless Saviour, (D. S.)

He's a Wonderful Savior to Me

Virgil P. Brock.

Blanche Kerr Brock.

1. I was lost in sin, but Je-sus res-cued me, He's a won-der-ful
2. He's a Friend so true, so pa-tient and so kind, He's a won-der-ful
3. He is al-ways near to com-fort and to cheer, He's a won-der-ful
4. Dear-er grows the love of Je-sus day by day, He's a won-der-ful

Sav-ior to me; I was bound by fear, but Je-sus set me free,
Sav-ior to me; Ev-'ry-thing I need in Him I al-ways find,
Sav-ior to me;(So wonderful!) He for-gives my sins, He dries my ev-'ry tear,
Sav-ior to me; Sweet-er is His grace while pressing on my way,

CHORUS.

He's a won-der-ful Sav-ior to me.(So won-der-ful!) For He's a won-der-ful

Sav-ior to me, won-der-ful! He's a won-der-ful Sav-ior to me; won-der-ful!

I was lost in sin, but Je-sus took me in: He's a wonderful Sav-ior to me.

216 Songs in the Mountains

JRR

John R. Rice

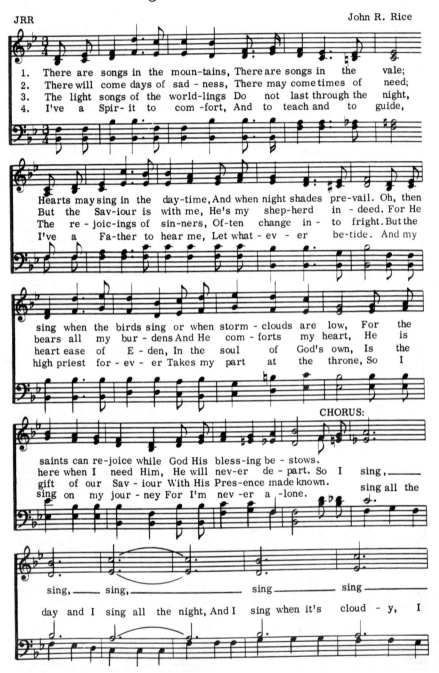

1. There are songs in the moun-tains, There are songs in the vale;
2. There will come days of sad - ness, There may come times of need;
3. The light songs of the world-lings Do not last through the night,
4. I've a Spir- it to com -fort, And to teach and to guide,

Hearts may sing in the day-time, And when night shades pre-vail. Oh, then
But the Sav-iour is with me, He's my shep-herd in - deed. For He
The re - joic-ings of sin-ners, Of-ten change in - to fright. But He
I've a Fa-ther to hear me, Let what - ev - er be-tide. And my

sing when the birds sing or when storm - clouds are low, For the
bears all my bur - dens And He com - forts my heart, He is
heart ease of E - den, In the soul of God's own, Is the
high priest for - ev - er Takes my part at the throne, So I

CHORUS:

saints can re-joice while God His bless-ing be - stows.
here when I need Him, He will nev-er de - part. So I sing, ____
gift of our Sav - iour With His Pres-ence made known.

sing all the

sing, ____ sing, ____ sing ____ sing ____

day and I sing all the night, And I sing when it's cloud - y, I

Songs in the Mountains

sing,————— For I'm hap-py in Je-sus, There's a song in my soul!
sing when it's light.

The Windows of Heaven 217

Arr. by John R. Rice

The win-dows of Heav-en are o - pen, The bless-ings are fall-ing to-night;

There's joy, joy, joy in my heart, since Je-sus made ev-'ry thing right; I

gave Him my old tat-tered gar-ment, He gave me a robe of pure white; I'm

feast-ing on man-na from Heav-en and that's why I'm hap-py to - night.

Only a Sinner

JAMES M. GRAY

DANIEL B. TOWNER

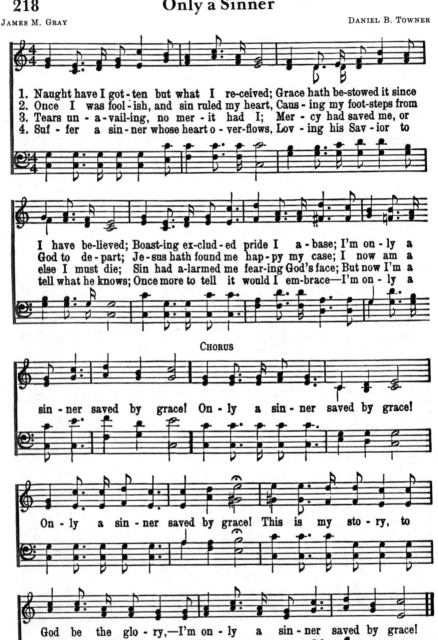

1. Naught have I got-ten but what I re-ceived; Grace hath be-stowed it since
2. Once I was fool-ish, and sin ruled my heart, Caus-ing my foot-steps from
3. Tears un-a-vail-ing, no mer-it had I; Mer-cy had saved me, or
4. Suf-fer a sin-ner whose heart o-ver-flows, Lov-ing his Sav-ior to

I have be-lieved; Boast-ing ex-clud-ed pride I a-base; I'm on-ly a
God to de-part; Je-sus hath found me hap-py my case; I now am a
else I must die; Sin had a-larmed me fear-ing God's face; But now I'm a
tell what he knows; Once more to tell it would I em-brace—I'm on-ly a

CHORUS

sin-ner saved by grace! On-ly a sin-ner saved by grace!

On-ly a sin-ner saved by grace! This is my sto-ry, to

God be the glo-ry,—I'm on-ly a sin-ner saved by grace!

Favorite song of Dr. Ed Nelson

Grace Greater Than Our Sin

JULIA H. JOHNSTON   DANIEL B. TOWNER

1. Mar-vel-ous grace of our lov-ing Lord, Grace that ex-ceeds our
2. Sin and de-spair like the sea waves cold, Threat-en the soul with
3. Dark is the stain that we can-not hide, What can a-vail to
4. Mar-vel-ous, in-fi-nite, match-less grace, Free-ly be-stowed on

sin and our guilt, Yon-der on Cal-va-ry's mount out-poured,
in-fi-nite loss; Grace that is great-er, yes, grace un-told,
wash it a-way? Look! there is flow-ing a crim-son tide;
all who be-lieve; You that are long-ing to see His face,

CHORUS

There where the blood of the Lamb was spilt.
Points to the Ref-uge, the Might-y Cross. Grace, grace,
Whit-er than snow you may be to-day.
Will you this mo-ment His grace re-ceive? Mar-vel-ous grace,

God's grace, Grace that will par-don and cleanse with-in; Grace,
In-fi-nite grace, Mar-vel-ous

grace, God's grace, Grace that is great-er than all our sin.
grace, In-fi-nite grace,

220 Wonderful Grace of Jesus

HALDOR LILLENAS

HALDOR LILLENAS

1. Won - der - ful grace of Je - sus, Great - er than all my sin; . .
2. Won - der - ful grace of Je - sus, Reach-ing to all the lost, . . .
3. Won - der - ful grace of Je - sus, Reach-ing the most de - filed, . .

How shall my tongue de - scribe it, Where shall its praise be - gin? . . .
By it I have been pardoned, Saved to the ut - ter - most, . . .
By its trans-form-ing pow - er, Mak - ing him God's dear child, . .

Tak - ing a - way my bur - den, Set - ting my spir - it free; . .
Chains have been torn a - sun - der, Giv - ing me lib - er - ty; . . .
Pur - chas-ing peace and heav - en, For all e - ter - ni - ty; . . .

For the won - der - ful grace of Je - sus reach - es me.
For the won - der - ful grace of Je - sus reach - es me.
And the won - der - ful grace of Je - sus reach - es me.

CHORUS

the matchless grace of Je-sus,
Won-der-ful the matchless grace of Je - - - sus, Deep-er than the

Wonderful Grace of Jesus

Sunshine in the Soul

Eliza E. Hewitt

John R. Sweney

1. There's sun-shine in my soul to-day, More glo - ri - ous and bright
2. There's mu - sic in my soul to-day, A car - ol to the King,
3. There's springtime in my soul to-day, For, when the Lord is near,
4. There's glad-ness in my soul to-day, And hope and praise and love,

Than glows in an - y earth-ly skies, For Je - sus is my light.
And Je - sus, lis - ten-ing, can hear The songs I can - not sing.
The dove of peace sings in my heart, The flow'rs of grace ap - pear.
For bless-ings which He gives me now, For joys "laid up" a - bove.

Refrain

O there's sun - shine, bless-ed sun - shine,
O there's sun - shine in the soul, bless - ed sun-shine in the soul,

When the peace-ful, hap - py mo - ments roll; When
hap - py mo - ments roll;

Je - sus shows His smil - ing face, There is sun-shine in the soul.

"Whosoever" Meaneth Me

J. Edwin McConnell

J. Edwin McConnell

1. I am hap-py to-day and the sun shines bright, The clouds have been
2. All my hopes have been raised, O His name be praised, His glo-ry has
3. O what won-der-ful love, O what grace di-vine, That Je-sus should

rolled a-way; For the Sav-ior said Who-so-ev-er will, May
filled my soul; I've been lift-ed up and from sin set free, His
die for me! I was lost in sin, for the world I pined, But

CHORUS

come with Him to stay (to stay). "Who-so-ev-er," sure-ly mean-eth me,
blood hath made me whole (me whole).
now I am set free (set free).

Sure-ly mean-eth me, O sure-ly mean-eth me; "Who-so-ev-er,"

sure-ly mean-eth me, "Who-so-ev-er," mean-eth me.
mean-eth me.

223

Victory in Jesus

E. M. B.

E. M. Bartlett

1. I heard an old, old sto-ry, How a Sav-ior came from glo-ry,
2. I heard a-bout His heal-ing, Of His cleans-ing pow'r re-veal-ing,
3. I heard a-bout a man-sion He has built for me in glo-ry,

How He gave His life on Cal-va-ry To save a wretch like me;
How He made the lame to walk a-gain And caused the blind to see;
And I heard a-bout the streets of gold Be-yond the crys-tal sea;

I heard a-bout His groan-ing, Of His pre-cious blood's a-ton-ing,
And then I cried "dear Je-sus, Come and heal my bro-ken spir-it,"
A-bout the an-gels sing-ing, And the old re-demp-tion sto-ry,

Then I re-pent-ed of my sins And won the vic-to-ry.
And some-how Je-sus came and bro't To me the vic-to-ry.
And some sweet day I'll sing up there The song of vic-to-ry.

CHORUS

O vic-to-ry in Je-sus, My Sav-ior, for-ev-er, He sought me and

Victory in Jesus

bo't me With His re-deem-ing blood; He loved me ere I knew Him And all my

love is due Him, He plunged me to vic-to-ry, Be-neath the cleans-ing flood.

O Happy Day

224

PHILIP DODDRIDGE

EDWARD F. RIMBAULT

1. { O hap-py day that fixed my choice On Thee, my Sav-ior and my God! }
   { Well may this glow-ing heart re-joice, And tell its rap-tures all a-broad. }

2. { O hap-py bond, that seals my vows To Him who mer-its all my love! }
   { Let cheer-ful an-thems fill His house, While to that sa-cred shrine I move. }

3. { 'Tis done: the great trans-ac-tion's done; I am my Lord's, and He is mine; }
   { He drew me and I fol-lowed on, Charmed to confess the voice di-vine. }

4. { Now rest, my long-di-vid-ed heart; Fixed on this bliss-ful cen-ter, rest; }
   { Nor ev-er from my Lord de-part, With Him of ev-'ry good possessed. }

FINE

Hap-py day, hap-py day, When Je-sus washed my sins a-way!

D. S.

He taught me how to watch and pray, And live re-joic-ing ev-'ry day;

225 There Shall Be Showers of Blessing

Daniel W. Whittle

James McGranahan

1. "There shall be show-ers of bless-ing:" This is the prom-ise of love;
2. "There shall be show-ers of bless-ing"—Pre-cious re-viv-ing a-gain;
3. "There shall be show-ers of bless-ing:" Send them up-on us, O Lord;
4. "There shall be show-ers of bless-ing:" Oh, that to-day they might fall,

There shall be sea-sons re-fresh-ing, Sent from the Sav-ior a-bove.
O-ver the hills and the val-leys, Sound of a-bun-dance of rain.
Grant to us now a re-fresh-ing, Come, and now hon-or Thy Word.
Now as to God we're con-fess-ing, Now as on Je-sus we call!

Chorus

Show - - ers of bless-ing, Show-ers of bless-ing we need:
Show - ers, show-ers of bless-ing,

Mer-cy-drops round us are fall-ing, But for the show-ers we plead.

Grace Weiser Davis

Chas. H. Gabriel

1. Since I lost my sins and I found my Sav-ior, There is glo - ry
2. Since He cleansed my heart, gave me sight for blindness, There is glo - ry
3. Since with God I've walked, hav-ing sweet com-mun-ion, There is glo - ry
4. Since I en-tered Canaan on my way to heav-en, There is glo - ry

in my soul! Since by faith I sought and ob-tained God's fa-vor, There is
in my soul! Since He touched and healed me in lov - ing kindness, There is
in my soul! Brighter grows each day in this heav'n-ly un - ion, There is
in my soul! Since the day my life to the Lord was giv - en, There is

CHORUS

glo - ry in my soul! There is glo - ry, glo-ry, there is glo - ry in my soul!

Ev - 'ry day bright-er grows, And I con-quer all my foes; There is glo - ry,

glo - ry, there is glo - ry in my soul! There is glo - ry in my soul!
glo - ry in my soul!

227 He Included Me

JOHNSON OATMAN, JR.

HAMPTON H. SEWELL

1. I am so hap-py in Christ to-day, That I go sing-ing a-long my way;
2. Glad-ly I read, "Who-so-ev-er may Come to the fountain of life to-day;"
3. Ever God's Spirit is saying, "Come!" Hear the Bride saying, "No longer roam;"
4. "Freely come drink," words the soul to thrill! O with what joy they my heart do fill!

Yes, I'm so hap-py to know and say, "Je-sus in-clud-ed me too."
But when I read it I al-ways say, "Je-sus in-clud-ed me too."
But I am sure while they're calling home, Je-sus in-clud-ed me too.
For when He said, "Who-so-ev-er will," Je-sus in-clud-ed me too.

CHORUS.

Je-sus in-clud-ed me, Yes, He in-clud-ed me, When the Lord said "Who-so-ev-er," He in-clud-ed me; Je-sus in-clud-ed me, Yes, He in-clud-ed me, When the Lord said "Who-so-ev-er," He included me. A-MEN.

Builded on the Rock

Mrs. C. R.   Mrs. C. Rice

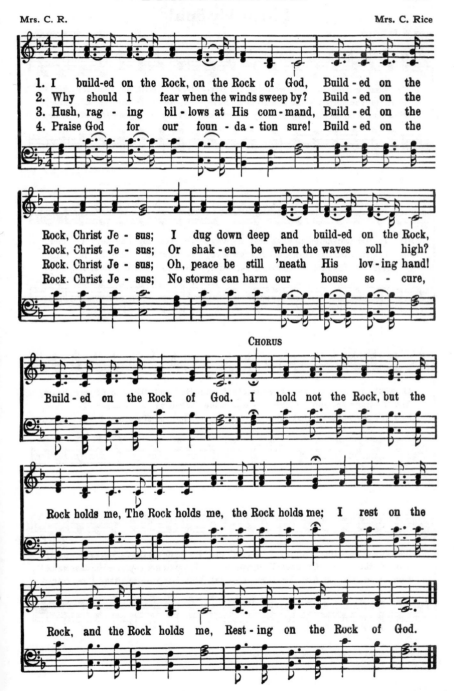

1. I build-ed on the Rock, on the Rock of God, Build-ed on the
2. Why should I fear when the winds sweep by? Build-ed on the
3. Hush, rag-ing bil-lows at His com-mand, Build-ed on the
4. Praise God for our foun-da-tion sure! Build-ed on the

Rock, Christ Je-sus; I dug down deep and build-ed on the Rock,
Rock, Christ Je-sus; Or shak-en be when the waves roll high?
Rock. Christ Je-sus; Oh, peace be still 'neath His lov-ing hand!
Rock. Christ Je-sus; No storms can harm our house se-cure,

CHORUS

Build-ed on the Rock of God. I hold not the Rock, but the

Rock holds me, The Rock holds me, the Rock holds me; I rest on the

Rock, and the Rock holds me, Rest-ing on the Rock of God.

229

Heaven Came Down and Glory
Filled My Soul

JOHN W. PETERSON

JOHN W. PETERSON

1. O what a won-der-ful, won-der-ful day— Day I will nev-er for-get;
2. Born of the Spir-it with life from a-bove In-to God's fam-'ly di-vine,
3. Now I've a hope that will sure-ly en-dure Aft-er the pass-ing of time;

Aft-er I'd wan-dered in dark-ness a-way, Je-sus my Sav-ior I met.
Jus-ti-fied ful-ly thru Cal-va-ry's love, O what a stand-ing is mine!
I have a fu-ture in heav-en for sure, There in those man-sions sub-lime.

O what a ten-der, com-pas-sion-ate friend—He met the need of my heart;
And the trans-ac-tion so quick-ly was made When as a sin-ner I came,
And it's be-cause of that won-der-ful day When at the cross I be-lieved;

Shad-ows dis-pel-ling, With joy I am tell-ing, He made all the dark-ness de-part!
Took of the of-fer Of grace He did prof-fer— He saved me, O praise His dear name!
Rich-es e-ter-nal And bless-ings su-per-nal From His pre-cious hand I re-ceived.

Heaven Came Down

230 Surely Goodness and Mercy

JOHN W. PETERSON
ALFRED B. SMITH

JOHN W. PETERSON

1. A pil-grim was I and a-wan-d'ring, In the cold night of sin I did roam, When Je-sus the kind Shep-herd found me, And now I am on my way home.

2. He re-stor-eth my soul when I'm wea-ry, He giv-eth me strength day by day; He leads me be-side the still wa-ters, He guards me each step of the way.

3. When I walk thro' the dark lone-some val-ley, My Sav-ior will walk with me there; And safe-ly His great hand will lead me To the man-sions He's gone to pre-pare.

CHORUS

Sure-ly good-ness and mer-cy shall fol-low me All the days, all the days of my life; Sure-ly good-ness and mer-cy shall fol-low

Surely Goodness and Mercy

231 Burdens Are Lifted at Calvary

JOHN M. MOORE   JOHN M. MOORE

1. Days are filled with sor-row and care, Hearts are lone-ly and drear;
2. Cast your care on Je-sus to-day, Leave your wor-ry and fear;
3. Trou-bled soul, the Sav-iour can see Ev - 'ry heart-ache and tear;

Bur-dens are lift - ed at Cal-va - ry, Je - sus is ver - y near.
Bur-dens are lift - ed at Cal-va - ry, Je - sus is ver - y near.
Bur-dens are lift - ed at Cal-va - ry, Je - sus is ver - y near.

CHORUS

Bur-dens are lift - ed at Cal - va - ry, Cal - va - ry, Cal - va - ry;

Bur-dens are lift - ed at Cal - va - ry, Je - sus is ver - y near.
ver-y near.

My Burdens Rolled Away

M. A. S.

Mrs. Minnie A. Steele

1. I re-mem-ber when my bur-dens rolled a-way, I had car-ried them for
2. I re-mem-ber when my bur-dens rolled a-way, That I feared would nev-er
3. I re-mem-ber when my bur-dens rolled a-way, That had hin-dered me for
4. I am sing-ing since my bur-dens rolled a-way, There's a song with-in my

years, night and day; When I sought the bless-ed Lord, and I took Him at His
leave night or day; Je-sus showed to me the loss, so I left them at the
years, night and day; As I sought the throne of grace, just a glimpse of Je-sus'
heart night and day; I am liv-ing for my King, and with joy I shout and

CHORUS

word, Then at once all my bur-dens rolled a-way. Rolled a-way, rolled a-
cross; I was glad when my bur-dens rolled a-way.
face, And I knew that my bur-dens could not stay.
sing Hal-le-lu-jah! all my bur-dens rolled a-way. Rolled a-way,

way, I am hap-py since my bur-dens rolled a-way; Rolled a-
rolled a-way, since my burdens rolled away;

way, rolled a-way, I am hap-py since my burdens rolled a-way.
Rolled a-way, rolled a-way,

Jesus Is All the World to Me

Will L. Thompson

Will L. Thompson

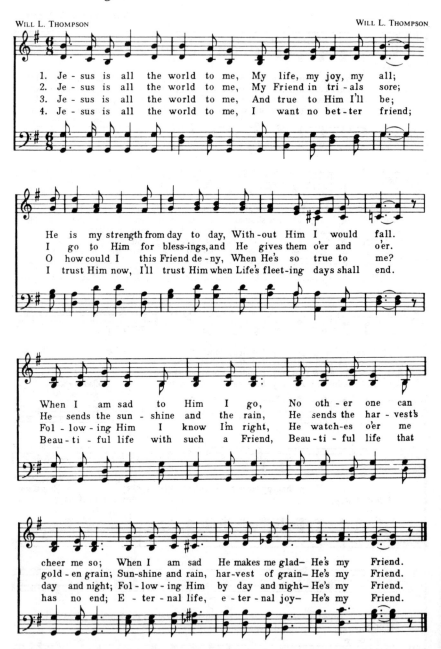

1. Je - sus is all the world to me, My life, my joy, my all;
2. Je - sus is all the world to me, My Friend in tri - als sore;
3. Je - sus is all the world to me, And true to Him I'll be;
4. Je - sus is all the world to me, I want no bet - ter friend;

He is my strength from day to day, With-out Him I would fall.
I go to Him for bless-ings, and He gives them o'er and o'er.
O how could I this Friend de - ny, When He's so true to me?
I trust Him now, I'll trust Him when Life's fleet-ing days shall end.

When I am sad to Him I go, No oth - er one can
He sends the sun - shine and the rain, He sends the har - vest's
Fol - low - ing Him I know I'm right, He watch-es o'er me
Beau-ti - ful life with such a Friend, Beau-ti - ful life that

cheer me so; When I am sad He makes me glad— He's my Friend.
gold - en grain; Sun-shine and rain, har-vest of grain— He's my Friend.
day and night; Fol - low - ing Him by day and night— He's my Friend.
has no end; E - ter - nal life, e - ter - nal joy— He's my Friend.

James G. Small

George C. Stebbins

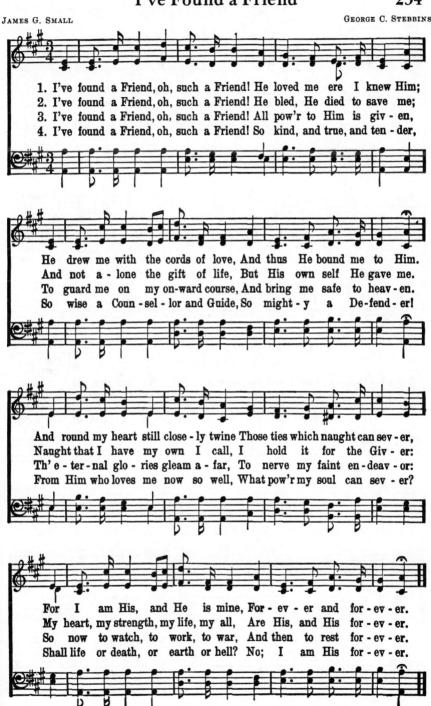

1. I've found a Friend, oh, such a Friend! He loved me ere I knew Him;
2. I've found a Friend, oh, such a Friend! He bled, He died to save me;
3. I've found a Friend, oh, such a Friend! All pow'r to Him is giv - en,
4. I've found a Friend, oh, such a Friend! So kind, and true, and ten - der,

He drew me with the cords of love, And thus He bound me to Him.
And not a - lone the gift of life, But His own self He gave me.
To guard me on my on-ward course, And bring me safe to heav - en.
So wise a Coun - sel - lor and Guide, So might - y a De-fend - er!

And round my heart still close - ly twine Those ties which naught can sev - er,
Naught that I have my own I call, I hold it for the Giv - er:
Th' e - ter - nal glo - ries gleam a - far, To nerve my faint en - deav - or:
From Him who loves me now so well, What pow'r my soul can sev - er?

For I am His, and He is mine, For - ev - er and for - ev - er.
My heart, my strength, my life, my all, Are His, and His for - ev - er.
So now to watch, to work, to war, And then to rest for - ev - er.
Shall life or death, or earth or hell? No; I am His for - ev - er.

A Child of the King

HARRIET E. BUELL

JOHN B. SUMMERS

1. My Fa - ther is rich in hous - es and lands, He hold - eth the
2. My Fa - ther's own Son, the Sav - iour of men, Once wan - dered on
3. I once was an out - cast stran - ger on earth, A sin - ner by
4. A tent or a cot - tage, why should I care? They're build-ing a

wealth of the world in His hands! Of ru - bies and dia-monds, of
earth as the poor - est of them; But now He is plead-ing our
choice, and an al - ien by birth; But I've been a - dopt - ed, my
pal - ace for me o - ver there; Tho' ex - iled from home, yet,

sil - ver and gold, His cof - fers are full, He has rich - es un - told.
par - don on high, That we may be His when He comes by and by.
name's writ-ten down, An heir to a man - sion, a robe, and a crown.
still I may sing: All glo - ry to God, I'm a child of the King.

CHORUS

I'm a child of the King, A child of the King:

With Je - sus my Sav - iour I'm a child of the King.

Moment by Moment

D. W. WHITTLE

MAY WHITTLE MOODY

1. Dy-ing with Je-sus, by death reckoned mine; Liv-ing with Je-sus, a
2. Nev-er a tri-al that He is not there, Nev-er a bur-den that
3. Nev-er a heart-ache and nev-er a groan; Nev-er a tear-drop and
4. Nev-er a weak-ness that He doth not feel, Nev-er a sick-ness that

new life di-vine; Look-ing to Je-sus till glo-ry doth shine, Mo-ment by
He doth not bear, Nev-er a sor-row that He doth not share, Mo-ment by
nev-er a moan; Nev-er a dan-ger but there on the throne, Mo-ment by
He can-not heal; Mo-ment by mo-ment, in woe or in weal, Je-sus my

CHORUS

mo-ment, O Lord, I am Thine.
mo-ment, I'm un-der His care. Mo-ment by mo-ment I'm kept in His love;
mo-ment He thinks of His own.
Sav-iour a-bides with me still.

Mo-ment by mo-ment I've life from a-bove; Look-ing to Je-sus till

glo-ry doth shine; Mo-ment by mo-ment, O Lord, I am Thine.

237 Springs of Living Water

JOHN W. PETERSON

JOHN W. PETERSON

1. I thirst-ed in the bar-ren land of sin and shame, And
2. How sweet the liv-ing wat-er from the hills of God, It
3. O sin-ner, won't you come to-day to Cal-va-ry, A

noth-ing sat-is-fy-ing there I found; But to the bless-ed cross of
makes me glad and hap-py all the way; Now glo-ry, grace and bless-ing
foun-tain there is flow-ing deep and wide; The Sav-iour now in-vites you

Christ one day I came, Where springs of liv-ing wat-er did a-bound.
mark the path I've trod, I'm shout-ing "Hal-le-lu-jah" ev-'ry day.
to the wat-er free, Where thirst-ing spir-its can be sat-is-fied.

CHORUS

Drink-ing at the springs of liv-ing wa-ter, Hap-py now am
Hap - py

I, My soul they sat-is-fy; Drink-ing at the
now am I, My soul they sat-is-fy; I'm

Springs of Living Water

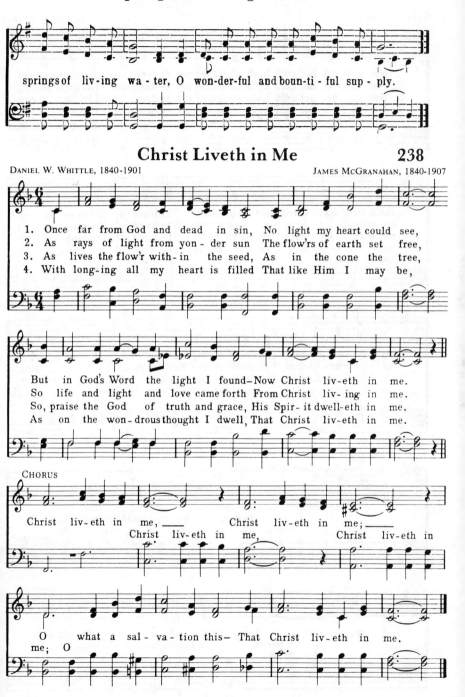

springs of liv-ing wa - ter, O won-der-ful and boun-ti - ful sup - ply.

Christ Liveth in Me 238

DANIEL W. WHITTLE, 1840-1901 JAMES McGRANAHAN, 1840-1907

1. Once far from God and dead in sin, No light my heart could see,
2. As rays of light from yon - der sun The flow'rs of earth set free,
3. As lives the flow'r with-in the seed, As in the cone the tree,
4. With long-ing all my heart is filled That like Him I may be,

But in God's Word the light I found—Now Christ liv-eth in me.
So life and light and love came forth From Christ liv-ing in me.
So, praise the God of truth and grace, His Spir-it dwell-eth in me.
As on the won-drous thought I dwell, That Christ liv-eth in me.

CHORUS

Christ liv-eth in me, ___ Christ liv-eth in me; ___
Christ liv-eth in me, Christ liv-eth in

O what a sal - va - tion this— That Christ liv-eth in me.
me; O

Nor Silver Nor Gold

James M. Gray

Daniel B. Towner

1. Nor sil - ver nor gold hath ob-tained my re-demp-tion, Nor rich - es of
2. Nor sil - ver nor gold hath ob-tained my re-demp-tion, The guilt on my
3. Nor sil - ver nor gold hath ob-tained my re-demp-tion, The ho - ly com-
4. Nor sil - ver nor gold hath ob-tained my re-demp-tion, The way in - to

earth could have saved my poor soul; The blood of the cross is my
con-science too heav - y had grown; The blood of the cross is my
mand-ment for - bade me draw near; The blood of the cross is my
heav - en could not thus be bought; The blood of the cross is my

on - ly foun - da - tion, The death of my Sav - ior now mak - eth me whole.
on - ly foun - da - tion, The death of my Sav - ior could on - ly a - tone.
on - ly foun - da - tion, The death of my Sav - ior re - mov - eth my fear.
on - ly foun - da - tion, The death of my Sav - ior re - demp-tion hath wrought

Chorus

I am re - deemed, ... but not with sil - ver;
I am re-deemed, I am re-deemed, but not with sil - ver;

I am bought, . but not with gold; Bought with a
I am bought, I am bought, but not with gold;

Nor Silver Nor Gold

price...... the blood of Je - sus, Pre-cious price of love un-told.
Bought with a price— the precious blood of Je-sus,

Hallelujah, 'Tis Done 240

P. P. B.

P. P. BLISS

1. 'Tis the prom - ise of God, full sal - va - tion to give
2. Tho' the path - way be lone - ly, and dan - ger - ous too,
3. Man - y loved ones have I in yon heav - en - ly throng,
4. There's a part in that cho - rus for you and for me,

Un - to him who on Je - sus, His Son, will be - lieve.
Sure - ly Je - sus is a - ble to car - ry me through.
They are safe now in glo - ry, and this is their song:
And the theme of our prais - es for - ev - er will be:

REFRAIN

Hal - le - lu - jah, 'tis done! I be - lieve on the Son; I am

1.
2.

saved by the blood of the cru - ci - fied One; cru - ci - fied One.

241 A New Name in Glory

C. Austin Miles   C. Austin Miles

1. I was once a sin-ner, but I came Par-don to re-ceive from my
2. I was humbly kneeling at the cross, Fearing naught but God's an-gry
3. In the Book 'tis written, "Saved by Grace," O the joy that came to my

Lord: This was free-ly giv-en, and I found That He al-ways kept His
frown; When the heavens opened and I saw That my name was writ-ten
soul! Now I am for-giv-en, and I know By the blood I am made

CHORUS

word (kept His word).
down (writ-ten down). There's a new name writ-ten down in glo-ry,
whole (am made whole).

And it's mine, O yes, it's mine! And the white-robed angels sing the
And it's mine, yes, it's mine!

sto-ry, "A sin-ner has come home." For there's a
has come home."

A New Name in Glory

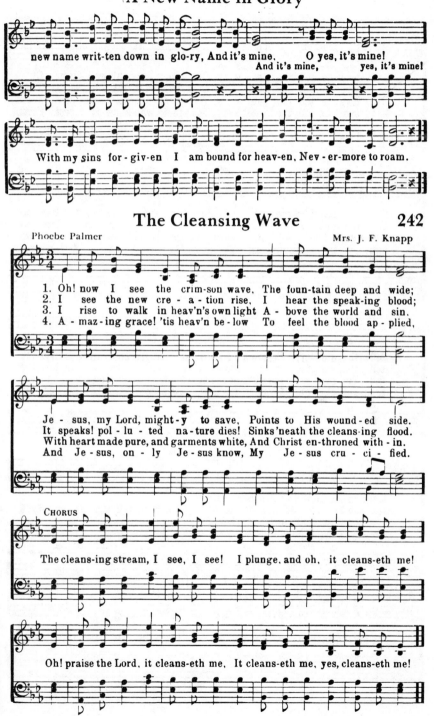

new name writ-ten down in glo-ry, And it's mine, O yes, it's mine!
And it's mine, yes, it's mine!

With my sins for-giv-en I am bound for heav-en, Nev-er-more to roam.

The Cleansing Wave 242

Phoebe Palmer

Mrs. J. F. Knapp

1. Oh! now I see the crim-son wave, The foun-tain deep and wide;
2. I see the new cre-a-tion rise, I hear the speak-ing blood;
3. I rise to walk in heav'n's own light A-bove the world and sin.
4. A-maz-ing grace! 'tis heav'n be-low To feel the blood ap-plied,

Je-sus, my Lord, might-y to save, Points to His wound-ed side.
It speaks! pol-lu-ted na-ture dies! Sinks 'neath the cleans-ing flood.
With heart made pure, and garments white, And Christ en-throned with-in.
And Je-sus, on-ly Je-sus know, My Je-sus cru-ci-fied.

CHORUS

The cleans-ing stream, I see, I see! I plunge, and oh, it cleans-eth me!

Oh! praise the Lord, it cleans-eth me, It cleans-eth me, yes, cleans-eth me!

I Love to Tell the Story

A. CATHERINE HANKEY

WILLIAM G. FISCHER

1. I love to tell the sto - ry Of un - seen things a - bove, Of
2. I love to tell the sto - ry, More won - der - ful it seems Than
3. I love to tell the sto - ry, 'Tis pleas - ant to re - peat What
4. I love to tell the sto - ry, For those who know it best Seem

Je - sus and His glo - ry, Of Je - sus and His love. I love to
all the gold - en fan - cies Of all our gold - en dreams. I love to
seems, each time I tell it, More won - der - ful - ly sweet. I love to
hun - ger - ing and thirst - ing To hear it like the rest. And when, in

tell the sto - ry, Be - cause I know 'tis true; It sat - is - fies my
tell the sto - ry, It did so much for me; And that is just the
tell the sto - ry, For some have nev - er heard The mes - sage of sal -
scenes of glo - ry, I sing the new, new song, 'Twill be the old, old

CHORUS

longings As noth - ing else can do.
rea - son I tell it now to thee. I love to tell the sto - ry, 'Twill
va - tion From God's own ho - ly Word.
sto - ry That I have loved so long.

be my theme in glo - ry To tell the old, old sto - ry Of Jesus and His love.

Edwin O. Excell

Edwin O. Excell

1. I have a song I love to sing, Since I have been re-deemed,
2. I have a Christ that sat-is-fies, Since I have been re-deemed,
3. I have a wit-ness bright and clear, Since I have been re-deemed,
4. I have a home pre-pared for me, Since I have been re-deemed,

Of my Re-deem-er, Sav-ior, King, Since I have been re-deemed.
To do His will my high-est prize, Since I have been re-deemed.
Dis-pel-ling ev-'ry doubt and fear, Since I have been re-deemed.
Where I shall dwell e-ter-nal-ly, Since I have been re-deemed.

CHORUS.

Since I . . . . have been re-deemed, Since I have been re-
Since I have been redeemed, Since I have been redeemed,

deemed, I will glo-ry in His name; Since I . . . . . have been re-
Since I have been redeemed, Since

deemed, I will glo-ry in my Sav-ior's name.
I have been re-deemed,

Heavenly Sunlight

H. J. ZELLEY

GEORGE H. COOK

1. Walk-ing in sun-light, all of my jour-ney; O - ver the moun-tains,
2. Shad-ows a - round me, shad-ows a - bove me, Nev-er con - ceal my
3. In the bright sun-light, ev - er re - joic - ing, Press-ing my way to

thro' the deep vale; Je - sus has said "I'll nev - er for - sake thee,"
Sav - iour and Guide; He is the light, in Him is no dark - ness;
man - sions a - bove; Sing-ing His prais - es glad - ly I'm walk - ing,

Prom - ise di - vine that nev - er can fail.
Ev - er I'm walk - ing close to His side. Heav-en - ly sun - light,
Walk-ing in sun - light, sun - light of love.

heav-en - ly sun - light, Flood-ing my soul with glo - ry di - vine: Hal-le-

lu - jah, I am re - joic - ing, Sing-ing His prais - es, Je - sus is mine.

Sunlight

Judson W. Van DeVenter

Winfield S. Weeden

1. I wan-dered in the shades of night, Till Je-sus came to me,
2. Tho' clouds may gath-er in the sky, And bil-lows round me roll,
3. While walk-ing in the light of God, I sweet com-mun-ion find;
4. I cross the wide ex-tend-ed fields, I jour-ney o'er the plain,
5. Soon I shall see Him as He is, The light that came to me;

And with the sun-light of His love Bid all my dark-ness flee.
How-ev-er dark the world may be I've sun-light in my soul.
I press with ho-ly vig-or on, And leave the world be-hind.
And in the sun-light of His love I reap the gold-en grain.
Be-hold the brightness of His face. Thro'-out e-ter-ni-ty.

Chorus

Sun-light, sun-light in my soul to-day. Sun-light, sun-light
to-day, yes,

all a-long the way; Since the Sav-ior found me,
nar-row way;

Took a-way my sin, I have had the sun-light of His love with-in.
load of sin,

Tell Me the Story of Jesus

FANNY J. CROSBY

JOHN R. SWENEY

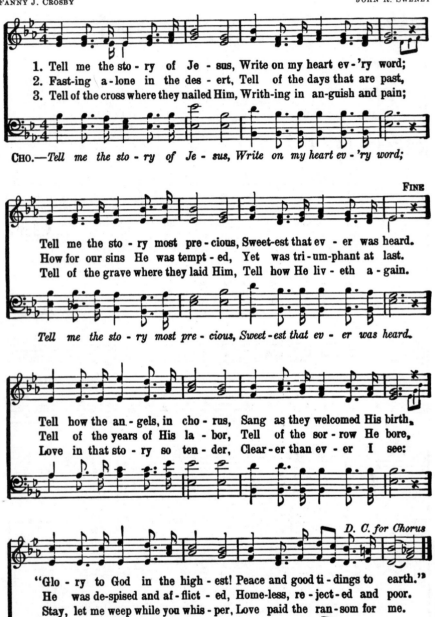

CHO.—*Tell me the sto - ry of Je - sus, Write on my heart ev - 'ry word;*

1. Tell me the sto - ry of Je - sus, Write on my heart ev - 'ry word;
2. Fast-ing a - lone in the des - ert, Tell of the days that are past,
3. Tell of the cross where they nailed Him, Writh-ing in an-guish and pain;

Tell me the sto - ry most pre - cious, Sweet-est that ev - er was heard.
How for our sins He was tempt - ed, Yet was tri - um-phant at last.
Tell of the grave where they laid Him, Tell how He liv - eth a - gain.

Tell me the sto - ry most pre - cious, Sweet-est that ev - er was heard.

Tell how the an - gels, in cho - rus, Sang as they welcomed His birth,
Tell of the years of His la - bor, Tell of the sor - row He bore,
Love in that sto - ry so ten - der, Clear-er than ev - er I see:

"Glo - ry to God in the high - est! Peace and good ti - dings to earth."
He was de-spised and af - flict - ed, Home-less, re - ject - ed and poor.
Stay, let me weep while you whis - per, Love paid the ran-som for me.

Tell Me the Old, Old Story

A. Catherine Hankey

William H. Doane

He Is So Precious to Me

CHARLES H. GABRIEL

CHARLES H. GABRIEL

1. So pre-cious is Je-sus, my Sav-ior, my King, His praise all the day
2. He stood at my heart's door 'mid sunshine and rain, And pa-tient-ly wait-
3. I stand on the moun-tain of bless-ing at last, No cloud in the heav-
4. I praise Him be-cause He ap-point-ed a place Where, some day, thro' faith

long with rap-ture I sing; To Him in my weak-ness for strength I can cling,
ed an en-trance to gain; What shame that so long He en-treat-ed in vain,
ens a shad-ow to cast; His smile is up-on me, the val-ley is past,
in His won-der-ful grace, I know I shall see Him—shall look on His face,

CHORUS. Faster.

For He is so pre-cious to me. For He is so pre-cious to me, ...
so pre-cious to me,

For He is so pre-cious to me; . . . . 'Tis Heav-en be-low
so pre-cious to me;

rit. . . .

My Re-deem-er to know, For He is so pre-cious to me. A-MEN.

I Know I Love Thee Better, Lord   250

FRANCES R. HAVERGAL

R. E. HUDSON

1. I know I love Thee bet-ter, Lord, Than an - y earth-ly joy;
2. I know that Thou art near-er still Than an - y earth-ly throng;
3. Thou hast put glad-ness in my heart; Then may I well be glad!
4. O Sav - iour, pre-cious Sav-iour mine! What will Thy pres-ence be,

For Thou hast giv - en me the peace Which noth-ing can de - stroy.
And sweet - er is the thought of Thee Than an - y love - ly song.
With-out the se - cret of Thy love I could not but be sad.
If such a life of joy can crown Our walk on earth with Thee?

CHORUS

The half has nev-er yet been told, Of love so full and free!
yet been told,

The half has nev-er yet been told, The blood—it cleans-eth me!
yet been told, cleans-eth me!

rit.

251   No, Not One!

JOHNSON OATMAN, JR.

GEORGE C. HUGG

1. There's not a friend like the low-ly Je-sus, No, not one! no, not one!
2. No friend like Him is so high and ho-ly, No, not one! no, not one!
3. There's not an hour that He is not near us, No, not one! no, not one!
4. Did ev-er saint find this Friend for-sake him? No, not one! no, not one!
5. Was e'er a gift like the Sav-ior giv-en? No, not one! no, not one!

None else could heal all our soul's dis-eas-es, No, not one! no, not one!
And yet no friend is so meek and low-ly, No, not one! no, not one!
No night so dark but His love can cheer us, No, not one! no, not one!
Or sin-ner find that He would not take him? No, not one! no, not one!
Will He re-fuse us a home in heav-en? No, not one! no, not one!

CHORUS

Je-sus knows all a-bout our strug-gles, He will guide till the day is done;

There's not a friend like the low-ly Je-sus, No, not one! no, not one!

The Lily of the Valley

CHARLES W. FRY

ARR. FROM WILLIAM S. HAYS

1. I have found a friend in Je-sus, He's ev-ery-thing to me, He's the
2. He all my griefs has tak-en, and all my sor-rows borne; In temp-
3. He will nev-er, nev-er leave me, nor yet for-sake me here, While I

fair-est of ten thou-sand to my soul; The Lil-y of the Val-ley,
ta-tion He's my strong and mighty tower; I have all for Him for-sak-en,
live by faith and do His bless-ed will; A wall of fire a-bout me,

D. S.—Lil-y of the Val-ley,

FINE.

in Him a-lone I see All I need to cleanse and make me ful-ly whole.
and all my i-dols torn From my heart, and now He keeps me by His power.
I've noth-ing now to fear, With His man-na He my hun-gry soul shall fill.

the Bright and Morn-ing Star, He's the fair-est of ten thou-sand to my soul.

In sor-row He's my com-fort, in trou-ble He's my stay,
Though all the world for-sake me, and Sa-tan tempt me sore,
Then sweep-ing up to glo-ry to see His bless-ed face,

D. S.

He tells me ev-ery care on Him to roll: He's the
Through Je-sus I shall safe-ly reach the goal: He's the
Where riv-ers of de-light shall ev-er roll: He's the

Seeking for Me

A. N.

E. E. HASTY

1. Je-sus my Sav-ior to Beth-le-hem came, Born in a man-ger to
2. Je-sus my Sav-ior, on Cal-va-ry's tree, Paid the great debt and my
3. Je-sus my Sav-ior, the same as of old, While I was wand'ring a-
4. Je-sus my Sav-ior shall come from on high—Sweet is the prom-ise as

sorrow and shame; Oh, it was wonderful—blest be His name! Seeking for me, for
soul He set free; Oh, it was wonderful—how could it be? Dy-ing for me, for
far from the fold, Gently and long did He plead with my soul, Calling for me, for
wea-ry years fly; Oh, I shall see Him decending the sky, Coming for me, for

REFRAIN   For me!........   For me!........

me! Seeking for me! Seeking for me! Seeking for me! Seeking for me!
me! Dy-ing for me! Dy-ing for me! Dy-ing for me! Dy-ing for me!
me! Calling for me! Calling for me! Calling for me! Call-ing for me!
me! Coming for me! Coming for me! Coming for me! Coming for me!

Oh, it was won-der-ful—blest be His name! Seeking for me, for me!
Oh, it was won-der-ful—how could it be? Dy-ing for me, for me!
Gen-tly and long did He plead with my soul, Call-ing for me, for me!
Oh, I shall see Him de-scending the sky, Com-ing for me, for me!

Oh, It Is Wonderful!

C. H. G. CHAS. H. GABRIEL

1. I stand all a-mazed at the love Je-sus of-fers me, Con-fused at the
2. I mar-vel that He would descend from His throne divine, To res-cue a
3. I think of His hands pierced and bleeding to pay the debt! Such mer-cy, such

grace that so ful-ly He proffers me; I trem-ble to know that for me He was
soul so re-bel-lious and proud as mine; That He should extend His great love un-to
love and de-vo-tion can I for-get? No, no! I will praise and a-dore at the

rit.

cru-ci-fied—That for me, a sin-ner, He suf-fered, He bled, and died.
such as I; Suf-fi-cient to own, to re-deem, and to jus-ti-fy.
mer-cy-seat, Un-til at the glo-ri-fied throne I kneel at His feet.

CHORUS *rit.*

Oh, it is won-der-ful that He should care for me, E-nough to
won-der-ful!

a tempo

die for me! Oh, it is won-der-ful, won-der-ful to me!
won-der-ful!

F. M. G.   F. M. Graham

1. There was a time on earth, When in the book of heav'n An old ac-count was
2. The old account was large, And growing ev-'ry day, For I was al-ways
3. When at the judgment bar, I stand be-fore my King, And He the book will
4. When in that hap-py home, My Sav-ior's home a-bove, I'll sing re-demp-tion's
5. O sin-ner, seek the Lord, Re-pent of all your sin, For thus He hath com-

stand-ing For sins yet un-for-giv'n; My name was at the top, And
sin-ning, And nev-er tried to pay; But when I looked a-head, And
o-pen, He can-not find a thing; Then will my heart be glad, While
sto-ry, And praise Him for His love; I'll not for-get that book, With
mand-ed, If you would en-ter in; And then if you should live A

man-y things be-low, I went un-to the keep-er, And set-tled long a-go.
saw such pain and woe, I said that I would set-tle, I set-tled long a-go.
tears of joy will flow Be-cause I had it set-tled, And set-tled long a-go.
pag-es white as snow, Be-cause I came and settled, And set-tled long a-go.
hun-dred years be-low, Up there you'll not re-gret it, You set-tled long a-go.

CHORUS

Long a-go,   Long a-go,   Yes, the
    Down on my knees,   I set-tled it all,

The Old Account Settled

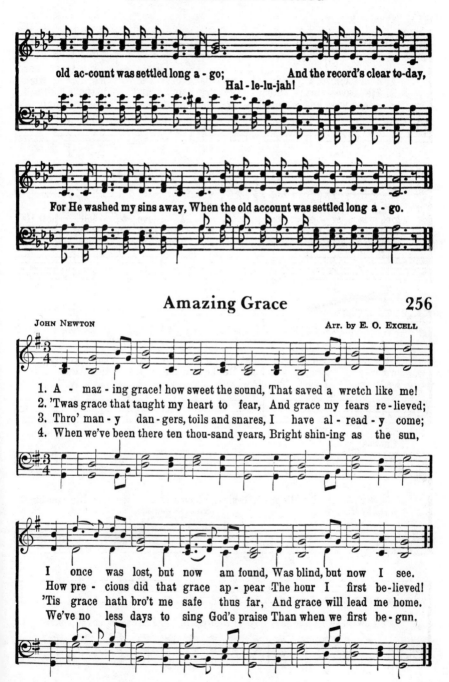

old ac-count was settled long a - go; And the record's clear to-day, Hal - le - lu-jah!

For He washed my sins away, When the old account was settled long a - go.

Amazing Grace

256

JOHN NEWTON

Arr. by E. O. EXCELL

1. A - maz - ing grace! how sweet the sound, That saved a wretch like me!
2. 'Twas grace that taught my heart to fear, And grace my fears re - lieved;
3. Thro' man - y dan - gers, toils and snares, I have al - read - y come;
4. When we've been there ten thou-sand years, Bright shin-ing as the sun,

I once was lost, but now am found, Was blind, but now I see.
How pre - cious did that grace ap - pear The hour I first be - lieved!
'Tis grace hath bro't me safe thus far, And grace will lead me home.
We've no less days to sing God's praise Than when we first be - gun.

Favorite song of Dr. Harold Henniger and Dr. Ford Porter.

257 Saved, Saved!

JACK P. SCHOLFIELD   JACK P. SCHOLFIELD

1. I've found a friend who is all to me,..... His
2. He saves me from ev-'ry sin and harm,. Se-
3. When poor and need-y and all a-lone,... In

love is ev-er true;...... I love to tell how He
cures my soul each day;...... I'm lean-ing strong on His
love He said to me,........ "Come un-to me and I'll

lift-ed me.... And what His grace can do for you...
might-y arm;.. I know He'll guide me all the way...
lead you home, To live with me e-ter-nal-ly."...

CHORUS.

Saved .... by His pow'r di-vine, Saved .... to new life sub-lime!
Saved by His pow'r,   Saved to new life,

rit.

Life now is sweet and my joy is com-plete, For I'm Saved, saved, saved!

Redeemed

258

FANNY J. CROSBY

WILLIAM J. KIRKPATRICK

1. Redeemed–how I love to pro-claim it! Redeemed by the blood of the Lamb;
2. Redeemed and so happy in Je - sus, No language my rap-ture can tell;
3. I think of my bless-ed Re-deem-er, I think of Him all the day long;
4. I know I shall see in His beau-ty The King in whose law I de - light;

Redeemed thro' His in - fi - nite mer - cy, His child, and for - ev - er, I am.
I know that the light of His presence With me doth con-tin - ual - ly dwell.
I sing, for I can-not be si - lent; His love is the theme of my song.
Who lov - ing - ly guardeth my footsteps, And giv-eth me songs in the night.

CHORUS

Re - deemed, .. re - deemed, .. Redeemed by the blood of the Lamb;
re-deemed, re-deemed,

Re - deemed, .. re - deemed, .. His child, and for-ev - er, I am.
re-deemed, re-deemed,

259 It Took a Miracle

JOHN W. PETERSON

JOHN W. PETERSON

1. My Fa-ther is om-nip-o-tent, And that you can't de-ny;
2. Tho here His glo-ry has been shown, We still can't ful-ly see
3. The Bi-ble tells us of His pow'r And wis-dom all way thru,

A God of might and mir-a-cles—'Tis writ-ten in the sky.
The won-ders of His might, His throne—'Twill take e-ter-ni-ty.
And ev-'ry lit-tle bird and flow'r Are tes-ti-mo-nies too.

CHORUS

It took a mir-a-cle to put the stars in place, It took a
mir-a-cle to hang the world in space; But when He saved my soul,
Cleansed and made me whole, It took a mir-a-cle of love and grace!

Saved by the Blood

S. J. Henderson

Daniel B. Towner

1. Saved by the blood of the Cru-ci-fied One! Now ran-somed from
2. Saved by the blood of the Cru-ci-fied One! The an-gels re-
3. Saved by the blood of the Cru-ci-fied One! The Fa-ther He
4. Saved by the blood of the Cru-ci-fied One! All hail to the

sin and a new work be-gun, Sing praise to the Fa-ther and
joic-ing be-cause it is done; A child of the Fa-ther, joint-
spake, and His will it was done; Great price of my par-don, His
Fa-ther, all hail to the Son, All hail to the Spir-it, the

praise to the Son, Saved by the blood of the Cru-ci-fied One!
heir with the Son, Saved by the blood of the Cru-ci-fied One!
own pre-cious Son; Saved by the blood of the Cru-ci-fied One!
great Three in One! Saved by the blood of the Cru-ci-fied One!

CHORUS

Saved! .. saved! .. My sins are all pardoned, my guilt is all gone!
Glo-ry, I'm saved! glo-ry, I'm saved!

Saved! .. saved! .. I am saved by the blood of the Cru-ci-fied One!
Glo-ry, I'm saved! glo-ry, I'm saved!

261 Saved!

OSWALD J. SMITH

ROGER M. HICKMAN

1. Saved! saved! saved! my sins are all for-giv'n; Christ is
2. Saved! saved! saved! by grace and grace a-lone; Oh, what
3. Saved! saved! saved! oh, joy be-yond com-pare! Christ my

mine! I'm on my way to heav'n; Once a guilt - - y
won - drous love to me was shown, In my stead Christ
life, and I His con-stant care; Yield-ing all and

sin-ner, lost, un-done, Now a child of God, saved thro' His Son.
Je-sus bled and died, Bore my sins, for me was cru-ci-fied.
trust-ing Him a-lone, Liv-ing now each moment as His own.

CHORUS

Saved! I'm saved thro' Christ, my all in all; .... Saved! I'm saved, what-
my all in all;

ev - er may be-fall; He died up-on the cross for me, He bore the aw-ful

Saved!

pen - al - ty; And now I'm saved e - ter - nal - ly—I'm saved! saved! saved!

Now I Belong to Jesus 262

NORMAN J. CLAYTON   NORMAN J. CLAYTON

1. Je - sus my Lord will love me for - ev - er, From Him no pow'r of e - vil can
2. Once I was lost in sin's deg - ra - da - tion, Je - sus came down to bring me sal -
3. Joy floods my soul for Je - sus has saved me, Freed me from sin that long had en -

sev - er, He gave His life to ran - som my soul, Now I be - long to Him;
va - tion, Lift - ed me up from sor - row and shame, Now I be - long to Him;
slaved me, His pre - cious blood He gave to redeem, Now I be - long to Him;

Chorus

Now I be - long to Je - sus, Je - sus be - longs to me,

Not for the years of time a - lone, But for e - ter - ni - ty.

If I Gained the World

ANNA ÖLANDER
Tr. Composite

Swedish

1. If I gained the world, but lost the Savior, Were my life worth liv-ing for a
2. Had I wealth and love in full-est measure, And a name revered both far and
3. O what emp-ti-ness!—without the Savior 'Mid the sins and sor-rows here be-
4. O the joy of hav-ing all in Je-sus! What a balm the bro-ken heart to

day? Could my yearn-ing heart find rest and com - fort In the
near, Yet no hope be-yond, no har-bor wait-ing, Where my
low! And e - ter - ni - ty, how dark with-out Him!—On - ly
heal! Ne'er a sin so great, but He'll for - give it, Nor a

things that soon must pass a - way? If I gained the world, but lost the
storm-tossed ves - sel I could steer; If I gained the world, but lost the
night and tears and end-less woe! What, tho' I might live with-out the
sor - row that He does not feel! If I have but Je - sus, on - ly

Sav - ior, Would my gain be worth the life - long strife? Are all
Sav - ior, Who en-dured the cross and died for me, Could then
Sav - ior, When I come to die, how would it be? O to
Je - sus,—Noth-ing else in all the world be - side— O then

If I Gained the World

earth-ly pleasures worth com-par-ing For a mo-ment with a Christ-filled life?
all the world af-ford a ref-uge, Whither, in my an-guish, I might flee?
face the val-ley's gloom with-out Him! And without Him all e - ter - ni - ty!
ev - 'ry-thing is mine in Je - sus; For my needs and more He will pro-vide.

Look to the Lamb of God   264

H. G. JACKSON

JAMES M. BLACK

1. If you from sin are long-ing to be free, Look to the Lamb of God;
2. When Satan tempts, and doubts and fears assail, Look to the Lamb of God;
3. Are you a-wea - ry, does the way seem long? Look to the Lamb of God;
4. Fear not when shadows on your path-way fall, Look to the Lamb of God;

He, to re-deem you, died on Cal - va - ry, Look to the Lamb of God.
You in His strength shall o-ver all pre-vail, Look to the Lamb of God.
His love will cheer and fill your heart with song, Look to the Lamb of God.
In joy or sor - row Christ is all in all, Look to the Lamb of God.

CHORUS

Look to the Lamb of God,   Look to the Lamb of God,
        the Lamb of God,   the Lamb of God,

For He a - lone is a - ble to save you, Look to the Lamb of God.

265 Ye Must Be Born Again

WILLIAM T. SLEEPER   GEORGE C. STEBBINS

1 A ru-ler once came to Je-sus by night, To ask Him the way of sal-
2. Ye children of men, at-tend to the word So sol-emn-ly ut-tered by
3. Oh, ye who would en-ter that glo-ri-ous rest, And sing with the ransomed the
4. A dear one in heaven thy heart yearns to see, At the beautiful gate may be

va-tion and light; The Mas-ter made an-swer in words true and plain,
Je-sus the Lord; And let not this mes-sage to you be in vain,
song of the blest; The life ev-er-last-ing if ye would ob-tain,
watching for thee; Then list to the note of this sol-emn re-frain,

CHORUS

"Ye must be born a-gain." .. "Ye must be born a-
a-gain.

gain, .. Ye must be born a-gain; .. I ver-i-ly,
a-gain,   a-gain;

ver-i-ly say un-to thee, Ye must be born a-gain." ...
a-gain.

Whiter Than Snow

JAMES NICHOLSON

WILLIAM G. FISCHER

1. Lord Je-sus, I long to be per-fect-ly whole; I want Thee for-ev-er to
2. Lord Je-sus, look down from Thy throne in the skies, And help me to make a com-
3. Lord Je-sus, for this I most hum-bly en-treat, I wait, bless-ed Lord, at Thy
4. Lord Je-sus, Thou seest I pa-tient-ly wait, Come now, and with-in me a

live in my soul, Break down ev-'ry i-dol, cast out ev-'ry foe;
plete sac-ri-fice; I give up my-self, and what-ev-er I know,
cru-ci-fied feet; By faith, for my cleans-ing, I see Thy blood flow,
new heart cre-ate; To those who have sought Thee, Thou nev-er saidst "No,"

CHORUS.

Now wash me, and I shall be whit-er than snow. Whit-er than snow, yes,

whit-er than snow; Now wash me, and I shall be whit-er than snow.

"Whosoever Will"

P. P. B.

P. P. Bliss

1. "Who-so-ev-er hear-eth," shout, shout the sound! Spread the bless-ed ti-dings
2. Who-so-ev-er com-eth need not de-lay, Now the door is o-pen,
3. "Who-so-ev-er will!" the prom-ise is se-cure; "Who-so-ev-er will," for-

all the world a-round; Tell the joy-ful news wher ev er man is found,
en-ter while you may; Je-sus is the true, the on-ly Liv-ing Way:
ev-er must en-dure; "Who-so-ev-er will!" 'tis life for-ev-er-more;

CHORUS

"Who-so-ev-er will may come." "Who-so-ev-er will, who-so-ev-er will!"

Send the proc-la-ma-tion o-ver vale and hill; 'Tis a lov-ing

Fa-ther calls the wan-derer home: "Who-so-ev-er will may come."

Favorite song of Dr. Hugh Pyle.

Look and Live

William A. Ogden

William A. Ogden

1. I've a mes-sage from the Lord, hal-le-lu-jah! The mes-sage un-to
2. I've a mes-sage full of love, hal-le-lu-jah! A mes-sage, O my
3. Life is of-fered un-to you, hal-le-lu-jah! E-ter-nal life thy
4. I will tell you how I came, hal-le-lu-jah! To Je-sus when He

you I'll give; 'Tis re-cord-ed in His Word, hal-le-lu-jah!
friend, for you; 'Tis a mes-sage from a-bove, hal-le-lu-jah!
soul shall have, If you'll on-ly look to Him, hal-le-lu-jah!
made me whole: 'Twas be-liev-ing on His name, hal-le-lu-jah!

Chorus

It is on-ly that you "look and live."
Je-sus said it and I know 'tis true. Look and live,
Look to Je-sus who a-lone can save. Look and live,
I trust-ed and He saved my soul.

my broth-er, live! Look to Je-sus now and live; 'Tis re-
my broth-er, live, look and live!

cord-ed in His Word, hal-le-lu-jah! It is on-ly that you "look and live."

269   Come and Dine

Words and Melody
C. B. Widmeyer

S. H. Bolton

1. Jesus has a table spread Where the saints of God are fed,
   With His manna He doth feed And sup-plies our ev-'ry need:
2. The dis-ci-ples came to land, Thus o-bey-ing Christ's command,
   There they found their hearts' de-sire, Bread and fish up-on the fire;
3. Soon the Lamb will take His bride To be ev-er at His side,
   O 'twill be a glo-rious sight, All the saints in spot-less white;

He in-vites His cho-sen peo-ple, "Come and dine;"
O 'tis sweet to sup with (Omit. . . . .)   Je-sus all the time!
For the Mas-ter called to them, "O come and dine;"
Thus He sat-is-fies the (Omit. . . . .)   hun-gry ev-'ry time.
All the host of heav-en will as-sem-bled be;
And with Je-sus they will (Omit. . . . .)   feast e-ter-nal-ly.

CHORUS

"Come and dine," the Master calleth, "Come and dine (O come and dine);" You may feast at

Je-sus' ta-ble all the time (O come and dine); He who fed the mul-ti-tude,

Turned the wa-ter in-to wine, To the hun-gry call-eth now, "Come and dine."

ERDMANN NEUMEISTER
TR. BY EMMA F. BEVAN

JAMES McGRANAHAN

1. Sin - ners Je - sus will re - ceive; Sound this word of grace to all
2. Come, and He will give you rest; Trust Him, for His word is plain;
3. Now my heart con-demns me not, Pure be - fore the law I stand;
4. Christ re - ceiv - eth sin - ful men, E - ven me with all my sin;

Who the heav'n - ly path-way leave, All who lin - ger, all who fall.
He will take the sin - ful - est; Christ re - ceiv - eth sin - ful men.
He who cleansed me from all spot, Sat - is - fied its last de-mand.
Purged from ev - 'ry spot and stain, Heav'n with Him I en - ter in.

REFRAIN

Sing it o'er . . . . . . and o'er a - gain; . . . . . . Christ re-
Sing it o'er a-gain, Sing it o'er a-gain; Christ re-

ceiv - - - eth sin-ful men; . . . . . Make the mes - - - sage
ceiv-eth sin - ful men, Christ re-ceiv-eth sin - ful men; Make the message plain,

clear and plain: . . . . . . Christ re - ceiv - eth sin - ful men.
Make the mes-sage plain:

Jesus Saves

Priscilla J. Owens

William J. Kirkpatrick

1. We have heard the joy - ful sound: Je - sus saves! Je - sus saves!
2. Waft it on the roll - ing tide; Je - sus saves! Je - sus saves!
3. Sing a - bove the bat - tle strife, Je - sus saves! Je - sus saves!
4. Give the winds a might - y voice, Je - sus saves! Je - sus saves!

Spread the ti - dings all a - round: Je - sus saves! Je - sus saves!
Tell to sin - ners far and wide: Je - sus saves! Je - sus saves!
By His death and end - less life, Je - sus saves! Je - sus saves!
Let the na - tions now re - joice,— Je - sus saves! Je - sus saves!

Bear the news to ev - 'ry land, Climb the steeps and cross the waves;
Sing, ye is - lands of the sea; Ech - o back, ye o - cean caves;
Sing it soft - ly thro' the gloom, When the heart for mer - cy craves;
Shout sal - va - tion full and free; High - est hills and deep - est caves;

On - ward!—'tis our Lord's com - mand; Je - sus saves! Je - sus saves!
Earth shall keep her ju - bi - lee: Je - sus saves! Je - sus saves!
Sing in tri - umph o'er the tomb,— Je - sus saves! Je - sus saves!
This our song of vic - to - ry,— Je - sus saves! Je - sus saves!

He Is Able to Deliver Thee

William A. Ogden

William A. Ogden

1. 'Tis the grand-est theme thro' the a-ges rung; 'Tis the grandest theme for a
2. 'Tis the grand-est theme in the earth or main; 'Tis the grandest theme for a
3. 'Tis the grand-est theme, let the ti-dings roll, To the guilt-y heart, to the

mor-tal tongue; 'Tis the grandest theme that the world e'er sung, "Our God is
mor-tal strain; 'Tis the grandest theme, tell the world a - gain, "Our God is
sin - ful soul; Look to God in faith, He will make thee whole, "Our God is

Chorus

a - ble to de - liv - er thee." He is a - - - - ble to de - liv - er thee,
a - ble, He is a - ble

He is a - - - - ble to de - liv - er thee; Tho' by sin op - prest,
a - ble, He is a - ble

Go to Him for rest; "Our God is a - ble to de - liv - er thee."

273   Turn Your Eyes Upon Jesus

H. H. L.   HELEN HOWARTH LEMMEL

With expression

1. O soul, are you wea-ry and troub-led? No light in the
2. Thro' death in-to life ev-er-last-ing He passed, and we
3. His word shall not fail you—He prom-ised; Be-lieve Him, and

dark-ness you see? There's light for a look at the Sav-ior,
fol-low Him there; O-ver us sin no more hath do-min-ion—
all will be well: Then go to a world that is dy-ing,

And life more a-bun-dant and free!
For more than con-qu'rors we are!
His per-fect sal-va-tion to tell!

REFRAIN

Turn your eyes up-on Je-sus, Look full in His won-der-ful face;.... And the things of
earth will grow strange-ly dim In the light of His glo-ry and grace.

The Light of the World Is Jesus

PHILIP P. BLISS   PHILIP P. BLISS

1. The whole world was lost in the dark-ness of sin; The Light of the
2. No dark-ness have we who in Je-sus a-bide, The Light of the
3. Ye dwell-ers in dark-ness with sin-blind-ed eyes, The Light of the
4. No need of the sun-light in heav-en, we're told, The Light of the

world is Je-sus; Like sun-shine at noon-day His glo-ry shone in,
world is Je-sus; We walk in the Light when we fol-low our Guide,
world is Je-sus; Go, wash at His bid-ding, and light will a-rise,
world is Je-sus; The Lamb is the Light in the Cit-y of Gold,

CHORUS

The Light of the world is Je-sus. Come to the Light, 'tis

shin-ing for thee; Sweet-ly the Light has dawned up-on me; Once I was

blind, but now I can see; The Light of the world is Je-sus.

Verily, Verily

G. M. J.   JAMES McGRANAHAN

1. Oh, what a Sav-ior, that He died for me! From con-dem-
2. All my in-iq-ui-ties on Him were laid, All my in-
3. Though poor and need-y I can trust my Lord, Though weak and
4. Though all un-wor-thy, yet I will not doubt, For him that

na-tion He hath made me free; "He that be-liev-eth on the
debt-ed-ness by Him was paid; All who be-lieve on Him, the
sin-ful I be-lieve His Word; Oh, glad mes-sage! ev-'ry
com-eth, He will not cast out; "He that be-liev-eth," oh, the

CHORUS

Son," saith He, "Hath ev-er-last-ing life." "Ver-i-ly, ver-i-ly,
Lord hath said, "Hath ev-er-last-ing life."
child of God "Hath ev-er-last-ing life."
good news shout, "Hath ev-er-last-ing life!"

I say un-to you," "Ver-i-ly, ver-i-ly," mes-sage ev-er new;

"He that be-liev-eth on the Son," 'tis true, "Hath ev-er-last-ing life"

Once for All

PHILIP P. BLISS

PHILIP P. BLISS

1. Free from the law, O hap-py con-di-tion, Je-sus hath
2. Now are we free—there's no con-dem-na-tion, Je-sus pro-
3. "Chil-dren of God," O glo-ri-ous call-ing, Sure-ly His

bled, and there is re-mis-sion; Cursed by the law and bruised by the
vides a per-fect sal-va-tion; "Come un-to Me," O hear His sweet
grace will keep us from fall-ing; Pass-ing from death to life at His

CHORUS

fall, Grace hath redeemed us once for all.
call, Come, and He saves us once for all. Once for all, O sin-ner, re-
call, Bless-ed sal-va-tion once for all.

ceive it, Once for all, O broth-er, be-lieve it; Cling to the

Cross, the bur-den will fall, Christ hath re-deemed us once for all.

Favorite song of Dr. Hugh Pyle.

Yes, I Know!

Mrs. A. W. W.

Mrs. Anna W. Waterman

1. Come, ye sin - - - ners, lost and hope - - - less, Je - sus'
1. Come, ye sin - ners, lost and hope-less, lost and hope-less,
2. To the faint.......... He giv - eth pow - - - er, Thro' the
2. To the faint He giv - eth pow - er, giv - eth pow - er,
3. In temp - ta - - - tion He is near thee, Holds the
3. In temp - ta - tion He is near thee, He is near thee,
4. He will keep.......... thee while the a - - - ges Roll thro'-
4. He will keep thee while the a - ges, while the a - ges,

blood........can make you free;.......... For He saved...... the worst a-
Je-sus' blood can make you free, can make you free; For He saved the worst a-
moun - - tains makes a way;.......... Find-eth wa - - - ter in the
Thro' the mountains makes a way, He makes a way; Find-eth wa - ter in the
pow'rs........ of hell at bay;.......... Guides you to........ the path of
Holds the pow'rs of hell at bay, of hell at bay; Guides you to the path of
out.......... e - ter - ni - ty;.......... Tho' earth hin - - ders and hell
Roll thro'-out e - ter - ni - ty, 'e - ter - ni - ty; Tho' earth hin-ders and hell

mong you, When He saved....... a wretch like me.............
mong you, worst among you, When He saved a wretch like me, a wretch like me.
des - - - ert, Turns the night...... to gold - en day.............
des - ert, in the des - ert, Turns the night to gold - en day, to gold - en day.
safe - - - ty, Gives you grace........ for ev - 'ry day.............
safe - ty, path of safe - ty, Gives you grace for ev - 'ry day, for ev - 'ry day.
rag - - - es, All must work........ for good to thee.............
rag - es, and hell rag - es, All must work for good to thee, for good to thee.

Chorus

And I know,................ yes, I know,................ Je - sus'
I sure - ly know, I sure - ly know,

Yes, I Know!

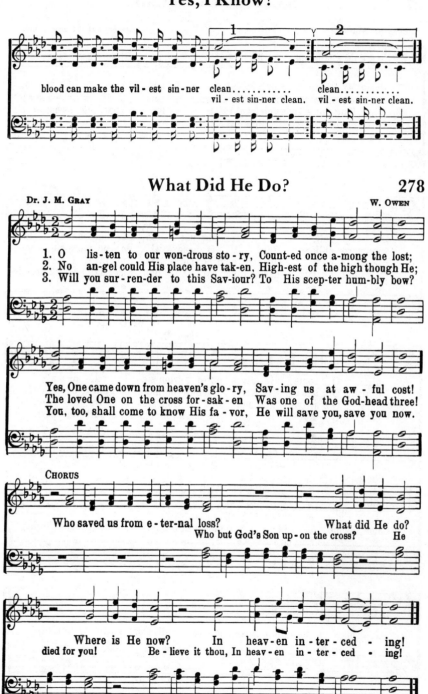

blood can make the vil - est sin - ner clean..........
vil - est sin - ner clean.
clean..........
vil - est sin-ner clean.

What Did He Do?   278

Dr. J. M. GRAY

W. OWEN

1. O lis-ten to our won-drous sto-ry, Count-ed once a-mong the lost;
2. No an-gel could His place have tak-en, High-est of the high though He;
3. Will you sur-ren-der to this Sav-iour? To His scep-ter hum-bly bow?

Yes, One came down from heaven's glo-ry, Sav-ing us at aw - ful cost!
The loved One on the cross for-sak-en Was one of the God-head three!
You, too, shall come to know His fa - vor, He will save you, save you now.

CHORUS

Who saved us from e - ter-nal loss?   What did He do?
Who but God's Son up-on the cross?   He

Where is He now?   In heav-en in - ter - ced - ing!
died for you!   Be - lieve it thou, In heav-en in - ter - ced - ing!

Edna R. Worrwell

Clarence B. Strouse. Arr.

1. Come, O come to the bless-ed Sav - ior, List, O list to His
2. Deep, deep, deep in the heart there whis - pers God's own voice to each
3. Long, long, long have you tried to sti - fle Yearnings sweet to a
4. Now, *now*, NOW as the Spir - it stirs ... you, Hard - en not your fast

lov - ing call, Of - fer - ing par - don, Pardon from sin to
way-ward child; Heed it! O heed it! Be no more sin - be-
life more pure; Quench them no lon - ger But in God rest se-
melt - ing heart; Take, take sal - va - tion Else shall your chance de-

all; O come, He gives par - don from sin to all, to all.
guiled, O heed His voice. be now no more be-guiled, be - guiled.
cure; O strive no more, but in God rest se - cure. se - cure.
part; O take it *now*, else shall your chance depart, de - part.

REFRAIN

Come, come to Je - sus, Come ere this mo - ment takes flight;

It may be now some-one's last call. last call to - night.

Honey in the Rock

F. A. G.

F. A. GRAVES

1. O my brother, do you know the Sav - ior, Who is won - drous
2. Have you "tasted that the Lord is gra - cious?" Do you walk in the
3. Do you pray un - to God the Fa - ther, "What wilt Thou have
4. Then go out thro' the streets and by - ways, Preach the word to the

kind and true? He's the "Rock of your sal - va - tion!"
way that's new? Have you drunk from the liv - ing foun - tain?
me to do?" Nev - er fear, He will sure - ly an - swer,
man - y or few; Say to ev - 'ry fall - en broth - er,

CHORUS

There's Hon-ey in the Rock for you. Oh, there's Honey in the Rock, my

broth-er, ... There's Hon-ey in the Rock for you; Leave your
my broth-er, for you;

rit.

sins for the blood to cov - er, There's Hon-ey in the Rock for you.
for you.

281

Why Do You Wait?

GEORGE F. ROOT

GEORGE F. ROOT

1. Why do you wait, dear broth-er, Oh, why do you tar - ry so long?
2. What do you hope, dear broth-er, To gain by a fur-ther de - lay?
3. Do you not feel, dear broth-er, His Spir - it now striv-ing with-in?
4. Why do you wait, dear broth-er? The harvest is pass-ing a - way;

Your Sav-ior is wait-ing to give you A place in His sanc-ti-fied throng.
There's no one to save you but Je - sus, There's no other way but His way.
Oh, why not ac-cept His sal - va - tion, And throw off your burden of sin?
Your Sav-ior is long-ing to bless you, There's danger and death in de-lay.

Chorus

Why not? why not? Why not come to Him now? now?

282

Just As I Am

CHARLOTTE ELLIOTT

WILLIAM B. BRADBURY

1. Just as I am, with-out one plea, But that Thy blood was shed for me,
2. Just as I am, and wait-ing not To rid my soul of one dark blot,
3. Just as I am, tho' tossed a-bout With many a con-flict, many a doubt,
4. Just as I am, poor, wretched, blind; Sight, riches, heal - ing of the mind,
5. Just as I am, Thou wilt re - ceive, Wilt welcome, pardon, cleanse, relieve;

Just As I Am

And that Thou bidd'st me come to Thee, O Lamb of God, I come! I come!
To Thee whose blood can cleanse each spot, O Lamb of God, I come! I come!
Fight-ings and fears with-in, with-out, O Lamb of God, I come! I come!
Yea, all I need, in Thee to find, O Lamb of God, I come! I come!
Be-cause Thy prom-ise I be-lieve, O Lamb of God, I come! I come!

Lord, I'm Coming Home

283

WILLIAM J. KIRKPATRICK

WILLIAM J. KIRKPATRICK

1. I've wan-dered far a-way from God, Now I'm com-ing home;
2. I've wast-ed man-y pre-cious years, Now I'm com-ing home;
3. I've tired of sin and stray-ing, Lord, Now I'm com-ing home;
4. My soul is sick, my heart is sore, Now I'm com-ing home;

FINE

The paths of sin too long I've trod, Lord, I'm com-ing home.
I now re-pent with bit-ter tears, Lord, I'm com-ing home.
I'll trust Thy love, be-lieve Thy word, Lord, I'm com-ing home.
My strength re-new, my hope re-store, Lord, I'm com-ing home.

D. S.—O-pen wide Thine arms of love, Lord, I'm com-ing home.

CHORUS

D. S.

Com-ing home, com-ing home, Nev-er-more to roam.

284 Jesus, I Come

WILLIAM T. SLEEPER

GEORGE C. STEBBINS

1. Out of my bond-age, sor-row and night, Je-sus, I come, Je-sus, I come;
2. Out of my shame-ful fail-ure and loss, Je-sus, I come, Je-sus, I come;
3. Out of un-rest and ar-ro-gant pride, Je-sus, I come, Je-sus, I come;
4. Out of the fear and dread of the tomb, Je-sus, I come, Je-sus, I come;

In-to Thy free-dom, glad-ness and light, Je-sus, I come to Thee;
In-to the glo-rious gain of Thy cross, Je-sus, I come to Thee;
In-to Thy bless-ed will to a-bide, Je-sus, I come to Thee;
In-to the joy and light of Thy home, Je-sus, I come to Thee;

Out of my sick-ness in-to Thy health, Out of my want and in-to Thy wealth,
Out of earth's sorrows in-to Thy balm, Out of life's storms and in-to Thy calm,
Out of my-self to dwell in Thy love, Out of de-spair in-to rap-tures a-bove,
Out of the depths of ru-in un-told, In-to the peace of Thy sheltering fold,

Out of my sin and in-to Thy-self, Je-sus, I come to Thee.
Out of dis-tress to ju-bi-lant psalm, Je-sus, I come to Thee.
Up-ward for aye on wings like a dove, Je-sus, I come to Thee.
Ev-er Thy glo-rious face to be-hold, Je-sus, I come to Thee.

Why Not Now?

Daniel W. Whittle

Charles C. Case

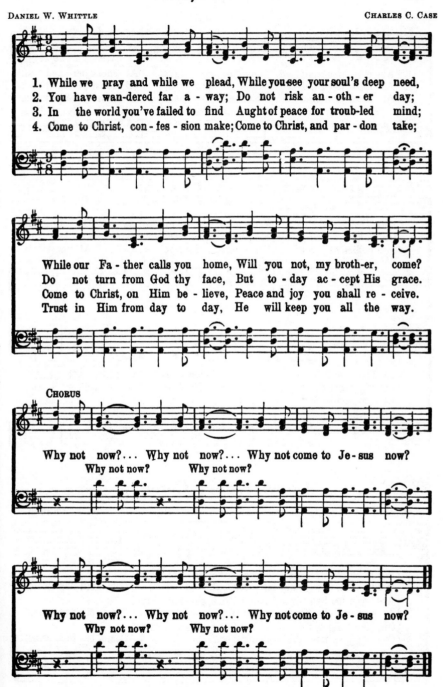

1. While we pray and while we plead, While you see your soul's deep need,
2. You have wan-dered far a - way; Do not risk an - oth - er day;
3. In the world you've failed to find Aught of peace for troub-led mind;
4. Come to Christ, con - fes - sion make; Come to Christ, and par - don take;

While our Fa - ther calls you home, Will you not, my broth-er, come?
Do not turn from God thy face, But to - day ac - cept His grace.
Come to Christ, on Him be - lieve, Peace and joy you shall re - ceive.
Trust in Him from day to day, He will keep you all the way.

Chorus

Why not now?... Why not now?... Why not come to Je - sus now?
Why not now? Why not now?

Why not now?... Why not now?... Why not come to Je - sus now?
Why not now? Why not now?

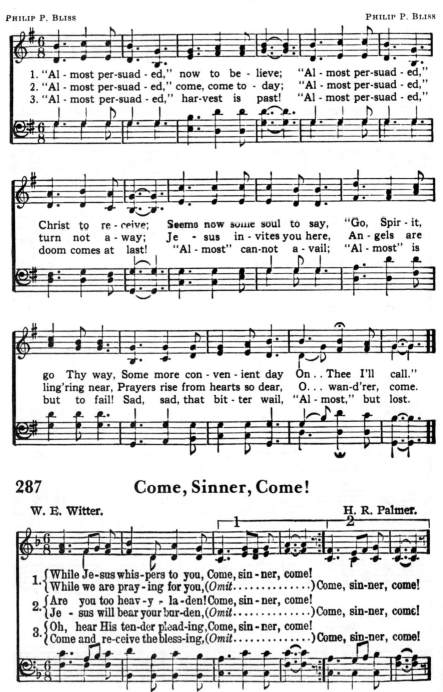

286 Almost Persuaded

Philip P. Bliss

Philip P. Bliss

1. "Al - most per-suad - ed," now to be - lieve; "Al - most per-suad - ed,"
2. "Al - most per-suad - ed," come, come to - day; "Al - most per-suad - ed,"
3. "Al - most per-suad - ed," har-vest is past! "Al - most per-suad - ed,"

Christ to re - ceive; Seems now some soul to say, "Go, Spir - it,
turn not a - way; Je - sus in - vites you here, An - gels are
doom comes at last! "Al - most" can-not a - vail; "Al - most" is

go Thy way, Some more con - ven - ient day On . . Thee I'll call."
ling'ring near, Prayers rise from hearts so dear, O . . . wan-d'rer, come.
but to fail! Sad, sad, that bit - ter wail, "Al - most," but lost.

287 Come, Sinner, Come!

W. E. Witter.

H. R. Palmer.

1. { While Je-sus whis-pers to you, Come, sin - ner, come!
     { While we are pray-ing for you,(Omit . . . .)Come, sin - ner, come!
2. { Are you too heav-y - la-den! Come, sin - ner, come!
     { Je - sus will bear your bur-den,(Omit . . . .)Come, sin - ner, come!
3. { Oh, hear His ten-der plead-ing, Come, sin - ner, come!
     { Come and re-ceive the bless-ing,(Omit . . . .)Come, sin - ner, come!

Come, Sinner, Come!

Now is the time to own Him, Come, sin-ner, come!
Now is the time to know Him, (*Omit* . . . .) Come, sin-ner, come!
Je - sus will not de-ceive you, Come, sin-ner, come!
Je - sus can now re-deem you, (*Omit* . . . .) Come, sin-ner, come!
While Je-sus whis-pers to you, Come, sin-ner, come!
While we are pray-ing for you, (*Omit* . . . .) Come, sin-ner, come!

Only Trust Him 288

JOHN H. STOCKTON   JOHN H. STOCKTON

1. Come, ev - 'ry soul by sin op-pressed, There's mer-cy with the Lord,
2. For Je - sus shed His pre-cious blood, Rich bless-ings to be - stow;
3. Yes, Je - sus is the Truth, the Way, That leads you in - to rest:
4. Come, then, and join this ho - ly band, And on to glo - ry go,

And He will sure - ly give you rest By trust-ing in His word.
Plunge now in - to the crim - son flood That wash - es white as snow.
Be - lieve in Him with-out de - lay, And you are ful - ly blest.
To dwell in that ce - les - tial land, Where joys im - mor-tal flow.

On - ly trust Him, on-ly trust Him, On - ly trust Him now.
He will save you, He will save you, He will (*Omit* . . . . .) save you now.

Come Unto Me

Charles P. Jones   Charles P. Jones

1. Hear the bless - ed Sav - ior call - ing the op-pressed, "O ye heav-y-
2. Are you dis - ap-point - ed, wan-d'ring here and there, Drag-ging chains of
3. Stum-bling on the moun - tains dark with sin and shame, Stumbling tow'rd the
4. Have you by temp - ta - tion of - ten con-quered been, Has a sense of

la - den, come to Me and rest; Come, no lon - ger tar - ry,
doubt and load - ed down with care? Do un - ho - ly feel - ings
pit of hell's con - sum - ing flame, By the pow'rs of sin de-
weak - ness brought dis - tress with - in? Christ will sanc - ti - fy you,

I your load will bear, Bring Me ev - 'ry bur - den, bring Me ev - 'ry care."
struggle in your breast? Bring your case to Je - sus, He will give you rest.
lud - ed and op-pressed, Hear the ten - der Shep-herd,—"Come to Me and rest."
if you'll claim His best, In the Ho - ly Spir - it, He will give you rest.

CHORUS

Come un-to Me; I . . . . will give you rest;
Come un - to Me,   Come un - to Me,   I will give you rest,   I will give you rest;

Take . . . . . My yoke up-on you, Hear . . . Me and be blest; . . . .
Take My yoke up - on you,   Take My yoke up-on you, Hear Me and be blest,   Hear Me and be blest;

Come Unto Me

I.........am meek and low - ly, Come......and trust My might;
I am meek and low - ly: I am meek and low-ly, Come and trust My might, Come and trust My might;

Come, My yoke is eas - - y, And.... My burden's light.
Come, O come, Come, My yoke is eas - y, Come, O come, Come, My burden's light.

Where He Leads Me

290

E. W. Blandly

J. S. Norris

1. I can hear my Sav - ior call - ing, I can hear my Sav - ior call - ing,
2. I'll go with Him thro' the gar - den, I'll go with Him thro' the gar - den,
3. I'll go with Him thro' the judg-ment, I'll go with Him thro' the judg-ment,
4. He will give me grace and glo - ry, He will give me grace and glo - ry,

REF.–Where He leads me I will fol - low, Where He leads me I will fol - low.

D. C. for Ref.

I can hear my Sav - ior call - ing, "Take thy cross and fol-low, fol - low Me."
I'll go with Him thro' the gar - den, I'll go with Him, with Him all the way.
I'll go with Him thro' the judgment, I'll go with Him, with Him all the way.
He will give me grace and glo-ry, And go with me, with me all the way.

Where He leads me I will fol - low, I'll go with Him, with Him all the way.

291 Jesus Is Calling

FANNY J. CROSBY

GEORGE C. STEBBINS

1. Je - sus is ten - der - ly call - ing thee home—Call - ing to - day,
2. Je - sus is call - ing the wea - ry to rest— Call - ing to - day,
3. Je - sus is wait - ing; O come to Him now— Wait - ing to - day,
4. Je - sus is plead - ing; O list to His voice: Hear Him to - day,

call - ing to - day; Why from the sun - shine of love wilt thou roam
call - ing to - day; Bring Him thy bur - den and thou shalt be blest:
wait - ing to - day; Come with thy sins; at His feet low - ly bow;
hear Him to - day; They who be - lieve on His name shall re - joice;

REFRAIN

Far - ther and far - ther a - way?
He will not turn thee a - way.
Come, and no lon - ger de - lay.
Quick - ly a - rise and a - way.

Call - - ing to - day, ...
Call - ing, call - ing to - day, to - day,

Call - - ing to - day, ...
Call - ing, call - ing to - day, to - day,

Je - - - - sus is
Je - sus is ten - der - ly

call - - - ing, is ten - der - ly call - ing to - day.
call - ing to - day,

Have You Any Room for Jesus?

SOURCE UNKNOWN
ARR. BY DANIEL W. WHITTLE

C. C. WILLIAMS

1. Have you an-y room for Je-sus, He who bore your load of sin?
2. Room for pleas-ure, room for busi-ness, But for Christ the Cru-ci-fied,
3. Have you an-y room for Je-sus, As in grace He calls a-gain?
4. Room and time now give to Je-sus, Soon will pass God's day of grace;

As He knocks and asks ad-mis-sion, Sin-ner, will you let Him in?
Not a place that He can en-ter, In the heart for which He died?
O to-day is time ac-cept-ed, To-mor-row you may call in vain.
Soon thy heart left cold and si-lent, And thy Sav-ior's pleading cease.

CHORUS

Room for Je-sus, King of glo-ry! Has-ten now His word o-bey;

Swing the heart's door wide-ly o-pen, Bid Him en-ter while you may.

293 Pass Me Not, O Gentle Savior

FANNY J. CROSBY

WILLIAM H. DOANE

1. Pass me not, O gen-tle Sav-ior, Hear my hum-ble cry; While on oth-ers
2. Let me at a throne of mer-cy Find a sweet re-lief; Kneel-ing there in
3. Trust-ing on-ly in Thy mer-it, Would I seek Thy face; Heal my wounded,
4. Thou the Spring of all my com-fort, More than life to me, Whom have I on

Thou art call-ing, Do not pass me by.
deep con-tri-tion, Help my un-be-lief.
bro-ken spir-it, Save me by Thy grace.
earth beside Thee? Whom in Heav'n but Thee?

CHORUS

Sav-ior, Sav-ior, Hear my humble

cry; While on oth-ers Thou art call-ing, Do not pass me by.

294 I Am Coming, Lord

LEWIS HARTSOUGH

LEWIS HARTSOUGH

1. I hear Thy welcome voice, That calls me, Lord, to Thee For cleansing in Thy
2. Tho' coming weak and vile, Thou dost my strength assure; Thou dost my vileness
3. 'Tis Je-sus calls me on To per-fect faith and love, To per-fect hope, and

pre-cious blood That flowed on Cal-va-ry.
ful-ly cleanse, Till spot-less all and pure.
peace, and trust, For earth and heav'n a-bove.

CHORUS

I am com-ing, Lord!

I Am Coming, Lord

Com-ing now to Thee! Wash me, cleanse me in the blood That flowed on Cal-va-ry!

Who at My Door Is Standing? 295

MARY B. C. SLADE

ASA B. EVERETT

1. Who at my door is stand-ing, Pa-tient-ly draw-ing near,
2. Lone-ly with-out He's stay-ing: Lone-ly with-in am I;
3. All through the dark hours drea-ry, Knock-ing a-gain is He;
4. Door of my heart, I has-ten! Thee will I o-pen wide.

En-trance with-in de-mand-ing? Whose is the voice I hear?
While I am still de-lay-ing, Will He not pass me by?
Je-sus, art Thou not wea-ry, Wait-ing so long for me?
Tho' He re-buke and chas-ten, He shall with me a-bide.

REFRAIN

Sweet-ly the tones are fall-ing: "O-pen the door for me!

If thou wilt heed My call-ing, I will a-bide with thee."

296 Softly and Tenderly Jesus Is Calling

WILL L. THOMPSON

WILL L. THOMPSON

1. Soft - ly and ten-der - ly Je - sus is call-ing, Call - ing for you and for me;
2. Why should we tarry when Jesus is plead-ing, Pleading for you and for me?
3. Time is now fleeting, the moments are passing, Passing from you and from me;
4. Oh! for the won-der-ful love He has promised, Promised for you and for me;

See, on the portals He's waiting and watching, Watching for you and for me.
Why should we linger and heed not His mercies, Mer-cies for you and for me?
Shadows are gathering, death-beds are coming, Com-ing for you and for me.
Tho' we have sinned, He has mercy and pardon, Par-don for you and for me.

CHORUS m   cresc.

Come home,.. come home,...... Ye who are wear-y, come home;...
Come home,   come home,

pp   ppp   rit.   pp

Ear-nest-ly, ten-der-ly, Je - sus is call-ing, Call-ing, O sin-ner, come home!

What Will You Do With Jesus?

Author Unknown

M. L. Stocks

1. Je - sus is stand-ing in Pi-late's hall—Friendless, for-sak-en, be-trayed by all:
2. Je - sus is stand-ing on tri - al still, You can be false to Him if you will,
3. Will you e-vade Him as Pi-late tried? Or will you choose Him, what-e'er be-tide?
4. Will you, like Peter, your Lord de-ny? Or will you scorn from His foes to fly,
5. "Je - sus, I give Thee my heart to-day! Je-sus, I'll fol - low Thee all the way,

Heark-en! what mean-eth the sud-den call! What will you do with Je - sus?
You can be faith-ful thro' good or ill: What will you do with Je - sus?
Vain - ly you strug-gle from Him to hide: What will you do with Je - sus?
Dar - ing for Je - sus to live or die? What will you do with Je - sus?
Glad - ly o - bey - ing Thee!" will you say: "This will I do with Je - sus!"

CHORUS

What will you do with Je - sus? Neu-tral you can - not be;

Some day your heart will be ask - ing, "What will He do with me?"

Let Him In

JONATHAN B. ATCHINSON   EDWIN O. EXCELL

1. There's a Stran-ger at the door, Let   Him in;
2. O - pen now to Him your heart, Let   Him in;
3. Hear you now His lov - ing voice? Let   Him in;
4. Now ad - mit the heav'n-ly Guest, Let   Him in;

Let the Sav-ior in,   Let the Sav-ior in;

He has been there oft be - fore, Let   Him in;
If you wait He will de - part, Let   Him in;
Now, oh, now make Him your choice, Let   Him in;
He will make for you a feast, Let   Him in;

Let the Sav-ior in,   Let the Sav-ior in;

Let Him in, ere He is gone, Let Him in, the Ho - ly One, Je - sus
Let Him in, He is your Friend, He your soul will sure de - fend, He will
He is stand-ing at your door, Joy to you He will re - store, And His
He will speak your sins for-giv'n, And when earth ties all are riv'n, He will

Christ, the Fa - ther's Son,   Let   Him in.
keep you to the end,   Let   Him in.
name you will a - dore,   Let   Him in.
take you home to heav'n,   Let   Him in.

Let the Sav-ior in,   Let the Sav-ior in.

Let Jesus Come Into Your Heart

Leila N. Morris

Leila N. Morris

1. If you are tired of the load of your sin, Let Je-sus come
2. If 'tis for pu-ri-ty now that you sigh, Let Je-sus come
3. If there's a tem-pest your voice can-not still, Let Je-sus come
4. If you would join the glad songs of the blest, Let Je-sus come

in-to your heart; If you de-sire a new life to be-gin,
in-to your heart; Fountains for cleans-ing are flow-ing near by,
in-to your heart; If there's a void this world nev-er can fill,
in-to your heart; If you would en-ter the man-sions of rest,

CHORUS

Let Je-sus come in-to your heart. Just now, your

doubt-ings give o'er; Just now, re-ject Him no more; Just now, throw

o-pen the door; Let Je-sus come in-to your heart.

300 Into My Heart

HARRY D. CLARKE

HARRY D. CLARKE

1. Come in-to my heart, bless-ed Je-sus, Come in-to my heart, I pray;
2. Come in-to my heart, bless-ed Je-sus, I need Thee thro' life's drear-y way;
3. Come in-to my heart, bless-ed Je-sus, And take all my guilt a-way;
4. Come in-to my heart, bless-ed Je-sus, O cleanse and il-lu-mine my soul;

My soul is so troub-led and wea-ry, Come in-to my heart to-day.
The bur-den of sin is so heav-y, Come in-to my heart to stay.
Then spotless I'll stand in Thy pres-ence, When breaks Thine e-ter-nal day.
Fill me with Thy won-der-ful Spir-it, Come in and take full con-trol.

CHORUS

In-to my heart, in-to my heart, Come in-to my heart, Lord Je-sus;

Come in to-day, Come in to stay, Come in-to my heart, Lord Je-sus.

I Am Resolved

PALMER HARTSOUGH

JAMES H. FILLMORE

1. I am re-solved no lon-ger to lin - ger, Charmed by the world's delight;
2. I am re-solved to go to the Sav-ior, Leav-ing my sin and strife;
3. I am re-solved to fol - low the Sav-ior, Faith-ful and true each day;
4. I am re-solved to en - ter the Kingdom, Leav-ing the paths of sin;

Things that are high-er, things that are no - bler, These have al-lured my sight.
He is the true One, He is the just One, He hath the words of life.
Heed what He say - eth, do what He will-eth, He is the liv - ing way.
Friends may op-pose me, foes may be - set me, Still will I en - ter in.

CHORUS

I will has-ten to Him, Has-ten so glad and free;
I will has-ten, has - ten to Him, Has-ten so glad and free;

Has-ten glad and free;

Je - - sus, Great-est, High-est, I will come to Thee.
Je - sus, Je - sus,

302 The Nail-Scarred Hand

Baylus B. McKinney

Baylus B. McKinney

1. Have you failed in your plan of your storm-tossed life? Place your hand in the
2. Are you walk-ing a-lone through the shad-ows dim? Place your hand in the
3. Would you fol-low the will of the ris-en Lord? Place your hand in the
4. Is your soul bur-dened down with its load of sin? Place your hand in the

nail-scarred hand; Are you wea-ry and worn from its toil and strife?
nail-scarred hand; Christ will com-fort your heart, put your trust in Him,
nail-scarred hand; Would you live in the light of His bless-ed Word?
nail-scarred hand; Throw your heart o-pen wide, let the Sav-iour in,

Chorus

Place your hand in the nail-scarred hand. Place your hand in the nail-scarred

hand, Place your hand in the nail-scarred hand; He will keep to the

end, He's your dear-est Friend, Place your hand in the nail-scarred hand.

Open Your Heart's Door

Words and music by Evangelist John R. Rice

John R. Rice

1. Je - sus is here, Je - sus is here, Here on the door - step He's
2. Who - so - e'er will, Who - so - e'er will, May take the wat - er of
3. Don't turn a - way, Don't turn a - way From the soft warn - ing, your
4. Je - sus, come in; Je - sus, come in; Oh, lift the bur - den, for -

wait ing so near, Not far a - way, but read - y to - day, Your poor
life to your fill. Je - sus has paid, His life down He laid, For all
con - science would say. God's brok - en laws, your sin and your fall, Oh, do
give all my sin. Con - quer, O mild one, my heart so wild, Take now

Chorus

lost soul this mo - ment to save.
your sins, a - tone - ment He made. O - pen your heart's door to Je - sus,
not grieve God's Spir - it who calls.
and cleanse and make me God's child.

He's stand - ing near, wait - ing to hear your heart's con - fes - sion and

He'll take po - ses - sion, So o - pen your heart's door and let Him come in.

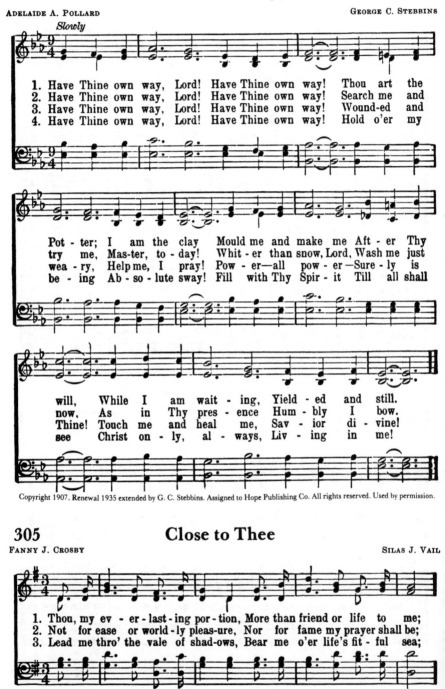

304 Have Thine Own Way, Lord!

ADELAIDE A. POLLARD

GEORGE C. STEBBINS

Slowly

1. Have Thine own way, Lord! Have Thine own way! Thou art the
2. Have Thine own way, Lord! Have Thine own way! Search me and
3. Have Thine own way, Lord! Have Thine own way! Wound-ed and
4. Have Thine own way, Lord! Have Thine own way! Hold o'er my

Pot - ter; I am the clay Mould me and make me Aft - er Thy
try me, Mas-ter, to - day! Whit - er than snow, Lord, Wash me just
wea - ry, Help me, I pray! Pow - er—all pow - er—Sure - ly is
be - ing Ab - so - lute sway! Fill with Thy Spir - it Till all shall

will, While I am wait - ing, Yield - ed and still.
now, As in Thy pres - ence Hum - bly I bow.
Thine! Touch me and heal me, Sav - ior di - vine!
see Christ on - ly, al - ways, Liv - ing in me!

305 Close to Thee

FANNY J. CROSBY

SILAS J. VAIL

1. Thou, my ev - er - last - ing por - tion, More than friend or life to me;
2. Not for ease or world - ly pleas-ure, Nor for fame my prayer shall be;
3. Lead me thro' the vale of shad-ows, Bear me o'er life's fit - ful sea;

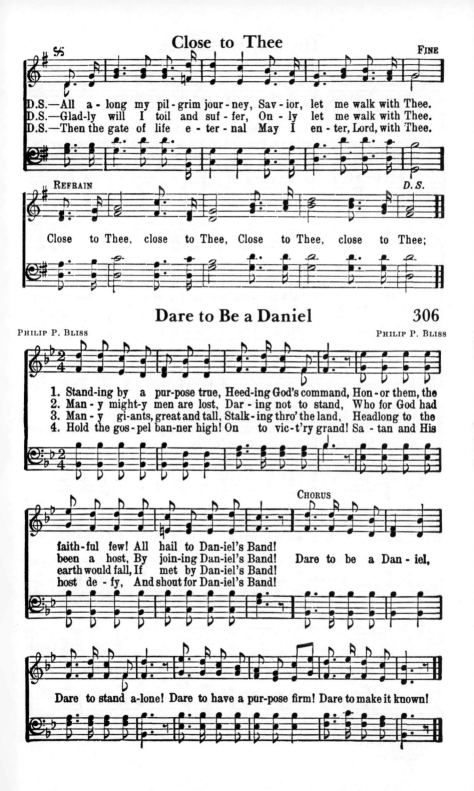

Close to Thee

FINE

D.S.—All a-long my pil-grim jour-ney, Sav-ior, let me walk with Thee.
D.S.—Glad-ly will I toil and suf-fer, On-ly let me walk with Thee.
D.S.—Then the gate of life e-ter-nal May I en-ter, Lord, with Thee.

REFRAIN   D. S.

Close to Thee, close to Thee, Close to Thee, close to Thee;

Dare to Be a Daniel

306

PHILIP P. BLISS   PHILIP P. BLISS

1. Stand-ing by a pur-pose true, Heed-ing God's command, Hon-or them, the
2. Man-y might-y men are lost, Dar-ing not to stand, Who for God had
3. Man-y gi-ants, great and tall, Stalk-ing thro' the land, Headlong to the
4. Hold the gos-pel ban-ner high! On to vic-t'ry grand! Sa-tan and His

CHORUS

faith-ful few! All hail to Dan-iel's Band!
been a host, By join-ing Dan-iel's Band!   Dare to be a Dan-iel,
earth would fall, If met by Dan-iel's Band!
host de-fy, And shout for Dan-iel's Band!

Dare to stand a-lone! Dare to have a pur-pose firm! Dare to make it known!

His Way With Thee

Cyrus S. Nusbaum   Cyrus S. Nusbaum

1. Would you live for Je - sus, and be al-ways pure and good? Would you walk with
2. Would you have Him make you free, and fol-low at His call? Would you know the
3. Would you in His king-dom find a place of con-stant rest? Would you prove Him

Him with - in the nar-row road? Would you have Him bear your burden, car - ry
peace that comes by giv-ing all? Would you have Him save you, so that you need
true in prov - i - den-tial test? Would you in His serv - ice la - bor al - ways

Chorus.

all your load? Let Him have His way with thee.
nev - er fall? Let Him have His way with thee. His pow'r can make you what you
at your best? Let Him have His way with thee.

ought to be; His blood can cleanse your heart and make you free; His love can fill your

rit.

soul, and you will see 'Twas best for Him to have His way with thee. A - men.

Follow On

W. O. CUSHING   ROBERT LOWRY

1. Down in the val-ley with my Sav-iour I would go, Where the flowers are
2. Down in the val-ley with my Sav-iour I would go, Where the storms are
3. Down in the val-ley, or up-on the moun-tain steep, Close be-side my

bloom-ing and the sweet wa-ters flow; Ev-ery-where He leads me I would
sweep-ing and the dark wa-ters flow; With His hand to lead me I will
Sav-iour would my soul ev-er keep; He will lead me safe-ly in the

fol-low, fol-low on, Walk-ing in His foot-steps till the crown be won.
nev-er, nev-er fear, Dan-ger can-not fright me if my Lord is near.
path that He has trod, Up to where they gath-er on the hills of God.

REFRAIN

Fol-low! fol-low! I would follow Je-sus! Anywhere, everywhere, I would follow on!

Fol-low! fol-low! I would follow Jesus! Everywhere He leads me I would follow on!

Is Your All on the Altar?

ELISHA A. HOFFMAN   ELISHA A. HOFFMAN

1. You have longed for sweet peace, and for faith to in-crease, And have ear-nest-ly,
2. Would you walk with the Lord, in the light of His Word, And have peace and con-
3. Oh, we nev - er can know what the Lord will be-stow Of the bless-ings for
4. Who can tell all the love He will send from a - bove, And how hap - py our

fer - vent-ly   prayed; But you can-not have rest   or be per - fect-ly blest
tent-ment al - way,   You must do His sweet will, to be free from all ill,
which we have prayed, Till our bod - y and soul He doth ful - ly con - trol,
hearts will be made, Of the fel - low-ship sweet we shall share at His feet,

CHORUS

Un - til all on the al - tar is   laid.
On the al - tar your all you must lay.   Is your all on the al - tar of
And our all on the al - tar is   laid.
When our all on the al - tar is   laid.

sac - ri - fice laid? Your heart, does the Spir-it con - trol? . . . You can on - ly be

blest and have peace and sweet rest, As you yield Him your bod - y and soul.

JUDSON W. VAN DEVENTER   WINFIELD S. WEEDEN

1. All to Je - sus I sur-ren - der, All to Him I free - ly give;
2. All to Je - sus I sur-ren - der, Hum - bly at His feet I bow,
3. All to Je - sus I sur-ren - der, Make me, Sav-ior, whol - ly Thine;
4. All to Je - sus I sur-ren - der, Lord, I give my - self to Thee;

I will ev - er love and trust Him, In His pres-ence dai - ly live.
World-ly pleas-ures all for-sak - en, Take me, Je - sus, take me now.
Let me feel the Ho - ly Spir - it,— Tru - ly know that Thou art mine.
Fill me with Thy love and pow - er, Let Thy bless-ing fall on me.

CHORUS

I sur-ren-der all,   I sur-ren-der all.
I sur-ren-der all,   I sur-ren-der all.

All to Thee, my bless - ed Sav - ior, I sur - ren - der all.

Favorite song of Dr. Fred D. Jarvis.

Open My Eyes, That I May See

CLARA H. SCOTT   CLARA H. SCOTT

1. O-pen my eyes, that I may see Glimps-es of truth Thou hast for me;
2. O-pen my ears, that I may hear Voi-ces of truth Thou send-est clear;
3. O-pen my mouth, and let me bear Glad-ly the warm truth ev-'ry-where;

Place in my hands the won-der-ful key That shall un-clasp, and set me free.
And while the wave-notes fall on my ear, Ev-'ry-thing false will dis-ap-pear.
O - pen my heart, and let me pre-pare Love with Thy chil-dren thus to share.

Si - lent-ly now I wait for Thee, Read-y, my God, Thy will to see;
Si - lent-ly now I wait for Thee, Read-y, my God, Thy will to see;
Si - lent-ly now I wait for Thee, Read-y, my God, Thy will to see;

O - pen my eyes, il - lu - mine me, Spir - it di - vine!
O - pen my ears, il - lu - mine me, Spir - it di - vine!
O - pen my heart, il - lu - mine me, Spir - it di - vine!   A - MEN.

I'll Be True, Precious Jesus

312

UNKNOWN

ELIZABETH PATE

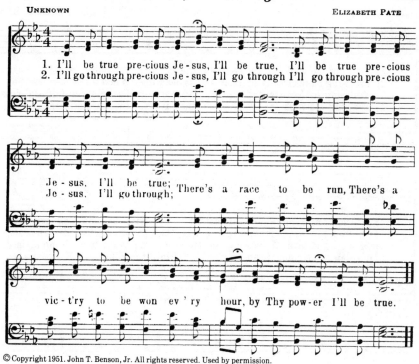

1. I'll be true pre-cious Je-sus, I'll be true, I'll be true pre-cious
2. I'll go through pre-cious Je-sus, I'll go through I'll go through pre-cious

Je-sus, I'll be true; There's a race to be run, There's a
Je-sus, I'll go through;

vic-t'ry to be won ev'ry hour, by Thy pow-er I'll be true.

Jesus Calls Us

313

MRS. CECIL F. ALEXANDER

GALILEE

WILLIAM H. JUDE

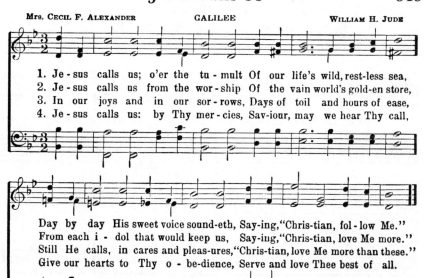

1. Je-sus calls us; o'er the tu-mult Of our life's wild, rest-less sea,
2. Je-sus calls us from the wor-ship Of the vain world's gold-en store,
3. In our joys and in our sor-rows, Days of toil and hours of ease,
4. Je-sus calls us: by Thy mer-cies, Sav-iour, may we hear Thy call,

Day by day His sweet voice sound-eth, Say-ing, "Chris-tian, fol-low Me."
From each i-dol that would keep us, Say-ing, "Chris-tian, love Me more."
Still He calls, in cares and pleas-ures, "Chris-tian, love Me more than these."
Give our hearts to Thy o-be-dience, Serve and love Thee best of all.

314 Stepping in the Light

ELIZA E. HEWITT

WILLIAM J. KIRKPATRICK

1. Try-ing to walk in the steps of the Sav-ior, Try-ing to fol-low our
2. Press-ing more close-ly to Him who is lead-ing, When we are tempted to
3. Walk-ing in foot-steps of gen-tle for-bear-ance, Foot-steps of faith-ful-ness,
4. Try-ing to walk in the steps of the Sav-ior, Up-ward, still upward we'll

Sav-ior and King; Shap-ing our lives by His bless-ed ex-am-ple,
turn from the way; Trust-ing the arm that is strong to de-fend us,
mer-cy and love, Look-ing to Him for the grace free-ly prom-ised,
fol-low our Guide; When we shall see Him, "the King in His beau-ty,"

CHORUS

Hap-py, how hap-py, the songs that we bring.
Hap-py, how hap-py, our prais-es each day. How beau-ti-ful to walk in the
Hap-py, how hap-py, our jour-ney a-bove.
Hap-py, how hap-py, our place at His side.

steps of the Sav-ior, Stepping in the light, Step-ping in the light; How

beau-ti-ful to walk in the steps of the Sav-ior, Led in paths of light.

I'll Live for Him
315

RALPH E. HUDSON

C. R. DUNBAR, 19th century

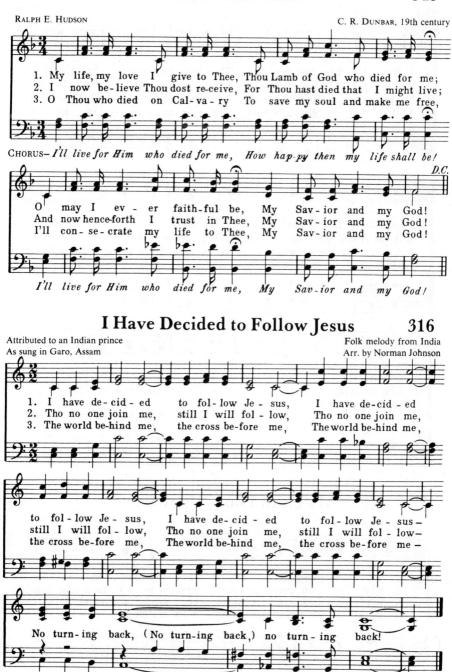

1. My life, my love I give to Thee, Thou Lamb of God who died for me;
2. I now be-lieve Thou dost re-ceive, For Thou hast died that I might live;
3. O Thou who died on Cal-va - ry To save my soul and make me free,

CHORUS— *I'll live for Him who died for me, How hap-py then my life shall be!*

D.C.

O may I ev - er faith-ful be, My Sav - ior and my God!
And now hence-forth I trust in Thee, My Sav - ior and my God!
I'll con - se - crate my life to Thee, My Sav - ior and my God!

I'll live for Him who died for me, My Sav-ior and my God!

I Have Decided to Follow Jesus
316

Attributed to an Indian prince
As sung in Garo, Assam

Folk melody from India
Arr. by Norman Johnson

1. I have de-cid - ed to fol-low Je - sus, I have de-cid - ed
2. Tho no one join me, still I will fol - low, Tho no one join me,
3. The world be-hind me, the cross be-fore me, The world be-hind me,

to fol-low Je - sus, I have de-cid - ed to fol-low Je - sus —
still I will fol - low, Tho no one join me, still I will fol - low
the cross be-fore me, The world be-hind me, the cross be-fore me —

No turn-ing back, (No turn-ing back,) no turn-ing back!

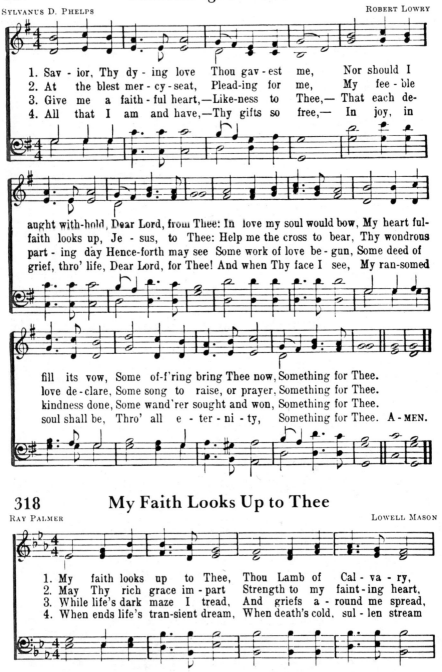

317

Something for Thee

SYLVANUS D. PHELPS

ROBERT LOWRY

1. Sav - ior, Thy dy - ing love Thou gav - est me, Nor should I
2. At the blest mer - cy - seat, Plead-ing for me, My fee - ble
3. Give me a faith - ful heart,—Like-ness to Thee,— That each de-
4. All that I am and have,—Thy gifts so free,— In joy, in

aught with-hold, Dear Lord, from Thee: In love my soul would bow, My heart ful-
faith looks up, Je - sus, to Thee: Help me the cross to bear, Thy wondrous
part - ing day Hence-forth may see Some work of love be - gun, Some deed of
grief, thro' life, Dear Lord, for Thee! And when Thy face I see, My ran-somed

fill its vow, Some of-f'ring bring Thee now, Something for Thee.
love de - clare, Some song to raise, or prayer, Something for Thee.
kindness done, Some wand'rer sought and won, Something for Thee.
soul shall be, Thro' all e - ter - ni - ty, Something for Thee. A - MEN.

318

My Faith Looks Up to Thee

RAY PALMER

LOWELL MASON

1. My faith looks up to Thee, Thou Lamb of Cal - va - ry,
2. May Thy rich grace im - part Strength to my faint - ing heart,
3. While life's dark maze I tread, And griefs a - round me spread,
4. When ends life's tran-sient dream, When death's cold, sul - len stream

My Faith Looks Up to Thee

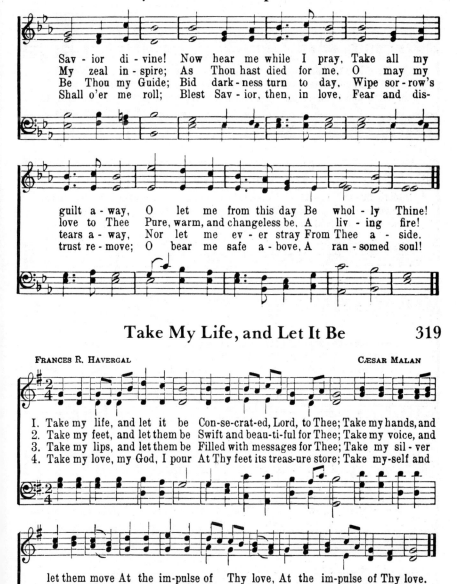

Sav - ior di - vine! Now hear me while I pray, Take all my
My zeal in - spire; As Thou hast died for me, O may my
Be Thou my Guide; Bid dark - ness turn to day, Wipe sor - row's
Shall o'er me roll; Blest Sav - ior, then, in love, Fear and dis-

guilt a - way, O let me from this day Be whol - ly Thine!
love to Thee Pure, warm, and changeless be, A liv - ing fire!
tears a - way, Nor let me ev - er stray From Thee a - side.
trust re - move; O bear me safe a - bove, A ran - somed soul!

Take My Life, and Let It Be 319

FRANCES R. HAVERGAL   CÆSAR MALAN

1. Take my life, and let it be Con-se-crat-ed, Lord, to Thee; Take my hands, and
2. Take my feet, and let them be Swift and beau-ti-ful for Thee; Take my voice, and
3. Take my lips, and let them be Filled with messages for Thee; Take my sil - ver
4. Take my love, my God, I pour At Thy feet its treas-ure store; Take my-self and

let them move At the im-pulse of Thy love, At the im-pulse of Thy love.
let me sing Al-ways, on - ly, for my King, Al-ways, on - ly, for my King.
and my gold, Not a mite would I with-hold, Not a mite would I with-hold.
I will be Ev - er, on - ly, all for Thee, Ev - er, on - ly, all for Thee.

More Like the Master

Charles H. Gabriel   Charles H. Gabriel

1. More like the Mas-ter I would ev-er be, More of His meek-ness,
2. More like the Mas-ter is my dai-ly prayer; More strength to car-ry
3. More like the Mas-ter I would live and grow; More of His love to

more hu-mil-i-ty; More zeal to la-bor, more cour-age to be true,
cross-es I must bear; More ear-nest ef-fort to bring His kingdom in;
oth-ers I would show; More self-de-ni-al, like His in Gal-i-lee,

rit.   CHORUS.

More con-se-cra-tion for work He bids me do...... Take Thou my
More of His Spir-it, the wan-der-er to win.....
More like the Mas-ter I long to ev-er be..... Take my heart, O

heart,.. I would be Thine a-lone;.. Take Thou my heart.. and
take my heart, I would be Thine a-lone; Take my heart, O take my heart and

make it all Thine own;.. Purge me from sin,.... O Lord, I now im-
make it all Thine own; Purge Thou me from ev'ry sin, O Lord, I

More Like the Master

plore, . . . Wash me and keep . . . me Thine for-ev - er - more.
now im-plore, Wash and keep, O wash and keep me Thine for-ev - er - more.

Sweet Hour of Prayer 321

WILLIAM W. WALFORD

WILLIAM B. BRADBURY

1. Sweet hour of prayer! sweet hour of prayer! That calls me from a world of care,
2. Sweet hour of prayer! sweet hour of prayer! Thy wings shall my pe - ti - tion bear
3. Sweet hour of prayer! sweet hour of prayer! May I thy con - so - la - tion share,

And bids me at my Fa-ther's throne Make all my wants and wish - es known;
To Him whose truth and faith-ful-ness En-gage the wait-ing soul to bless;
Till, from Mount Pisgah's loft - y height, I view my home, and take my flight:

In sea - sons of dis-tress and grief, My soul has oft - en found re - lief,
And since He bids me seek His face, Be-lieve His word and trust His grace,
This robe of flesh I'll drop, and rise To seize the ev - er - last - ing prize;

And oft es - caped the tempter's snare By thy re-turn, sweet hour of prayer.
I'll cast on Him my ev - 'ry care, And wait for thee, sweet hour of prayer.
And shout, while passing thro' the air, Farewell, farewell, sweet hour of prayer.

Ashamed of Jesus

Joseph Griggs.

E. O. Excell.

1. Je - sus, and shall it ev - er be, A mor - tal man a - shamed of Thee? A - shamed of Thee, whom an - gels praise, Whose glo - ries shine thro' end - less days?

2. A - shamed of Je - sus! soon - er far Let eve - ning blush to own a star; He sheds the beams of light di - vine O'er this be - night - ed soul of mine.

3. A - shamed of Je - sus! that dear Friend, On whom my hopes of Heav'n de - pend? No! when I blush be this my shame, That I no more re - vere His name.

4. A - shamed of Je - sus! yes, I may, When I've no guilt to wash a - way, No tear to wipe, no good to crave, No fears to quell, no soul to save.

CHORUS.

A - shamed.... of Je - sus, I nev - er, I nev - er will be;......

A-shamed of Je-sus, a-shamed of Je-sus, I nev-er, I nev-er, I nev-er will be;

For Je - - sus, my Sav - iour is not a-shamed of me.

Je-sus my Sav-iour, for Je-sus, my Sav-iour,

Sweet Will of God

Leila N. Morris

Leila N. Morris

DUET

1. My stub-born will at last hath yield-ed; I would be Thine, and
2. I'm tired of sin, foot-sore and wea-ry, The dark-some path hath
3. Thy pre-cious will, O con-qu'ring Sav-ior, Doth now em-brace and
4. Shut in with Thee, O Lord, for-ev-er, My way-ward feet no

Thine a-lone; And this the prayer my lips are bring-ing,
drear-y grown, But now a light has ris'n to cheer me;
com-pass me; All dis-cords hushed, my peace a riv-er,
more to roam; What pow'r from Thee my soul can sev-er?

rit. CHORUS

"Lord, let in me Thy will be done."
I find in Thee my Star, my Sun. Sweet will of God, still
My soul a pris-oned bird set free.
The cen-ter of God's will my home.

fold me clos-er, Till I am whol-ly lost in Thee; Sweet will of

God, still fold me clos-er, Till I am whol-ly lost in Thee.

324

Back to Bethel

B. B. McK.

B. B. McKinney.

1. Back to the Bi-ble, the true Liv-ing Word, Sweet-est old sto-ry that
2. Back to the beau-ti-ful path I once trod, Back to the church and the
3. Back to the giv-ing of mon-ey and time, Back to the life of con-
4. Back to the prayer-life in Christ I once knew, Back to its beau-ti-ful

ev - er was heard; Back to the joy-life my soul longs to know,
peo - ple of God; Out of the cold world of sin and its woe,
tent-ment sub-lime, Back to pro-tec-tion the world can-not know,
life-cleans-ing dew, Back to help oth-ers to con-quer each foe,

CHORUS

Beth - el is call-ing, and I must go. Back to Beth-el

I must go, Back where the riv-ers of sweet wa-ters flow, Back to the

true life my soul longs to know, Beth-el is call-ing, and I must go.

Nothing Between

Words and Music by C. A. TINDLEY   Arr. by F. A. CLARK

1. Noth-ing be-tween my soul and the Sav-iour, Naught of this world's de-
2. Noth-ing be-tween like world-ly pleas-ure; Hab-its of life, though
3. Noth-ing be-tween, like pride or sta-tion; Self or friends shall
4. Noth-ing be-tween, e'en man-y hard tri-als, Tho' the whole world a-

lu - sive dream: I have re-nounced all sin - ful pleas-ure,
harmless they seem, Must not my heart from Him ev - er sev - er,—
not in - ter - vene; Tho' it may cost me much trib - u - la - tion,
gainst me con-vene; Watching with prayer and much self-de - ni - al, I'll

CHORUS

Je - sus is mine, there's nothing be-tween.
He is my all, there's nothing be-tween. Noth-ing be-tween my soul and the
I am re-solved, there's nothing be-tween.
tri-umph at last, with nothing be-tween.

Sav-iour, So that His bless - ed face may be seen; Noth-ing pre-vent-ing the

least of His fa - vor, Keep the way clear! Let noth - ing be - tween.

Yield Not to Temptation

HORATIO R. PALMER   HORATIO R. PALMER

1. Yield not to temp-ta - tion, For yield-ing is sin, Each vic - t'ry will
2. Shun e - vil com-pan-ions, Bad lan-guage dis-dain, God's name hold in
3. To him that o'er-com-eth God giv-eth a crown, Thro' faith we shall

help you Some oth - er to win; Fight man-ful - ly on-ward,
rev-'rence, Nor take it in vain; Be thought-ful and ear - nest,
con - quer, Though of - ten cast down; He who is our Sav-ior,

Dark pas-sions sub-due, Look ev - er to Je - sus, He will car-ry you through.
Kind-heart-ed and true, Look ev - er to Je - sus, He will car-ry you through.
Our strength will re - new, Look ev - er to Je - sus, He will car-ry you through.

CHORUS

Ask the Sav - ior to help you, Com - fort, strengthen, and keep you,

He is will - ing to aid you, He will car - ry you through.

Give Me Thy Heart

Eliza E. Hewitt

William J. Kirkpatrick

1. "Give me thy heart," says the Fa-ther a-bove— No gift so pre-cious to
2. "Give me thy heart," says the Sav-ior of men, Call-ing in mer-cy a-
3. "Give me thy heart," says the Spir-it di-vine, "All that thou hast to my

Him as our love; Soft-ly He whis-pers wher-ev-er thou art,
gain and a-gain; "Turn now from sin and from e-vil de-part—
keep-ing re-sign; Grace more a-bound-ing is mine to im-part—

CHORUS

"Grate-ful-ly trust me and give me thy heart."
Have I not died for thee? give me thy heart." "Give me thy heart,
Make full sur-ren-der and give me thy heart."

Give me thy heart"— Hear the soft whisper, wher-ev-er thou art; From this dark

world He would draw thee a-part, Speak-ing so ten-der-ly, "Give me thy heart."

328 More Love to Thee

ELIZABETH P. PRENTISS

WILLIAM H. DOANE

1. More love to Thee, O Christ, More love to Thee! Hear Thou the
2. Once earth-ly joy I craved, Sought peace and rest; Now Thee a-
3. Let sor-row do its work, Send grief and pain; Sweet are Thy
4. Then shall my lat-est breath Whis-per Thy praise; This be the

prayer I make On bend-ed knee; This is my ear-nest plea:
lone I seek, Give what is best; This all my prayer shall be:
mes-sen-gers, Sweet their re-frain, When they can sing with me,
part-ing cry My heart shall raise; This still its prayer shall be:

More love, O Christ, to Thee, More love to Thee, More love to Thee!

329 All for Jesus

MARY D. JAMES

Arranged

1. All for Je-sus, all for Je-sus! All my be-ing's ransomed pow'rs:
2. Let my hands perform His bid-ding, Let my feet run in His ways;
3. Since my eyes were fixed on Je-sus, I've lost sight of all be-side;
4. Oh, what won-der! how a-maz-ing! Je-sus, glo-rious King of kings,

All my tho'ts and words and do - ings, All my days and all my hours.
Let my eyes see Je - sus on - ly, Let my lips speak forth His praise.
So en-chained my spir-it's vi - sion, Look-ing at the Cru - ci - fied.
Deigns to call me His be - lov - ed, Lets me rest be-neath His wings.

All for Je-sus! all for Je - sus! All my days and all my hours; hours.
All for Je-sus! all for Je - sus! Let my lips speak forth His praise; praise.
All for Je-sus! all for Je - sus! Look-ing at the Cru-ci-fied; fied.
All for Je-sus! all for Je - sus! Rest-ing now beneath His wings; wings.

MARY B. C. SLADE

Footprints of Jesus

330

ASA B. EVERETT

1. Sweet-ly, Lord, have we heard Thee call-ing, "Come, fol-low Me!" And we
2. Though they lead o'er the cold, dark mountains, Seek-ing His sheep, Or a-
3. If they lead thro' the tem-ple ho - ly, Preaching the Word, Or in
4. Then at last, when on high He sees us, Our jour-ney done, We will

CHORUS

see where Thy foot-prints falling Lead us to Thee.
long by Si - lo-am's fountains, Help-ing the weak: Foot-prints of Je-sus, that
homes of the poor and low-ly, Serv-ing the Lord:
rest where the steps of Je - sus End at His throne.

make the pathway glow! We will follow the steps of Je-sus wher-e'er they go.

331 Just a Closer Walk With Thee

Anon.

Arr. for John T. Benson

1. I am weak but Thou art strong (Thou art strong), Je-sus keep me from all
2. Thru this world of toil and snares (toil and snares), If I fal-ter, Lord, who
3. When my fee-ble life is o'er (life is o'er), Time for me will be no

wrong (from all wrong); I'll be sat-is-fied as long (just as long), As I walk let me
cares (Lord, who cares)? Who with me my burden shares (burden shares)? None but Thee, dear
more (be no more); Guide me gently, safely o'er (safely o'er), To Thy king-dom

CHORUS.

walk close to Thee (close to Thee).
Lord, none but Thee (none but Thee). Just a closer walk with Thee (walk with Thee),
shore, to Thy shore (to Thy shore).

Grant it, Je-sus, is my plea (hum-ble plea); Dai-ly walk-ing close to

Thee (close to Thee), Let it be, dear Lord, let it be (let it be).

Trust and Obey

JOHN H. SAMMIS   DANIEL B. TOWNER

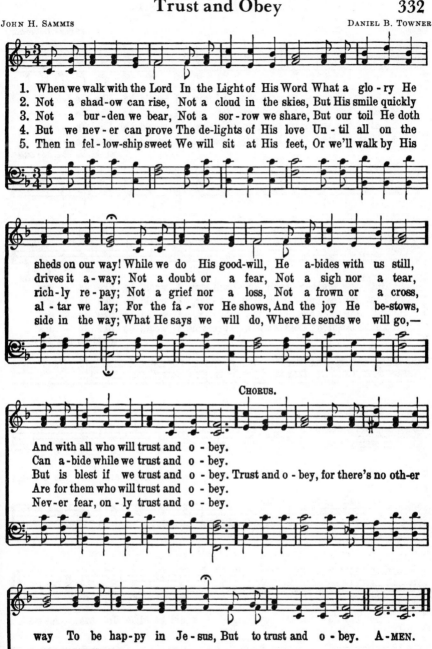

1. When we walk with the Lord In the Light of His Word What a glo-ry He
2. Not a shad-ow can rise, Not a cloud in the skies, But His smile quickly
3. Not a bur-den we bear, Not a sor-row we share, But our toil He doth
4. But we nev-er can prove The de-lights of His love Un-til all on the
5. Then in fel-low-ship sweet We will sit at His feet, Or we'll walk by His

sheds on our way! While we do His good-will, He a-bides with us still,
drives it a-way; Not a doubt or a fear, Not a sigh nor a tear,
rich-ly re-pay; Not a grief nor a loss, Not a frown or a cross,
al-tar we lay; For the fa-vor He shows, And the joy He be-stows,
side in the way; What He says we will do, Where He sends we will go,—

CHORUS.

And with all who will trust and o-bey.
Can a-bide while we trust and o-bey.
But is blest if we trust and o-bey. Trust and o-bey, for there's no oth-er
Are for them who will trust and o-bey.
Nev-er fear, on-ly trust and o-bey.

way To be hap-py in Je-sus, But to trust and o-bey. A-MEN.

333 I Would Be Like Jesus

JAMES ROWE   BENTLEY D. ACKLEY

1. Earth-ly pleas-ures vain-ly call me; I would be like Je - sus;
2. He has bro-ken ev - 'ry fet - ter, I would be like Je - sus;
3. All the way from earth to Glo - ry, I would be like Je - sus;
4. That in Heav-en He may meet me, I would be like Je - sus;
                                        would be like Je-sus;

Noth-ing world-ly shall en-thrall me; I would be like Je - sus.
That my soul may serve Him bet - ter, I would be like Je - sus.
Tell - ing o'er and o'er the sto - ry, I would be like Je - sus.
That His words "Well done" may greet me, I would be like Je - sus.
                                        would be like Je-sus.

CHORUS.

Be like Je - sus, this my song, In the home and in the throng;

Be like Je - sus, all day long! I would be like Je - sus. A - MEN.

O to Be Like Thee!

THOMAS O. CHISHOLM

WILLIAM J. KIRKPATRICK

1. O to be like Thee! bless-ed Re-deem-er, This is my con-stant
2. O to be like Thee! full of com-pas-sion, Lov-ing, for-giv-ing,
3. O to be like Thee! low-ly in spir-it, Ho-ly and harm-less,
4. O to be like Thee! Lord, I am com-ing, Now to re-ceive th'a-
5. O to be like Thee! while I am plead-ing, Pour out Thy Spir-it,

long-ing and prayer; Glad-ly I'll for-feit all of earth's treas-ures,
ten-der and kind, Help-ing the help-less, cheer-ing the faint-ing,
pa-tient and brave; Meek-ly en-dur-ing cru-el re-proach-es,
noint-ing di-vine; All that I am and have I am bring-ing.
fill with Thy love; Make me a tem-ple meet for Thy dwell-ing,

CHORUS

Je-sus, Thy per-fect like-ness to wear.
Seek-ing the wan-d'ring sin-ner to find.
Will-ing to suf-fer oth-ers to save.   O to be like Thee!
Lord, from this mo-ment all shall be Thine.
Fit me for life and heav-en a-bove.

O to be like Thee, Bless-ed Re-deem-er, pure as Thou art; Come in Thy

sweet-ness, come in Thy full-ness; Stamp Thine own im-age deep on my heart.

Where He Leads I'll Follow

WILLIAM A. OGDEN

WILLIAM A. OGDEN

1. Sweet are the prom-is-es, Kind is the word, Dear-er far than
2. Sweet is the ten-der love Je-sus hath shown, Sweet-er far than
3. List to His lov-ing words, "Come un-to Me;" Wea-ry, heav-y-

an-y mes-sage man ev-er heard; Pure was the mind of Christ,
an-y love that mor-tals have known; Kind to the err-ing one,
la-den, there is sweet rest for thee; Trust in His prom-is-es,

Sin-less I see; He the great ex-am-ple is, and pat-tern for me.
Faith-ful is He; He the great ex-am-ple is, and pat-tern for me.
Faith-ful and sure; Lean up-on the Sav-ior, and thy soul is se-cure.

CHORUS

Where . . . . He leads I'll fol - - - low,
Where He leads I'll fol-low, Where He leads I'll fol-low,

Fol - - - low all the way. Fol-low Je-sus ev-'ry day.
Fol-low all the way, yes, fol-low all the way.

Wherever He Leads I'll Go

B. B. McK.

B. B. McKinney

1. "Take up thy cross and fol - low Me," I heard my Mas - ter say;
2. He drew me clos - er to His side, I sought His will to know,
3. It may be through the shad-ows dim, Or o'er the storm - y sea,
4. My heart, my life, my all I bring To Christ who loves me so;

"I gave My life to ran - som thee, Sur - ren-der your all to - day."
And in that will I now a - bide, Wher-ev - er He leads I'll go.
I take my cross and fol - low Him, Wher-ev - er He lead-eth me.
He is my Mas - ter, Lord, and King, Wher-ev - er He leads I'll go.

CHORUS

Wher - ev - er He leads I'll go, . . . Wher-ev - er He leads I'll go, . . .

I'll fol-low my Christ who loves me so, Wher-ev - er He leads I'll go.

337 Make Me a Blessing

IRA B. WILSON

GEORGE S. SCHULER

Slowly

1. Out in the high-ways and by-ways of life, Man-y are wea-ry and sad; . . . .
2. Tell the sweet sto-ry of Christ and His love, Tell of His pow'r to for-give; . . . .
3. Give as 'twas giv-en to you in your need, Love as the Mas-ter loved you; . . . .

are wea-ry and sad;
His pow'r to for-give;
the Mas-ter loved you;

Car-ry the sunshine where darkness is rife,
Oth-ers will trust Him if on-ly you prove
Be to the help-less a help-er in-deed,

rit.

Mak-ing the sor-row-ing glad. . . .
True, ev-'ry mo-ment you live. . . . .
Un-to your mis-sion be true. . . . .

CHORUS *Men or Unison*

Make me a bless-ing,

Women

Make me a bless-ing, Out of my life . . . may Je-

Out of my life

Men

rit.

Unison

Women

sus shine; . . Make me a bless-ing, O Sav-ior,

Make Me a Blessing

I pray...... Make me a bless-ing to some-one to-day.
I pray Thee, my Sav-ior,

Tenors

More About Jesus

ELIZA E. HEWITT

JOHN R. SWENEY

338

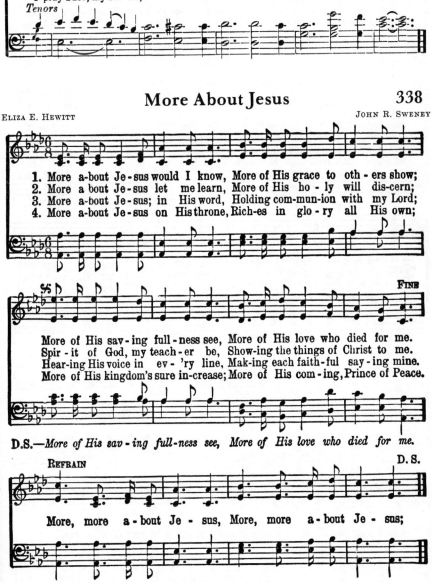

1. More a-bout Je-sus would I know, More of His grace to oth-ers show;
2. More a-bout Je-sus let me learn, More of His ho-ly will dis-cern;
3. More a-bout Je-sus; in His word, Holding com-mun-ion with my Lord;
4. More a-bout Je-sus on His throne, Rich-es in glo-ry all His own;

FINE

More of His sav-ing full-ness see, More of His love who died for me.
Spir-it of God, my teach-er be, Show-ing the things of Christ to me.
Hear-ing His voice in ev-'ry line, Mak-ing each faith-ful say-ing mine.
More of His kingdom's sure in-crease; More of His com-ing, Prince of Peace.

D.S.—*More of His sav-ing full-ness see, More of His love who died for me.*

REFRAIN

D. S.

More, more a-bout Je-sus, More, more a-bout Je-sus;

339   If Jesus Goes With Me

C. Austin Miles

C. Austin Miles

1. It may be in the val-ley, where countless dangers hide; It may be in the
2. It may be I must car-ry the bless-ed word of life A-cross the burning
3. But if it be my por-tion to bear my cross at home, While others bear their
4. It is not mine to ques-tion the judg-ments of my Lord, It is but mine to

sun - shine that I, in peace, a - bide; But this one thing I know—if
des - erts to those in sin - ful strife; And tho' it be my lot to
bur - dens be - yond the bil - low's foam, I'll prove my faith in Him—con-
fol - low the lead-ings of His Word; But if to go or stay, or

it be dark or fair, If Je - sus is with me, I'll go an - y - where!
bear my col - ors there, If Je - sus goes with me, I'll go an - y - where!
fess His judgments fair, And, if He stays with me, I'll stay an - y - where!
wheth-er here or there, I'll be, with my Sav - ior, Con-tent an - y - where!

CHORUS

If Je-sus goes with me, I'll go.... An - y - where! 'Tis heaven to me, Wher-
I'll go

e'er I may be, If He is there! I count it a priv - i - lege here.. His
His cross, His

If Jesus Goes with Me

cross to bear;.. If Je-sus goes with me, I'll go... An-y-where!
cross, His cross to bear;

Channels Only

340

MARY E. MAXWELL

ADA R. GIBBS

1. How I praise Thee, pre-cious Sav - ior, That Thy love laid hold of me;
2. Emp-tied that Thou shouldest fill me, A clean ves - sel in Thy hand;
3. Wit-ness-ing Thy pow'r to save me, Set - ting free from self and sin;
4. Je - sus, fill now with Thy Spir - it Hearts that full sur-ren-der know;

Thou hast saved and cleansed and filled me That I might Thy chan-nel be.
With no pow'r but as Thou giv - est Gra-cious-ly with each com-mand.
Thou who bought-est to pos-sess me, In Thy full - ness, Lord, come in.
That the streams of liv-ing wa - ter From our in - ner man may flow.

CHORUS

Chan-nels on - ly, bless-ed Mas - ter, But with all Thy won-drous pow'r

Flow-ing thro' us, Thou canst use us Ev - 'ry day and ev - 'ry hour.

341 Living for Jesus

Thomas O. Chisholm

C. Harold Lowden

Not fast

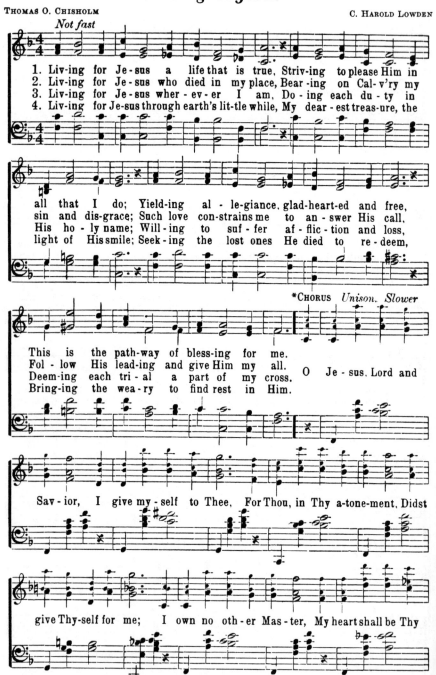

1. Liv-ing for Je-sus a life that is true, Striv-ing to please Him in
2. Liv-ing for Je-sus who died in my place, Bear-ing on Cal-v'ry my
3. Liv-ing for Je-sus wher-ev-er I am, Do-ing each du-ty in
4. Liv-ing for Je-sus through earth's lit-tle while, My dear-est treas-ure, the

all that I do; Yield-ing al-le-giance, glad-heart-ed and free,
sin and dis-grace; Such love con-strains me to an-swer His call,
His ho-ly name; Will-ing to suf-fer af-flic-tion and loss,
light of His smile; Seek-ing the lost ones He died to re-deem,

CHORUS Unison. Slower

This is the path-way of bless-ing for me.
Fol-low His lead-ing and give Him my all.
Deem-ing each tri-al a part of my cross.
Bring-ing the wea-ry to find rest in Him.

O Je-sus, Lord and Sav-ior, I give my-self to Thee, For Thou, in Thy a-tone-ment, Didst give Thy-self for me; I own no oth-er Mas-ter, My heart shall be Thy

Living for Jesus

throne, My life I give, hence-forth to live, O Christ, for Thee a - lone.

Take Time to Be Holy

342

WILLIAM D. LONGSTAFF

GEORGE C. STEBBINS

1. Take time to be ho - ly, Speak oft with thy Lord; A - bide in Him al - ways, And feed on His Word. Make friends of God's chil - dren; Help those who are weak; For - get - ting in noth - ing His bless - ing to seek.

2. Take time to be ho - ly, The world rush - es on;.. Spend much time in se - cret With Je - sus a - lone; By look - ing to Je - sus, Like Him thou shalt be;.. Thy friends in thy con - duct His likeness shall see..

3. Take time to be ho - ly, Let Him be thy Guide, And run not be - fore Him, What - ev - er be - tide;.. In joy or in sor - row, Still fol - low thy Lord, And, look - ing to Je - sus, Still trust in His Word.

4. Take time to be ho - ly, Be calm in thy soul;. Each tho't and each mo - tive Be - neath His con - trol;.. Thus led by His Spir - it To foun - tains of love, Thou soon shalt be fit - ted For serv - ice a - bove.

343 Draw Me Nearer

FANNY J. CROSBY

WILLIAM H. DOANE

1. I am Thine, O Lord, I have heard Thy voice, And it told Thy love to me; But I long to rise in the arms of faith, And be clos-er drawn to Thee.

2. Con-se-crate me now to Thy serv-ice, Lord, By the pow'r of grace di-vine; Let my soul look up with a stead-fast hope, And my will be lost in Thine.

3. Oh, the pure de-light of a sin-gle hour That be-fore Thy throne I spend, When I kneel in prayer, and with Thee, my God, I com-mune as friend with friend!

4. There are depths of love that I can-not know Till I cross the nar-row sea; There are heights of joy that I may not reach Till I rest in peace with Thee.

REFRAIN

Draw me near - er, near- er, bless-ed Lord, To the cross where Thou hast died; Draw me near - er, near - er, near - er, bless - ed Lord, To Thy pre - cious, bleed - ing side.

Higher Ground

JOHNSON OATMAN, JR.

CHARLES H. GABRIEL

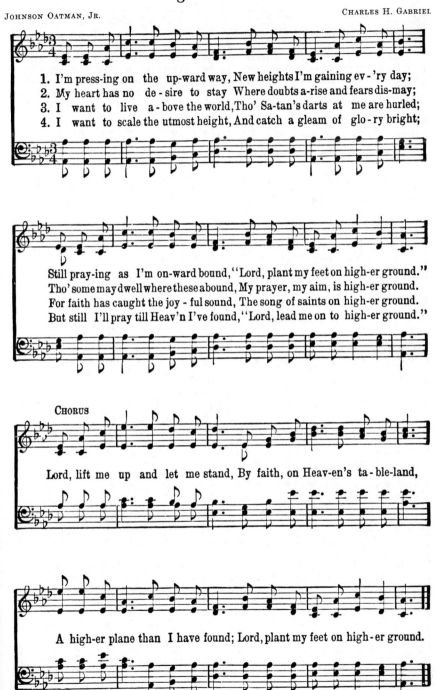

1. I'm press-ing on the up-ward way, New heights I'm gaining ev-'ry day;
2. My heart has no de-sire to stay Where doubts a-rise and fears dis-may;
3. I want to live a-bove the world, Tho' Sa-tan's darts at me are hurled;
4. I want to scale the utmost height, And catch a gleam of glo-ry bright;

Still pray-ing as I'm on-ward bound, "Lord, plant my feet on high-er ground."
Tho' some may dwell where these abound, My prayer, my aim, is high-er ground.
For faith has caught the joy-ful sound, The song of saints on high-er ground.
But still I'll pray till Heav'n I've found, "Lord, lead me on to high-er ground."

CHORUS

Lord, lift me up and let me stand, By faith, on Heav-en's ta-ble-land,

A high-er plane than I have found; Lord, plant my feet on high-er ground.

Christ Is All

1. I en-tered once a home of care, For age and pen-u-ry were
2. I stood be-side a dy-ing bed, Where lay a child with ach-ing
3. I saw the mar-tyr at the stake, The flames could not his cour-age
4. I saw the gos-pel her-ald go To Afric's sand and Greenland's
5. I dreamed that hoar-y time had fled, And earth and sea gave up their
6. Then come to Christ, O come to-day, The Fa-ther, Son, and Spir-it

there, Yet peace and joy with-al; I asked the lone-ly moth-er
head, Wait-ing for Je-sus' call; I marked his smile,'twas sweet as
shake, Nor death his soul ap-pall; I asked him whence his strength was
snow, To save from Sa-tan's thrall: Nor home nor life he count-ed
dead, A fire dissolved this ball; I saw the church's ran-som'd
say; The Bride re-peats the call; For He will cleanse your guilt-y

whence Her help-less wid-ow-hood's de-fence, She told me,"Christ was all."
May, And as his spir-it passed a-way, He whispered,"Christ is all."
giv'n—He look'd tri-umph-ant-ly to heav'n, And answered,"Christ is all."
dear, Midst wants and per-ils owned no fear, He felt that,"Christ is all."
throng, I heard the bur-den of their song, 'Twas"Christ is all in all."
stains, His love will soothe your wea-ry pains, For "Christ is all in all."

Christ is all, all in all, She told me,"Christ was all."
Christ is all, all in all, He whispered,"Christ is all."
Christ is all, all in all, And an-swered,"Christ is all."
Christ is all, all in all, He felt that "Christ is all."
Christ is all, all in all, 'Twas "Christ is all in all."
Christ is all, all in all, For "Christ is all in all."

Give Me Jesus

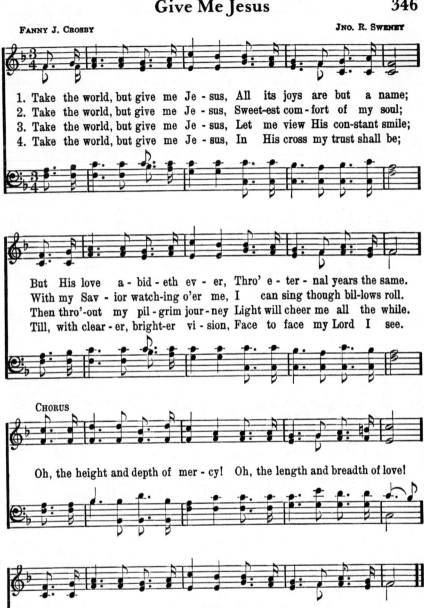

346

FANNY J. CROSBY

JNO. R. SWENEY

1. Take the world, but give me Je - sus, All its joys are but a name;
2. Take the world, but give me Je - sus, Sweet-est com - fort of my soul;
3. Take the world, but give me Je - sus, Let me view His con-stant smile;
4. Take the world, but give me Je - sus, In His cross my trust shall be;

But His love a - bid - eth ev - er, Thro' e - ter - nal years the same.
With my Sav - ior watch-ing o'er me, I can sing though bil-lows roll.
Then thro'-out my pil - grim jour-ney Light will cheer me all the while.
Till, with clear - er, bright-er vi - sion, Face to face my Lord I see.

CHORUS

Oh, the height and depth of mer - cy! Oh, the length and breadth of love!

Oh, the full - ness of re-demp-tion, Pledge of end - less life a - bove!

347   I Want That Mountain!

Words and Music
By Bill Harvey

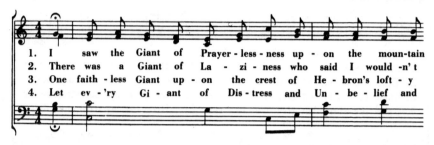

1. I saw the Giant of Prayer-less-ness up-on the moun-tain
2. There was a Giant of La-zi-ness who said I would-n't
3. One faith-less Giant up-on the crest of He-bron's loft-y
4. Let ev-'ry Gi-ant of Dis-tress and Un-be-lief and

high; He laughed so hard at my un-bend-ed knee. No
go and wit-ness for the One who set me free. I'll
height has vowed that he's the one to make me flee. I'll
Sin get read-y now to va-cate, for you see: I've

long-er in the Wil-der-ness I'll stay, and so I cry:--
come from out the Wil-der-ness, I'll wit-ness now I know;- I
climb from out the Wil-der-ness! and trust Je-ho-vah's might! -
come from out the Wil-der-ness! I know I'm going to win!--

Chorus

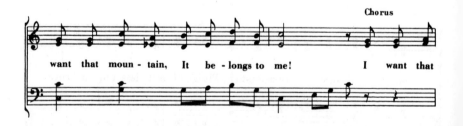

want that moun-tain, It be-longs to me! I want that

I Want That Mountain!

moun - tain! I want that moun - tain! Where the milk and hon - ey flow, Where the grapes of Esh - col grow. I want that moun - tain! I want that moun - tain! The Moun - tain that my Lord has giv - en me.

Constantly Abiding

MRS. WILL L. MURPHY

MRS. WILL L. MURPHY

1. There's a peace in my heart that the world nev-er gave, A peace it can
2. All the world seemed to sing of a Sav-ior and King, When peace sweetly
3. This treas-ure I have in a tem-ple of clay, While here on His

not take a-way; Tho' the tri-als of life may surround like a cloud,
came to my heart; Troubles all fled a-way and my night turned to day,
foot-stool I roam; But He's coming to take me some glo-ri-ous day,

CHORUS

I've a peace that has come there to stay!
Bless-ed Je-sus, how glorious Thou art!
O-ver there to my heav-en-ly home!

Con - - - stant-ly a-
Con-stant-ly a-bid - ing,

bid - - - ing, Je - - - sus is mine;.........
con-stant-ly a-bid-ing, Je-sus is mine, yes, Je-sus is mine;

Con - - - stant-ly a-bid - - - ing, rap - - ture di-
Con-stant-ly a-bid - ing, con-stant-ly a-bid-ing, rap-ture di-vine, O

Constantly Abiding

vine; He nev-er leaves me lone - - - ly, whis-pers,
rap-ture di-vine; He nev-er leaves me, nev-er leaves me lone-ly, whis-pers,

O. so kind:— "I will nev-er leave thee," Je - sus is mine.
whis-pers, O so kind:— nev-er leave thee," Je-sus, Je-sus is mine.

Holy Ghost, With Light Divine 349

ANDREW REED

LOUIS M. GOTTSCHALK
Arr. by EDWIN P. PARKER

1. Ho - ly Ghost, with light di-vine, Shine up - on this heart of mine;
2. Ho - ly Ghost, with pow'r di-vine, Cleanse this guilt-y heart of mine;
3. Ho - ly Ghost, with joy di-vine, Cheer this sad-dened heart of mine;
4. Ho - ly Spir - it, all di-vine, Dwell with-in this heart of mine;

Chase the shade of night a - way, Turn my dark-ness in - to day.
Long has sin, with-out con-trol, Held do - min - ion o'er my soul.
Bid my man-y woes de - part, Heal my wound-ed, bleed-ing heart.
Cast down ev - 'ry i - dol-throne, Reign su-preme, and reign a-lone. A-MEN.

350 Ho! Every One That Is Thirsty

L. J. R.

Lucy J. Rider

1. Ho! ev-'ry one that is thirst-y in spir-it, Ho! ev-'ry
2. Child of the world, are you tired of your bon-dage? Wea-ry of
3. Child of the king-dom, be filled with the Spir-it, Noth-ing but

one that is wea-ry and sad, Come to the foun-tain, there's
earth-joys, so false, so un-true; Thirst-ing for God, and His
full-ness thy long-ing can meet. 'Tis the en-due-ment for

full-ness in Je-sus, All that you're long-ing for, come and be glad.
full-ness of bless-ing? List to the prom-ise— a mes-sage for you.
life and for ser-vice; Thine is the prom-ise, so cer-tain, so sweet.

CHORUS.

"I will pour wa-ter on him who is thirst-y, I will pour

floods up-on the dry ground; O-pen your heart for the gift I am

Ho! Every One That Is Thirsty

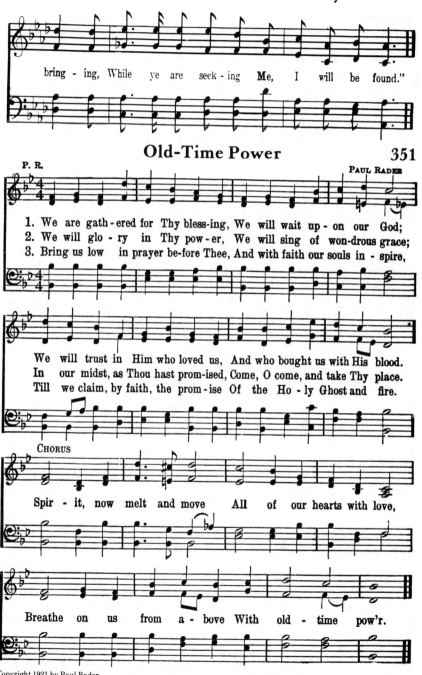

bring - ing, While ye are seek - ing Me, I will be found."

Old-Time Power

351

P. R.

PAUL RADER

1. We are gath-ered for Thy bless-ing, We will wait up-on our God;
2. We will glo-ry in Thy pow-er, We will sing of won-drous grace;
3. Bring us low in prayer be-fore Thee, And with faith our souls in-spire,

We will trust in Him who loved us, And who bought us with His blood.
In our midst, as Thou hast prom-ised, Come, O come, and take Thy place.
Till we claim, by faith, the prom-ise Of the Ho-ly Ghost and fire.

CHORUS

Spir - it, now melt and move All of our hearts with love,

Breathe on us from a-bove With old-time pow'r.

352   Spirit of God, Descend Upon My Heart

GEORGE CROLY

FREDERICK C. ATKINSON

1. Spir-it of God, de-scend up-on my heart;
2. Hast Thou not bid us love Thee, God and King?
3. Teach me to feel that Thou art al-ways nigh;
4. Teach me to love Thee as Thine an-gels love,

Wean it from earth, through all its puls-es move;
All, all Thine own, soul, heart and strength and mind;
Teach me the strug-gles of the soul to bear,
One ho-ly pas-sion fill-ing all my frame;

Stoop to my weak-ness, might-y as Thou art,
I see Thy cross— there teach my heart to cling:
To check the ris-ing doubt, the reb-el sigh;
The bap-tism of the heav'n-de-scend-ed Dove,

And make me love Thee as I ought to love.
O let me seek Thee, and O let me find.
Teach me the pa-tience of un-an-swered prayer.
My heart an al-tar, and Thy love the flame. A - MEN.

Pentecostal Power

Charlotte G. Homer

Chas. H. Gabriel

1. Lord, as of old at Pen - te - cost Thou didst Thy pow'r dis - play,
2. For might-y works for Thee pre-pare, And strengthen ev - 'ry heart;
3. All self con-sume, all sin de-stroy! With ear - nest zeal en - due
4. Speak, Lord! be-fore Thy throne we wait, Thy prom - ise we be - lieve,

With cleans-ing, pu - ri - fy - ing flame De-scend on us to - day.
Come, take pos - ses - sion of Thine own, And nev - er-more de - part.
Each wait-ing heart to work for Thee; O Lord, our faith re - new!
And will not let Thee go un - til The bless-ing we re - ceive.

Chorus

Lord, send the old - time pow'r, the Pen - te - cos - tal pow'r! Thy flood-gates of bless-ing on us throw o - pen wide! Lord, send the old - time pow'r, the Pen - te - cos - tal pow'r, That sinners be con-vert-ed and Thy name glo - ri-fied!

354 Blessed Quietness

Manie P. Ferguson

W. S. Marshall
Arr. by James M. Kirk

1. Joys are flow-ing like a riv-er, Since the Com-fort-er has come;
2. Bring-ing life and health and glad-ness, All a-round this heav'nly Guest,
3. Like the rain that falls from heav-en, Like the sun-light from the sky,
4. See, a fruit-ful field is grow-ing, Bless-ed fruit of right-eous-ness;
5. What a won-der-ful sal-va-tion, Where we al-ways see His face!

He a-bides with us for-ev-er, Makes the trust-ing heart His home.
Ban-ished un-be-lief and sad-ness, Changed our wea-ri-ness to rest.
So the Ho-ly Ghost is giv-en, Com-ing on us from on high.
And the streams of life are flow-ing In the lone-ly wil-der-ness.
What a per-fect hab-i-ta-tion, What a qui-et rest-ing place!

Refrain

Bless-ed qui-et-ness, ho-ly qui-et-ness, What as-sur-ance in my soul!

rit.

On the storm-y sea, He speaks peace to me, How the bil-lows cease to roll!

Breathe on Me

EDWIN HATCH

B. B. McKINNEY

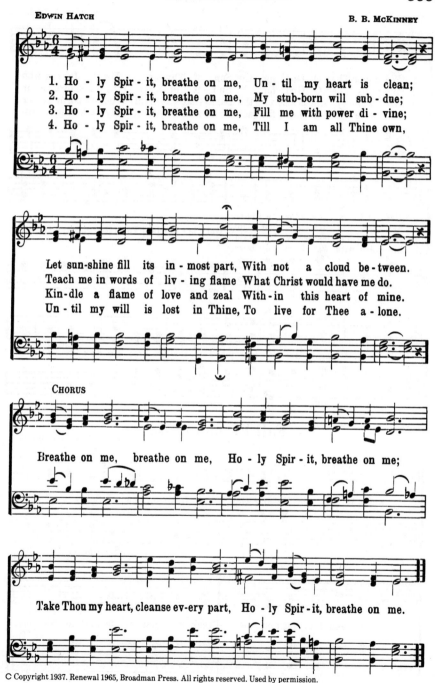

1. Ho - ly Spir - it, breathe on me, Un - til my heart is clean;
2. Ho - ly Spir - it, breathe on me, My stub-born will sub - due;
3. Ho - ly Spir - it, breathe on me, Fill me with power di - vine;
4. Ho - ly Spir - it, breathe on me, Till I am all Thine own,

Let sun-shine fill its in - most part, With not a cloud be - tween.
Teach me in words of liv - ing flame What Christ would have me do.
Kin-dle a flame of love and zeal With - in this heart of mine.
Un - til my will is lost in Thine, To live for Thee a - lone.

CHORUS

Breathe on me, breathe on me, Ho - ly Spir - it, breathe on me;

Take Thou my heart, cleanse ev-ery part, Ho - ly Spir - it, breathe on me.

356

Revive Us Again

WILLIAM P. MACKAY

JOHN J. HUSBAND

1. We praise Thee, O God! for the Son of Thy love, For Je-sus who
2. We praise Thee, O God! for Thy Spir-it of light, Who has shown us our
3. All glo-ry and praise to the Lamb that was slain, Who has borne all our
4. Re-vive us a-gain; fill each heart with Thy love; May each soul be re-

died, and is now gone a-bove.
Sav-ior, and scat-tered our night. Hal-le-lu-jah! Thine the glo-ry; Hal-le-
sins, and has cleansed ev-'ry stain.
kin-dled with fire from a-bove.

lu-jah! A-men! Hal-le-lu-jah! Thine the glo-ry; Re-vive us a-gain.

357

Fall Fresh on Me

Arr. by B. B. McKINNEY

Spir-it of the liv-ing God, Fall fresh on me, Spir-it of the

D. S.—*Spir-it of the*

liv-ing God, Fall fresh on me. Break me, melt me, mould me, fill me.

liv-ing God, Fall fresh on me.

ALFRED MIDLANE   JAMES McGRANAHAN

1. Re - vive Thy work, O Lord! Thy might - y arm make bare;
2. Re - vive Thy work, O Lord! Dis - turb this sleep of death;
3. Re - vive Thy work, O Lord! Cre - ate soul-thirst for Thee;
4. Re - vive Thy work, O Lord! Ex - alt Thy pre - cious name;

Speak with the voice that wakes the dead, And make Thy peo - ple hear.
Quick - en the smoul-d'ring em - bers now By Thine al - might - y breath.
But hun-g'ring for the bread of life, Oh, may our spir - its be!
And, by the Ho - ly Ghost, our love For Thee and Thine in - flame.

CHORUS

Re - vive! . . . re - vive! . . . And give re - fresh-ing show'rs;
Re - vive Thy work! re - vive Thy work! And give, oh, give re - fresh-ing show'rs;

The glo - ry shall be all Thine own; The bless-ing shall be ours.

Bring Your Vessels, Not a Few

Leila N. Morris

Leila N. Morris

1. Are you look-ing for the full-ness of the bless-ing of the Lord
2. Bring your emp-ty earth-en ves-sels, clean thro' Je-sus' pre-cious blood,
3. Like the cruse of oil un-fail-ing is His grace for-ev-er-more,

In your heart and life to-day? Claim the prom-ise of your Fa-ther,
Come, ye need-y, one and all; And in hu-man con-se-cra-tion
And His love un-chang-ing still; And ac-cord-ing to His prom-ise

come ac-cord-ing to His word, In the bless-ed old-time way.
wait be-fore the throne of God, Till the Ho-ly Ghost shall fall.
with the Ho-ly Ghost and pow'r, He will ev-'ry ves-sel fill.

Chorus

He will fill your heart to-day to o-ver-flow - - - ing, As the
He will fill your heart to o-ver-flow-ing,

Lord commandeth you, "Bring your vessels, not a few;" He will fill your heart to-
He will fill

Bring Your Vessels, Not a Few

day to o-ver-flow - - - ing With the Ho - ly Ghost and pow'r.
your   heart to o-ver-flow-ing,

Fill Me Now

360

ELWOOD H. STOKES

JOHN R. SWENEY

1. Hov - er o'er me, Ho - ly Spir - it, Bathe my trem-bling heart and brow;
2. Thou canst fill me, gra-cious Spir - it, Though I can - not tell Thee how;
3. I am weak-ness, full of weak-ness, At Thy sa - cred feet I bow;
4. Cleanse and com-fort, bless and save me, Bathe, O bathe my heart and brow;

Fill me with Thy hal-lowed pres-ence, Come, O come and fill me now.
But I need Thee, great-ly need Thee, Come, O come and fill me now.
Blest, di - vine, e - ter - nal Spir - it, Fill with pow'r, and fill me now.
Thou art com-fort-ing and sav - ing, Thou art sweet-ly fill - ing now.

CHORUS

Fill me now, fill me now, Je - sus, come and fill me now;

Fill me with Thy hal-lowed pres-ence, Come, O come and fill me now.

The Comforter Has Come

FRANK BOTTOME

361

WILLIAM J. KIRKPATRICK

1. O spread the ti-dings 'round, wher-ev-er man is found, Wher-
2. The long, long night is past, the morn-ing breaks at last, And
3. Lo, the great King of kings, with heal-ing in His wings, To
4. O bound-less love di-vine! how shall this tongue of mine To

ev - er hu-man hearts and hu-man woes a-bound; Let ev-'ry Christian
hushed the dreadful wail and fu-ry of the blast, As o'er the gold-en
ev-'ry cap-tive soul a full de-liv'rance brings; And thro' the va-cant
wond'ring mor-tals tell the matchless grace di-vine—That I, a child of

D.S.—*Ho-ly Ghost from Heav'n, The Fa-ther's promise giv'n; O spread the ti-dings*

tongue pro-claim the joy-ful sound: The Com-fort-er has come!
hills the day ad-vanc-es fast! The Com-fort-er has come!
cells the song of tri-umph rings; The Com-fort-er has come!
hell, should in His im-age shine! The Com-fort-er has come!

'round, wher-ev-er man is found—The Com-fort-er has come!

CHORUS

The Com-fort-er has come, The Com-fort-er has come! The

Come, Holy Spirit

Words and music by Evangelist John R. Rice

John R. Rice

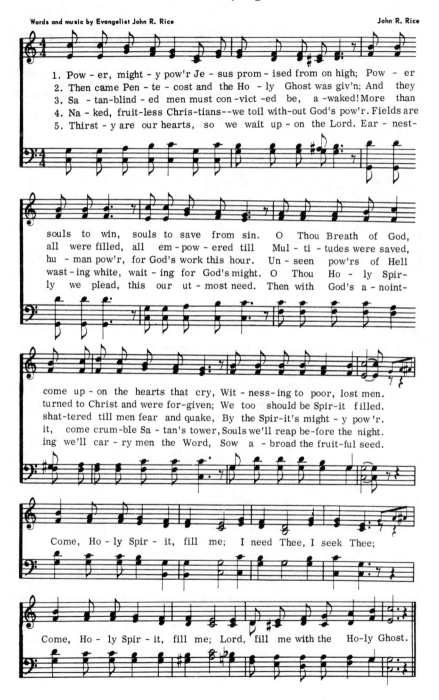

1. Pow - er, might - y pow'r Je - sus prom - ised from on high; Pow - er
2. Then came Pen - te - cost and the Ho - ly Ghost was giv'n; And they
3. Sa - tan-blind - ed men must con - vict - ed be, a -waked! More than
4. Na - ked, fruit-less Chris-tians--we toil with-out God's pow'r. Fields are
5. Thirst - y are our hearts, so we wait up - on the Lord. Ear - nest-

souls to win, souls to save from sin. O Thou Breath of God,
all were filled, all em - pow - ered till Mul - ti - tudes were saved,
hu - man pow'r, for God's work this hour. Un - seen pow'rs of Hell
wast - ing white, wait - ing for God's might. O Thou Ho - ly Spir-
ly we plead, this our ut - most need. Then with God's a - noint-

come up - on the hearts that cry, Wit - ness-ing to poor, lost men.
turned to Christ and were for-given; We too should be Spir-it filled.
shat-tered till men fear and quake, By the Spir-it's might - y pow'r.
it, come crum-ble Sa - tan's tower, Souls we'll reap be-fore the night.
ing we'll car - ry men the Word, Sow a - broad the fruit-ful seed.

Come, Ho - ly Spir - it, fill me; I need Thee, I seek Thee;

Come, Ho - ly Spir - it, fill me; Lord, fill me with the Ho - ly Ghost.

363 Have You Prayed It Through?

Rev. W. C. POOLE

B. D. ACKLEY

1. Have you prayed all night, Till the break of day, And the morn-ing light
2. Did you pray it through Till the an-swer came? There's a prom-ise true
3. As the Mas-ter prayed In the gar-den lone, Let your prayer be made

Drove the dark a-way? Did you lin-ger there, Till the morn-ing dew,
For your faith to claim; At the place of prayer Je-sus waits for you,
To the Fa-ther's throne; If you seek His will He will an-swer you;

CHORUS

In pre-vail-ing prayer—Did you pray it through?
Did you meet Him there, Did you pray it through? Did you pray till the an-swer
Are you trust-ing still, Have you prayed it through?

came, Did you plead in the Sav-iour's name? Have you
till it came, in His name?

prayed all night till the morn-ing light, Did you pray till the an-swer came?

I Am Praying for You

S. O'MALLEY CLUFF

IRA D. SANKEY

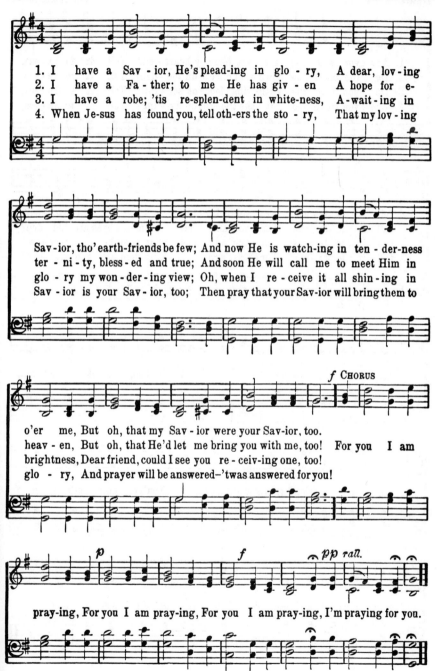

1. I have a Sav-ior, He's plead-ing in glo-ry, A dear, lov-ing
2. I have a Fa-ther; to me He has giv-en A hope for e-
3. I have a robe; 'tis re-splen-dent in white-ness, A-wait-ing in
4. When Je-sus has found you, tell oth-ers the sto-ry, That my lov-ing

Sav-ior, tho' earth-friends be few; And now He is watch-ing in ten-der-ness
ter-ni-ty, bless-ed and true; And soon He will call me to meet Him in
glo-ry my won-der-ing view; Oh, when I re-ceive it all shin-ing in
Sav-ior is your Sav-ior, too; Then pray that your Sav-ior will bring them to

f CHORUS

o'er me, But oh, that my Sav-ior were your Sav-ior, too.
heav-en, But oh, that He'd let me bring you with me, too! For you I am
brightness, Dear friend, could I see you re-ceiv-ing one, too!
glo-ry, And prayer will be answered–'twas answered for you!

p   *f*   *pp rall.*

pray-ing, For you I am pray-ing, For you I am pray-ing, I'm praying for you.

365   Tell It to Jesus

JEREMIAH E. RANKIN   EDMUND S. LORENZ

1. Are you wea - ry, are you heav - y-heart - ed? Tell it to Je - sus,
2. Do the tears flow down your cheeks un-bid - den? Tell it to Je - sus,
3. Do you fear the gath-'ring clouds of sor - row? Tell it to Je - sus,
4. Are you troub - led at the thought of dy - ing? Tell it to Je - sus,

Tell it to Je - sus; Are you griev - ing o - ver joys de - part - ed?
Tell it to Je - sus; Have you sins that to men's eyes are hid - den?
Tell it to Je - sus; Are you anx - ious what shall be to - mor-row?
Tell it to Je - sus; For Christ's com-ing King-dom are you sigh-ing?

CHORUS

Tell it to Je - sus a - lone. Tell it to Je - sus, tell it to Je - sus,

He is a friend that's well known; You've no oth - er

such a friend or broth - er, Tell it to Je - sus a - lone.

'Tis the Blessed Hour of Prayer

Fanny J. Crosby

William H. Doane

1. 'Tis the bless-ed hour of prayer, when our hearts low-ly bend,
2. 'Tis the bless-ed hour of prayer, when the Sav-iour draws near,
3. 'Tis the bless-ed hour of prayer, when the tempt-ed and tried
4. At the bless-ed hour of prayer, trust-ing Him we be-lieve

And we gath-er to Je-sus, our Sav-iour and Friend; If we
With a ten-der com-pas-sion His chil-dren to hear; When He
To the Sav-iour who loves them their sor-row con-fide; With a
That the bless-ings we're need-ing we'll sure-ly re-ceive; In the

come to Him in faith, His pro-tec-tion to share, What a balm for the
tells us we may cast at His feet ev-ery care, What a balm for the
sym-pa-thiz-ing heart He re-moves ev-ery care; What a balm for the
full-ness of this trust we shall lose ev-ery care; What a balm for the

CHORUS

wea-ry! O how sweet to be there! Bless-ed hour of prayer, Bless-ed

hour of prayer; What a balm for the wea-ry! O how sweet to be there!

367 Did You Think to Pray?

Mrs. M. A. Kidder

W. O. Perkins

1. Ere you left your room this morning, Did you think to pray? In the name of
2. When you met with great temp-ta-tion, Did you think to pray? By His dy - ing
3. When your heart was filled with an-ger, Did you think to pray? Did you plead for
4. When sore tri - als came up - on you, Did you think to pray? When your soul was

Christ our Sav - ior, Did you sue for lov-ing fa - vor, As a shield to-day?
love and mer - it, Did you claim the Ho-ly Spir - it As your guide and stay?
grace, my broth-er, That you might forgive an-oth - er Who had crossed your way?
bowed in sor - row, Balm of Gil-ead did you bor - row, At the gates of day?

D. S.—*So in sor-row and in glad - ness, Don't for-get to pray.*

CHORUS

D. S.

Oh, how pray-ing rests the wea - ry! Prayer will change the night to day;

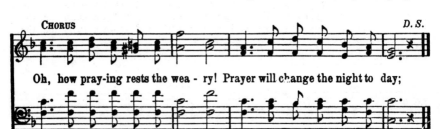

368 From Every Stormy Wind

Hugh Stowell

Thomas Hastings

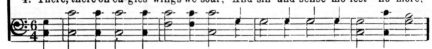

1. From ev - 'ry storm-y wind that blows, From ev -'ry swell-ing tide of woes,
2. There is a place where Je-sus sheds The oil of glad-ness on our heads;
3. There is a scene where spirits blend, Where friend holds fellowship with friend:
4. There, there on ea-gles' wings we soar, And sin and sense mo-lest no more,

From Every Stormy Wind

There is a calm. a sure re-treat: 'Tis found be-neath the mer-cy seat.
A place than all be-sides more sweet: It is the blood-bought mer-cy seat.
Tho' sun-dered far. by faith they meet A-round one com-mon mer-cy seat.
And heav'n comes down our souls to greet, When glo-ry crowns the mer-cy seat.

What a Friend We Have in Jesus 369

JOSEPH SCRIVEN   CHARLES C. CONVERSE

1. What a Friend we have in Je - sus, All our sins and griefs to bear!
2. Have we tri - als and temp - ta - tions? Is there troub-le an - y - where?
3. Are we weak and heav-y - la - den, Cumbered with a load of care?—

What a priv - i - lege to car - ry Ev - 'ry-thing to God in prayer!
We should nev-er be dis - cour-aged, Take it to the Lord in prayer.
Pre - cious Sav-ior, still our ref - uge,—Take it to the Lord in prayer.

O what peace we oft - en for - feit, O what need-less pain we bear,
Can we find a friend so faith - ful Who will all our sor-rows share?
Do thy friends despise, for-sake thee? Take it to the Lord in prayer;

All be-cause we do not car - ry Ev - 'ry-thing to God in prayer!
Je - sus knows our ev - 'ry weak - ness, Take it to the Lord in prayer.
In His arms He'll take and shield thee, Thou wilt find a sol - ace there.

370 I'm Leaning on Jesus

J.R.R.

John R. Rice

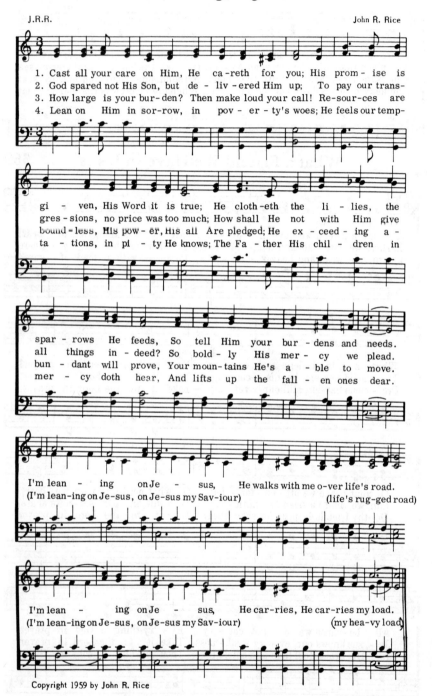

1. Cast all your care on Him, He ca-reth for you; His prom-ise is
2. God spared not His Son, but de-liv-ered Him up; To pay our trans-
3. How large is your bur-den? Then make loud your call! Re-sour-ces are
4. Lean on Him in sor-row, in pov-er-ty's woes; He feels our temp-

gi-ven, His Word it is true; He cloth-eth the li-lies, the
gres-sions, no price was too much; How shall He not with Him give
bound-less, His pow-er, His all Are pledged; He ex-ceed-ing a-
ta-tions, in pi-ty He knows; The Fa-ther His chil-dren in

spar-rows He feeds, So tell Him your bur-dens and needs.
all things in-deed? So bold-ly His mer-cy we plead.
bun-dant will prove, Your moun-tains He's a-ble to move.
mer-cy doth hear, And lifts up the fall-en ones dear.

I'm lean-ing on Je-sus, He walks with me o-ver life's road.
(I'm lean-ing on Je-sus, on Je-sus my Sav-iour)   (life's rug-ged road)

I'm lean-ing on Je-sus, He car-ries, He car-ries my load.
(I'm lean-ing on Je-sus, on Je-sus my Sav-iour)   (my hea-vy load)

Copyright 1959 by John R. Rice

I Must Tell Jesus

Elisha A. Hoffman

Elisha A. Hoffman

1. I must tell Je - sus all of my tri - als; I can - not bear these
2. I must tell Je - sus all of my troub- les; He is a kind, com-
3. Tempted and tried I need a great Sav - ior, One who can help my
4. O how the world to e - vil al - lures me! O how my heart is

bur - dens a - lone; In my dis - tress He kind - ly will help me;
pas - sion - ate Friend; If I but ask Him, He will de - liv - er,
bur - dens to bear; I must tell Je - sus, I must tell Je - sus;
tempt - ed to sin! I must tell Je - sus, and He will help me

He ev - er loves and cares for His own.
Make of my troub - les quick - ly an end.
He all my cares and sor - rows will share.
O - ver the world the vic - t'ry to win.

CHORUS

I must tell Je - sus!

I must tell Je - sus! I can - not bear my bur - dens a - lone; I must tell

Je - sus! I must tell Je - sus! Je - sus can help me, Je - sus a - lone.

Favorite song of songleader Lindsay Terry.

372 Ask and Seek and Knock

J. R. R.

JOHN R. RICE

1. Is there an - y - thing too hard for God to do?
2. Do you think He does not love e - nough to give.
3. When we read the Book of God we see His grace
4. We may ask "in Je - sus' name," or "ask in faith,"

Is there aught be - yond His pow'r? He com - mand - ed us to
All His chil - dren want and need? His be - lov - ed Son He
In His prom - is - es all through. Ev - 'ry word re - veals that
Pray u - nit - ed or a - lone. We may pray with trem - bling

o - pen wide our mouth, We should ask our needs this hour.
gave to save our souls; He would give all else in - deed!
God does an - swer prayer. We should claim each prom - ise true.
faith, but pray we should, We should plead till it is done!

CHORUS

We should ask and seek, Keep knock - ing at the door, at Je - sus' feet.

We have not our needs, Be - cause we do not plead with Je - sus.

Pray About Everything

373

J. R. M.

JOY RICE MARTIN

1. Once I was bur-dened with man-y a care; Prob-lems too hard for my weak soul to bear; Then in God's Word came a mes-sage so clear;
2. Ask of your Fa-ther, He lov-eth to please; Un-lock His treas-ure, He gives us the keys; Claim-ing this prom-ise, I dropped to my knees:
3. Doubt-ing and fret-ting can on-ly bring shame; Wor-ry and fear will dis-hon-or His name; Go to your Sav-iour His prom-ise to claim:
4. Rich-es in Je-sus, a-bun-dant and free, Needs in our work or what-ev-er it be; Ours for the ask-ing! This on-ly His plea:

CHORUS

Pray a-bout ev-'ry thing__ Prayer is a wonder-ful (ev-'ry thing) thing__ Prayer is a won-der-ful thing.__Bless-ing all ours with-out meas-ure; So pray a-bout ev-'ry thing. (ev-'ry thing)

Copyright 1965 by John R. Rice in "Revival Specials No. 2"

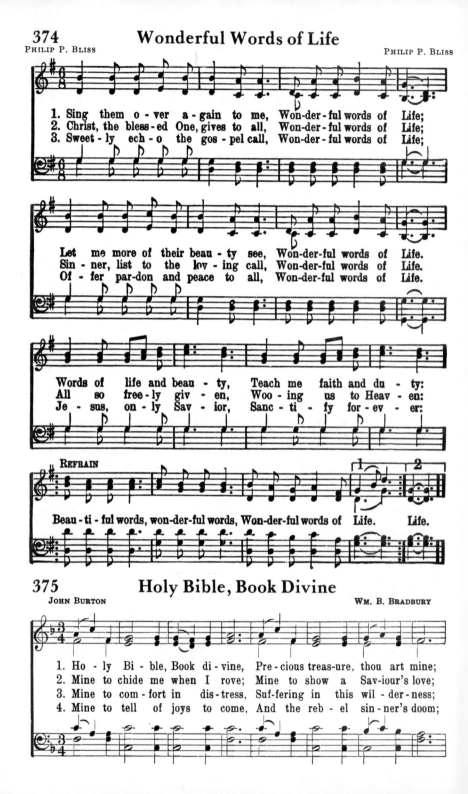

374 Wonderful Words of Life

PHILIP P. BLISS

PHILIP P. BLISS

1. Sing them o-ver a-gain to me, Won-der-ful words of Life;
2. Christ, the bless-ed One, gives to all, Won-der-ful words of Life;
3. Sweet-ly ech-o the gos-pel call, Won-der-ful words of Life;

Let me more of their beau-ty see, Won-der-ful words of Life.
Sin - ner, list to the lov-ing call, Won-der-ful words of Life.
Of - fer par-don and peace to all, Won-der-ful words of Life.

Words of life and beau - ty, Teach me faith and du - ty:
All so free-ly giv - en, Woo - ing us to Heav - en:
Je - sus, on - ly Sav - ior, Sanc - ti - fy for - ev - er:

REFRAIN

Beau - ti - ful words, won-der-ful words, Won-der-ful words of Life. Life.

375 Holy Bible, Book Divine

JOHN BURTON

WM. B. BRADBURY

1. Ho - ly Bi - ble, Book di - vine, Pre - cious treas-ure, thou art mine;
2. Mine to chide me when I rove; Mine to show a Sav-iour's love;
3. Mine to com - fort in dis - tress, Suf-fering in this wil - der - ness;
4. Mine to tell of joys to come, And the reb - el sin - ner's doom;

Holy Bible, Book Divine

Mine to tell me whence I came; Mine to teach me what I am;
Mine thou art to guide and guard; Mine to pun-ish or re-ward;
Mine to show, by liv-ing faith, Man can tri-umph o-ver death;
O thou ho-ly Book di-vine, Pre-cious treas-ure, thou art mine.

Break Thou the Bread of Life   376

MARY ANN LATHBURY   WILLIAM F. SHERWIN

1. Break Thou the bread of life, Dear Lord, to me, As Thou didst
2. Bless Thou the truth, dear Lord To me— to me— As Thou didst
3. Thou art the bread of life, O Lord, to me, Thy ho-ly
4. O send Thy Spir-it, Lord, Now un-to me, That He may

break the loaves Be-side the sea; Be-yond the sa-cred page
bless the bread By Gal-i-lee; Then shall all bond-age cease,
Word the truth That sav-eth me; Give me to eat and live
touch my eyes, And make me see: Show me the truth con-cealed

I seek Thee, Lord; My spir-it pants for Thee, O liv-ing Word.
All fet-ters fall; And I shall find my peace, My All in All.
With Thee a-bove; Teach me to love Thy truth, For Thou art love.
With-in Thy Word, And in Thy book re-vealed I see the Lord.

My Mother's Bible

Evangelist M. B. WILLIAMS

CHARLIE D. TILLMAN

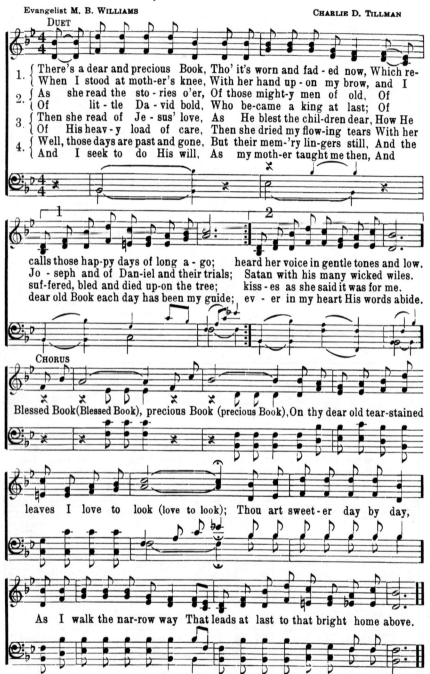

1. There's a dear and precious Book, Tho' it's worn and fad-ed now, Which re-
   When I stood at moth-er's knee, With her hand up-on my brow, and I
2. As she read the sto-ries o'er, Of those might-y men of old, Of
   Of lit-tle Da-vid bold, Who be-came a king at last; Of
3. Then she read of Je-sus' love, As He blest the chil-dren dear, How He
   Of His heav-y load of care, Then she dried my flow-ing tears With her
4. Well, those days are past and gone, But their mem-'ry lin-gers still, And the
   And I seek to do His will, As my moth-er taught me then, And

calls those hap-py days of long a-go; heard her voice in gentle tones and low.
Jo-seph and of Dan-iel and their trials; Satan with his many wicked wiles.
suf-fered, bled and died up-on the tree; kiss-es as she said it was for me.
dear old Book each day has been my guide; ev-er in my heart His words abide.

CHORUS

Blessed Book(Blessed Book), precious Book (precious Book),On thy dear old tear-stained
leaves I love to look (love to look); Thou art sweet-er day by day,
As I walk the nar-row way That leads at last to that bright home above.

I Know the Bible Is True 378

Gene Routh.

B. B. McKinney.

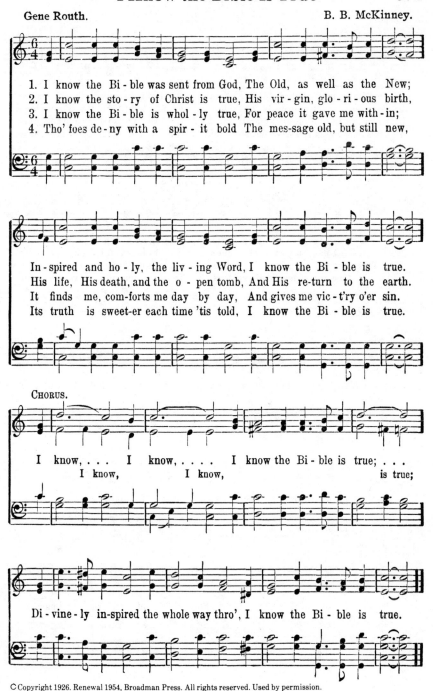

1. I know the Bi - ble was sent from God, The Old, as well as the New;
2. I know the sto - ry of Christ is true, His vir - gin, glo - ri - ous birth,
3. I know the Bi - ble is whol - ly true, For peace it gave me with - in,
4. Tho' foes de - ny with a spir - it bold The mes-sage old, but still new,

In - spired and ho - ly, the liv - ing Word, I know the Bi - ble is true.
His life, His death, and the o - pen tomb, And His re-turn to the earth.
It finds me, com-forts me day by day, And gives me vic - t'ry o'er sin.
Its truth is sweet-er each time 'tis told, I know the Bi - ble is true.

CHORUS.

I know, . . . I know, ... I know the Bi - ble is true; . . .
I know, I know, is true;

Di - vine - ly in-spired the whole way thro', I know the Bi - ble is true.

379 Thy Word Have I Hid in My Heart

From Psalm 119
Adapted by Ernest O. Sellers

Ernest O. Sellers

1. Thy Word is a lamp to my feet, A light to my path al - way,
2. For - ev - er, O Lord, is Thy Word Es-tab-lished and fixed on high;
3. At morn-ing, at noon, and at night I ev - er will give Thee praise;
4. Thru Him whom Thy Word hath fore-told, The Sav-ior and Morn - ing Star,

To guide and to save me from sin And show me the heav'n-ly way.
Thy faith-ful-ness un - to all men A - bid-eth for - ev - er nigh.
For Thou art my por-tion, O Lord, And shall be thru all my days!
Sal - va-tion and peace have been brought To those who have strayed a - far.

CHORUS

Thy Word have I hid in my heart, (in my heart,) That I might not

sin a-gainst Thee; (a-gainst Thee;) That I might not sin, that

I might not sin, Thy Word have I hid in my heart.

Standing on the Promises

381 The Old Book and the Old Faith

GEORGE H. CARR, 20th century

GEORGE H. CARR

1. 'Mid the storms of doubt and un-be-lief we fear, Stands a Book e-
2. 'Tis the Book that tells us of the Fa-ther's love, When He sent His
3. 'Tis the Book that tells us of the will of God And the Sav-ior's
4. 'Tis the Book that tells us of e-ter-nal life, Aft-er faith-ful

ter-nal that the world holds dear; Thru the rest-less a-ges it re-
Son to us from heav'n a-bove, Who by rich-est prom-ise cre-ates
teachings while the earth He trod— How He soothed earth's sor-rows and re-
serv-ice in a world of strife; And this glo-rious tri-umph o-ver

mains the same—'Tis the Book of God, and the Bi-ble is its name!
hope with-in, For 'tis thru His blood we are saved from ev-'ry sin!
lieved its woe, Thru whom strength is giv-en to con-quer ev-'ry foe!
death's dark fears Is the world's best gift in an age of count-less tears!

CHORUS

The old Book and the old Faith Are the Rock on which I stand!
The grand old Book and the dear old Faith on which I stand!

The Old Book and the Old Faith

The old Book and the old Faith Are the bul-wark of the land!
The grand old Book and the dear old Faith

Thru storm and stress they stand the test, In ev-'ry clime and na-tion blest;

The old Book and the old Faith Are the hope of ev-'ry land!
The grand old Book and the dear old Faith

GRAND CHORUS AT CLOSE
(*May be omitted*)

O the grand old Book and the dear old Faith Are the Rock on which I stand!

O the grand old Book and the dear old Faith Are the hope of ev-'ry land!

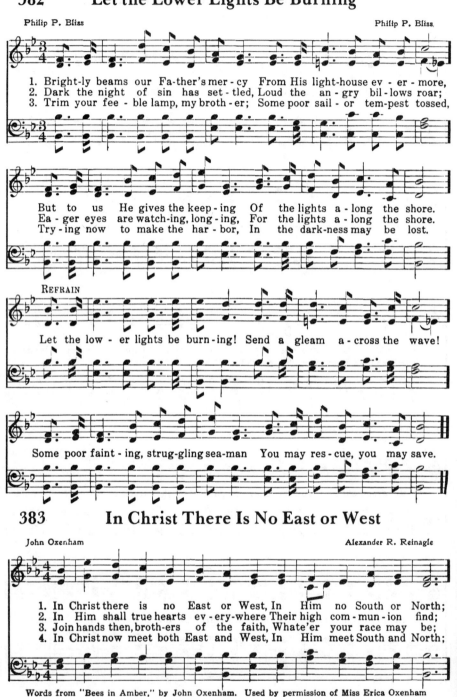

382   Let the Lower Lights Be Burning

Philip P. Bliss

Philip P. Bliss

1. Bright-ly beams our Fa-ther's mer-cy From His light-house ev-er-more,
2. Dark the night of sin has set-tled, Loud the an-gry bil-lows roar;
3. Trim your fee-ble lamp, my broth-er; Some poor sail-or tem-pest tossed,

But to us He gives the keep-ing Of the lights a-long the shore.
Ea-ger eyes are watch-ing, long-ing, For the lights a-long the shore.
Try-ing now to make the har-bor, In the dark-ness may be lost.

REFRAIN

Let the low-er lights be burn-ing! Send a gleam a-cross the wave!

Some poor faint-ing, strug-gling sea-man You may res-cue, you may save.

383   In Christ There Is No East or West

John Oxenham

Alexander R. Reinagle

1. In Christ there is no East or West, In Him no South or North;
2. In Him shall true hearts ev-ery-where Their high com-mun-ion find;
3. Join hands then, broth-ers of the faith, Whate'er your race may be;
4. In Christ now meet both East and West, In Him meet South and North;

Words from "Bees in Amber," by John Oxenham. Used by permission of Miss Erica Oxenham

In Christt There Is No East or West

But one great fel-low-ship of love Throughout the whole wide earth.
His serv-ice is the gold-en cord Close-bind-ing all man-kind.
Who serves my Fa-ther as a son Is sure-ly kin to me.
All Christ-ly souls are one in Him Throughout the whole wide earth. A-MEN.

Work, for the Night Is Coming 384

Annie L. Coghill
Alt. by Lowell Mason

Lowell Mason

1. Work, for the night is com-ing, Work thro' the morn-ing hours;
2. Work, for the night is com-ing, Work thro' the sun-ny noon;
3. Work, for the night is com-ing, Un-der the sun-set skies;

Work while the dew is spark-ling; Work 'mid spring-ing flowers.
Fill bright-est hours with la-bor, Rest comes sure and soon.
While their bright tints are glow-ing, Work, for day-light flies.

Work when the day grows bright-er, Work in the glow-ing sun;
Give ev-er-fly-ing min-ute Some-thing to keep in store;
Work till the last beam fad-eth, Fad-eth to shine no more;

Work, for the night is com-ing, When man's work is done.
Work, for the night is com-ing, When man works no more.
Work, while the night is dark-'ning, When man's work is o'er. A-MEN.

Throw Out the Life-Line

Edward S. Ufford
Arr. by George C. Stebbins

Edward S. Ufford

1. Throw out the Life-Line a-cross the dark wave, There is a broth-er whom
2. Throw out the Life-Line with hand quick and strong: Why do you tar-ry, why
3. Throw out the Life-Line to dan-ger fraught men, Sink-ing in an-guish where
4. Soon will the sea-son of res-cue be o'er, Soon will they drift to e-

some one should save; Some-bod-y's broth-er! oh, who then will dare To
lin-ger so long? See! he is sink-ing; oh, has-ten to-day—And
you've nev-er been: Winds of temp-ta-tion and bil-lows of woe Will
ter-ni-ty's shore; Haste then, my broth-er, no time for de-lay, But!

REFRAIN

throw out the Life-Line, his per-il to share?
out with the Life-Boat! a-way, then, a-way! Throw out the Life-Line!
soon hurl them out where the dark wa-ters flow.
throw out the Life-Line and save them to-day.

Throw out the Life-Line! Some-one is drift-ing a-way; Throw out the

Life-Line! Throw out the Life-Line! Some one is sink-ing to-day.

We've a Story to Tell to the Nations

H. ERNEST NICHOL

H. ERNEST NICHOL

1. We've a sto - ry to tell to the na - tions That shall turn their hearts
2. We've a song to be sung to the na - tions That shall lift their hearts
3. We've a mes - sage to give to the na - tions, That the Lord who reign-
4. We've a Sav - ior to show to the na - tions Who the path of sor-

to the right, A sto - ry of truth and mer - cy, A
to the Lord, A song that shall con - quer e - vil And
eth a - bove Hath sent us His Son to save us, And
row hath trod, That all of the world's great peo - ples Might

sto - ry of peace and light, A sto - ry of peace and light.
shat - ter the spear and sword, And shat - ter the spear and sword.
show us that God is love, And show us that God is love.
come to the truth of God, Might come to the truth of God.

CHORUS

For the darkness shall turn to dawn - ing, And the dawn-ing to noonday bright,

rall.

And Christ's great kingdom shall come to earth, The kingdom of love and light.

387 Will There Be Any Stars?

ELIZA E. HEWITT

JOHN R. SWENEY

1. I am think-ing to-day of that beau-ti-ful land I shall reach when the
2. In the strength of the Lord let me la-bor and pray, Let me watch as a
3. Oh, what joy it will be when His face I be-hold, Liv-ing gems at His

sun go-eth down; When thro' wonderful grace by my Sav-ior I stand, Will there
win-ner of souls; That bright stars may be mine in the glo-ri-ous day, When His
feet to lay down; It would sweeten my bliss in the cit-y of gold, Should there

CHORUS.

be an-y stars in my crown?
praise like the sea-bil-low rolls. Will there be an-y stars, an-y stars in my
be an-y stars in my crown.

crown When at evening the sun go-eth down? . . . When I wake with the blest
go-eth down?

In the mansions of rest, Will there be an-y stars in my crown? .. A-MEN.
an-y stars in my crown?

A Passion for Souls

HERBERT G. TOVEY

FOSS L. FELLERS

388

1. Give me a pas - sion for souls, dear Lord, A pas - sion to save the lost;
2. Though there are dan - gers un - told and stern Con - front - ing me in the way,
3. How shall this pas - sion for souls be mine? Lord, make Thou the an - swer clear;

O that Thy love were by all a - dored, And wel - comed at an - y cost.
Will - ing - ly still would I go, nor turn, But trust Thee for grace each day.
Help me to throw out the old Life-Line To those who are strug - gling near.

CHORUS.

Je - sus, I long, I long to be win - ning Men who are lost, and con - stant - ly sin - ning; O may this hour be one of be - gin - ning The sto - ry of par - don to tell.

389 So Send I You

E. Margaret Clarkson

John W. Peterson

1. So send I you to la-bor un-re-ward-ed, To serve un-
2. So send I you to bind the bruised and bro-ken, O'er wand'ring
3. So send I you to lone-li-ness and long-ing, With heart a-
4. So send I you to leave your life's am-bi-tion, To die to
5. So send I you to hearts made hard by hat-red, To eyes made

paid, un-loved, un-sought, un-known, To bear re-buke, to suf-fer
souls to work, to weep, to wake, To bear the bur-dens of a
hung'ring for the loved and known, For-sak-ing home and kin-dred,
dear de-sire, self-will re-sign, To la-bor long, and love where
blind be-cause they will not see, To spend, tho' it be blood, to

scorn and scoff-ing— So send I you to toil for Me a-lone.
world a-wea-ry— So send I you to suf-fer for My sake.
friend and dear one— So send I you to know My love a-lone.
men re-vile you— So send I you to lose your life in Mine.
spend and spare not— So send I you to taste of Cal-va-ry.

*CHORUS

"As the Fa-ther hath sent me, So send I you."

*Effective if sung only after the last verse.

Send the Light

CHARLES H. GABRIEL   CHARLES H. GABRIEL

1. There's a call comes ring-ing o'er the rest-less wave, "Send the light! ...
2. We have heard the Mac-e-do-nian call to-day, "Send the light! ...
3. Let us pray that grace may ev-'ry-where a-bound; Send the light! ...
4. Let us not grow wea-ry in the work of love, Send the light! ...

Send the light!

Send the light!"   There are souls to res-cue, there are souls to save,
Send the light!"   And a gold-en of-f'ring at the cross we lay,
Send the light!   And a Christ-like spir-it ev-'ry-where be found,
Send the light!   Let us gath-er jew-els for a crown a-bove,

Send the light!

REFRAIN

Send the light! ... Send the light! ... Send the light! ... the
Send the light!   Send the light!   Send the light!

bless-ed gos-pel light; Let it shine ... from shore to
the   bless-ed gos-pel light;   Let it shine

shore! .... shine ... for-ev-er-more. ....
from shore to shore!   Let it shine   for-ev-er-more.

391 ## Rescue the Perishing

FANNY J. CROSBY

WILLIAM H. DOANE

1. Res - cue the per-ish-ing, Care for the dy - ing, Snatch them in pit - y from
2. Tho' they are slighting Him, Still He is wait-ing, Wait-ing the pen - i - tent
3. Down in the hu-man heart, Crushed by the tempter, Feel-ings lie bur - ied that
4. Res - cue the per-ish-ing, Du - ty de-mands it; Strength for thy la-bor the

sin and the grave; Weep o'er the er - ring one, Lift up the fall - en,
child to re - ceive; Plead with them ear-nest-ly, Plead with them gen-tly,
grace can re - store; Touched by a lov - ing heart, Wak-ened by kind-ness,
Lord will pro - vide; Back to the nar-row way Pa - tient - ly win them;

CHORUS

Tell them of Je - sus the migh - ty to save.
He will for - give if they on - ly be-lieve. Res-cue the per - ish-ing,
Chords that are bro - ken will vi - brate once more.
Tell the poor wan-d'rer a Sav - ior has died.

Care for the dy - ing; Je - sus is mer - ci - ful, Je - sus will save.

Seeking the Lost

WILLIAM A. OGDEN

WILLIAM A. OGDEN

1. Seek-ing the lost, yes, kind-ly en-treat-ing Wan-der-ers on the moun-tain a-stray; "Come un-to Me," His mes-sage re-peat-ing, Words of the Mas-ter speak-ing to-day.
2. Seek-ing the lost and point-ing to Je-sus Souls that are weak and hearts that are sore, Lead-ing them forth in ways of sal-va-tion, Show-ing the path to life ev-er-more.
3. Thus I would go on mis-sions of mer-cy, Fol-low-ing Christ from day un-to day, Cheer-ing the faint and rais-ing the fall-en, Point-ing the lost to Je-sus, the Way.

CHORUS

Go-ing a-far up-on the moun-tain,
In-to the fold of my Re-deem-er,

Go-ing a-far . . . . up-on the moun-tain, . . Bring-ing the
In-to the fold . . . . of my Re-deem-er, . . . Je-sus, the

Bring-ing the wan-d'rer back a-gain, back a-gain,
Je-sus, the Lamb for sin-ners (Omit . . . .) slain, for sin-ners slain,

wan - - - d'rer back a-gain . . .
Lamb . . . . for sin-ners (Omit . . .) slain. . . . .

Bringing in the Sheaves

KNOWLES SHAW

GEORGE A. MINOR

1. Sow - ing in the morn - ing, sow-ing seeds of kind - ness, Sow-ing in the
2. Sow - ing in the sun - shine, sow-ing in the shad - ows, Fear-ing nei - ther
3. Go - ing forth with weep-ing, sow-ing for the Mas - ter, Tho' the loss sus-

noon - tide and the dew - y eve; Wait-ing for the har - vest,
clouds nor win-ter's chill ing breeze, By and by the har - vest,
tained our spir - it oft - en grieves; When our weep-ing's o - ver,

and the time of reap-ing, We shall come re - joic - ing, bring-ing in the sheaves.
and the la - bor end - ed, We shall come re - joic - ing, bring-ing in the sheaves.
He will bid us wel-come, We shall come re - joic - ing, bring-ing in the sheaves.

CHORUS

Bring-ing in the sheaves, bring-ing in the sheaves, We shall come re-joic-
Bring-ing in the sheaves, bring-ing in the sheaves, We shall come re-joic-

1. ing, bring - ing in the sheaves; 2. ing, bring - ing in the sheaves.

Help Somebody Today

CARRIE E. BRECK

CHARLES H. GABRIEL

1. Look all a-round you, find some one in need, Help some-bod-y to - day!
2. Man - y are wait-ing a kind, lov-ing word, Help some-bod-y to - day!
3. Man - y have bur-dens too heav-y to bear, Help some-bod-y to - day!
4. Some are dis-cour-aged and wea-ry in heart, Help some-bod-y to - day!

Tho' it be lit - tle—a neigh-bor-ly deed— Help some-bod-y to - day!
Thou hast a mes-sage, O let it be heard, Help some-bod-y to - day!
Grief is the por-tion of some ev - 'ry-where, Help some-bod-y to - day!
Some one the jour-ney to heav-en should start, Help some-bod-y to - day!

CHORUS

Help some-bod - y to - day, ... Some-bod - y a-long life's way; . . . Let
to-day,   home-ward way;

sor-row be end-ed, The friendless befriended, Oh, help some-bod-y to - day!

Must I Go, and Empty-Handed?

C. C. Luther

George C. Stebbins

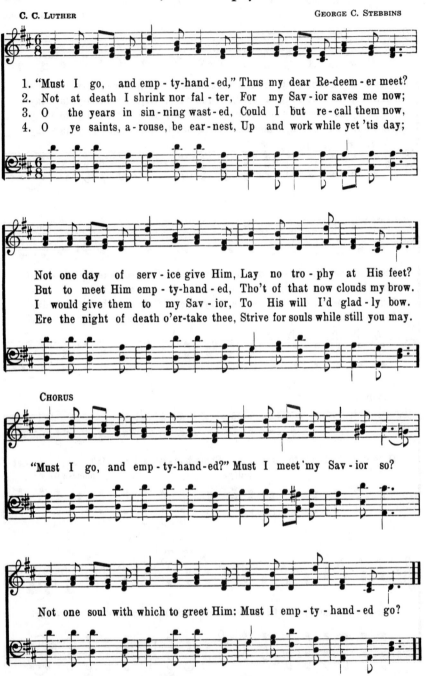

1. "Must I go, and emp-ty-hand-ed," Thus my dear Re-deem-er meet?
2. Not at death I shrink nor fal-ter, For my Sav-ior saves me now;
3. O the years in sin-ning wast-ed, Could I but re-call them now,
4. O ye saints, a-rouse, be ear-nest, Up and work while yet 'tis day;

Not one day of serv-ice give Him, Lay no tro-phy at His feet?
But to meet Him emp-ty-hand-ed, Tho't of that now clouds my brow.
I would give them to my Sav-ior, To His will I'd glad-ly bow.
Ere the night of death o'er-take thee, Strive for souls while still you may.

Chorus

"Must I go, and emp-ty-hand-ed?" Must I meet 'my Sav-ior so?

Not one soul with which to greet Him: Must I emp-ty-hand-ed go?

He Was Not Willing

L. R. M.

LUCY R. MEYER

1. "He was not will-ing that an-y should per'-ish;" Je-sus en-throned in the
2. "He was not will-ing that an-y should per-ish:" Clothed in our flesh with its
3. Plen-ty for pleas-ure, but lit-tle for Je-sus; Time for the world with its
4. "He was not will-ing that an-y should per-ish;" Am I His fol-low-er,

glo-ry a-bove, Saw our poor fall-en world, pit-ied our sor-rows, Poured out His
sor-row and pain, Came He to seek the lost, com-fort the mourn-er, Heal the heart
trou-bles and toys, No time for Je-sus' work, feed-ing the hun-gry, Lift-ing lost
and can I live Long-er at ease with a soul go-ing down-ward, Lost for the

life for us, won-der-ful love! Per-ish-ing, per-ish-ing! Throng-ing our path-way,
bro-ken by sor-row and shame. Per-ish-ing, per-ish-ing! Har-vest is pass-ing,
souls to e-ter-ni-ty's joys. Per-ish-ing, per-ish-ing! Hark, how they call us;
lack of the help I might give? Per-ish-ing, per-ish-ing! Thou wast not will-ing;

Hearts break with bur-dens too heav-y to bear: Je-sus would save, but there's
Reap-ers are few and the night draw-eth near: Je-sus is call-ing thee,
Bring us your Sav-ior, oh, tell us of Him! We are so wea-ry, so
Mas-ter, for-give, and in-spire us a-new; Ban-ish our world-li-ness

no one to tell them, No one to lift them from sin and de-spair.
haste to the reap-ing, Thou shalt have souls, pre-cious souls for thy hire.
heav-i-ly la-den, And with long weep-ing our eyes have grown dim.
help us to ev-er Live with e-ter-ni-ty's val-ues in view.

397 Make Me a Channel of Blessing

H. G. S.

H. G. SMYTH

1. Is your life a chan-nel of bless-ing? Is the love of God flow-ing thro' you? Are you tell-ing the lost of the Sav-iour? Are you read-y His serv-ice to do?
2. Is your life a chan-nel of bless-ing? Are you bur-dened for those that are lost? Have you urged up-on those who are stray-ing, The Sav-iour who died on the cross?
3. Is your life a chan-nel of bless-ing? Is it dai-ly tell-ing for Him? Have you spo-ken the word of sal-va-tion To those who are dy-ing in sin?
4. We can-not be chan-nels of bless-ing If our lives are not free from known sin; We will bar-ri-ers be and a hin-drance To those we are try-ing to win.

CHORUS

Make me a chan-nel of bless-ing to-day, Make me a chan-nel of bless-ing, I pray; My life pos-sess-ing, my serv-ice bless-ing, Make me a chan-nel of bless-ing to-day.

In the Service of the King

ALFRED H. ACKLEY   BENTLEY D. ACKLEY

1. I am hap-py in the serv-ice of the King, I am
2. I am hap-py in the serv-ice of the King, I am
3. I am hap-py in the serv-ice of the King, I am
4. I am hap-py in the serv-ice of the King, I am

hap-py, oh, so hap-py; I have peace and joy that
hap-py, oh, so hap-py; Thro' the sun-shine and the
hap-py, oh, so hap-py; To His guid-ing hand for-
hap-py, oh, so hap-py; All that I pos-sess to

noth-ing else can bring, In the serv-ice of the King.
shad-ow I can sing, In the serv-ice of the King.
ev-er I will cling, In the serv-ice of the King.
Him I glad-ly bring, In the serv-ice of the King.

CHORUS

In the serv-ice of the King, Ev-'ry tal-ent I will bring;

I have peace and joy and bless-ing In the serv-ice of the King.

Copyright 1912 by B. D. Ackley. ©Renewed 1940 (extended), The Rodeheaver Co., Owner. Used by Permission.

399 Go Ye Into All the World

James McGranahan   James McGranahan

1. Far, far a-way, in hea-then darkness dwell-ing, Mil-lions of souls for-
2. See o'er the world wide-o-pen doors in-vit-ing, Sol-diers of Christ, a-
3. "Why will ye die?" the voice of God is call-ing, "Why will ye die?" re-
4. God speed the day, when those of ev-'ry na-tion "Glo-ry to God!" tri-

ev-er may be lost; Who, who will go, sal-va-tion's sto-ry tell-ing,
rise and en-ter in! Chris-tians, a-wake! your forc-es all u-nit-ing,
ech-o in His name; Je-sus hath died to save from death ap-pall-ing,
um-phant-ly shall sing; Ran-somed, redeemed, re-joic-ing in sal-va-tion,

Chorus

Look-ing to Je-sus, minding not the cost?
Send forth the gospel, break the chains of sin. "All pow'r is giv-en un-to Me,
Life and sal-va-tion therefore go pro-claim.
Shout Hal-le-lu-jah, for the Lord is King.

All pow'r is giv-en un-to Me, Go ye in-to all the world and

preach the gos-pel, And lo, I am with you al-way."

O Zion, Haste

MARY A. THOMSON

400

JAMES WALCH

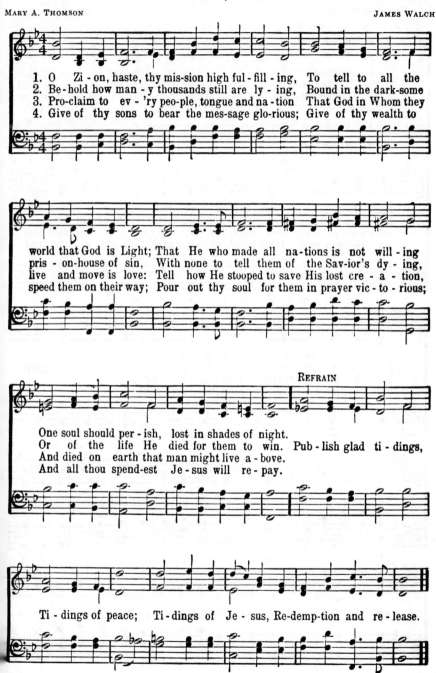

1. O Zi-on, haste, thy mis-sion high ful-fill-ing, To tell to all the
2. Be-hold how man-y thousands still are ly-ing, Bound in the dark-some
3. Pro-claim to ev-'ry peo-ple, tongue and na-tion That God in Whom they
4. Give of thy sons to bear the mes-sage glo-rious; Give of thy wealth to

world that God is Light; That He who made all na-tions is not will-ing
pris-on-house of sin, With none to tell them of the Sav-ior's dy-ing,
live and move is love: Tell how He stooped to save His lost cre-a-tion,
speed them on their way; Pour out thy soul for them in prayer vic-to-rious;

One soul should per-ish, lost in shades of night.
Or of the life He died for them to win.
And died on earth that man might live a-bove.
And all thou spend-est Je-sus will re-pay.

REFRAIN

Pub-lish glad ti-dings,

Ti-dings of peace; Ti-dings of Je-sus, Re-demp-tion and re-lease.

401 Tell It Again

Mrs. M. B. C. SLADE · R. M. MCINTOSH

1. In - to the tent where a gip - sy boy lay, Dy - ing a - lone at the
2. "Did He so love me, a poor lit - tle boy? Send un - to me the good
3. Bend-ing we caught the last words of his breath, Just as he en-tered the
4. Smil-ing, he said, as his last sigh he spent, "I am so glad that for

close of the day, News of sal - va - tion we car - ried, said he:
ti - dings of joy? Need I not per - ish? my hand will He hold?
val - ley of death: "God sent His Son!" "Who - so - ev - er," said He:
me He was sent!" Whis-pered, while low sank the sun in the west,

"No - bod - y ev - er has told it to me!"
No - bod - y ev - er the sto - ry has told!" Tell it a - gain!
"Then I am sure that He sent Him for me!"
"Lord, I be - lieve, tell it now to the rest!"

REFRAIN

Tell it a - gain! Sal - va-tion's sto-ry re-peat o'er and o'er, Till none can

say of the chil-dren of men, "No-bod - y ev - er has told me be-fore."

It Pays to Serve Jesus

F. C. H.

FRANK C. HUSTON

1. The serv-ice of Je-sus true pleas-ure af-fords, In Him there is
2. It pays to serve Je-sus what-e'er may be-tide, It pays to be
3. Tho' sometimes the shad-ows may hang o'er the way, And sor-rows may

joy with-out an al-loy; 'Tis heav-en to trust Him and rest on His
true what-e'er you may do; 'Tis rich-es of mer-cy in Him to a-
come to beck-on us home, Our pre-cious Re-deem-er each toil will re-

CHORUS

words; It pays to serve Je-sus each day.
bide; It pays to serve Je-sus each day. It pays to serve Je-sus, it
pay; It pays to serve Je-sus each day.

pays ev-'ry day, It pays ev-'ry step of the way; ..... Tho' the pathway to
ev-'ry step of the way;

glo-ry may sometimes be drear, You'll be hap-py each step of the way.

Speak, My Lord

G. B.   George Bennard

1. Hear the Lord of har-vest sweet-ly call-ing, "Who will go and work for Me to-day? Who will bring to Me the lost and dy-ing? Who will point them to the nar-row way?"

2. When the coal of fire . . . touched the proph-et, Mak-ing him as pure, as pure can be; When the voice of God said, "Who'll go for us?" Then he an-swered, "Here I am, send me."

3. Mil-lions now in sin and shame are dy-ing; Lis-ten to their sad and bit-ter cry; Has-ten, broth-er, has-ten to the res-cue; Quick-ly an-swer, "Mas-ter, here am I."

4. Soon the time for reap-ing will be o-ver; Soon we'll gath-er for the har-vest-home; May the Lord of har-vest smile up-on us, May we hear His bless-ed, "Child, well done."

CHORUS

Speak, my Lord, speak, my Lord, Speak, and I'll be quick to an-swer Thee; Speak, my Lord, speak, my Lord, Speak, and I will answer, "Lord, send me."

Have I Done My Best for Jesus?

ENSIGN EDWIN YOUNG

HARRY E. STORRS

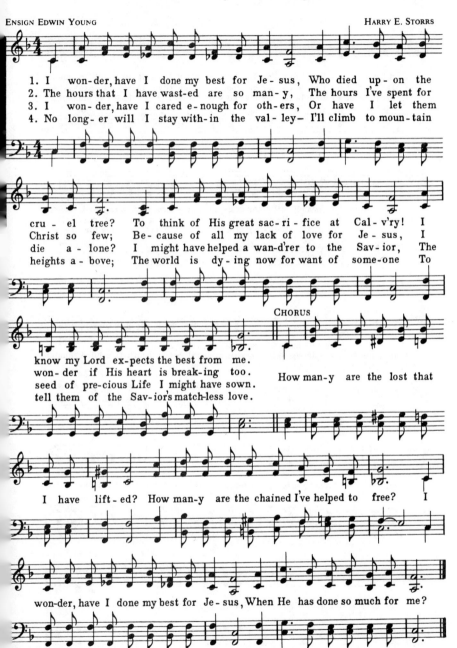

1. I won-der, have I done my best for Je-sus, Who died up-on the
2. The hours that I have wast-ed are so man-y, The hours I've spent for
3. I won-der, have I cared e-nough for oth-ers, Or have I let them
4. No long-er will I stay with-in the val-ley— I'll climb to moun-tain

cru - el tree? To think of His great sac-ri-fice at Cal-v'ry! I
Christ so few; Be-cause of all my lack of love for Je-sus, I
die a - lone? I might have helped a wan-d'rer to the Sav-ior, The
heights a-bove; The world is dy-ing now for want of some-one To

CHORUS

know my Lord ex-pects the best from me.
won-der if His heart is break-ing too.
seed of pre-cious Life I might have sown.
tell them of the Sav-ior's match-less love.

How man-y are the lost that

I have lift-ed? How man-y are the chained I've helped to free? I

won-der, have I done my best for Je-sus, When He has done so much for me?

Set My Soul Afire

Words and Music by
GENE BARTLETT

1. Set my soul a - fire, Lord, for Thy Ho - ly Word, Burn it deep with-in me,
2. Set my soul a - fire, Lord, for the lost in sin, Give to me a pas - sion
3. Set my soul a - fire, Lord, in my dai - ly life, Far too long I've wandered

let your voice be heard; Mil-lions grope in dark-ness in this day and hour,
as I seek to win; Help me not to fal - ter, nev - er let me fail,
in this day of strife; Noth - ing else will mat - ter but to live for Thee,

CHORUS

I will be your wit-ness, fill me with Thy pow'r.
Fill me with Thy Spir - it, let Thy will pre-vail. Set my soul a-fire, Lord, set my
I will be your wit-ness as you live in me.

soul a - fire, Make my life a wit-ness of Thy sav-ing pow'r. Millions grope in

dark-ness, wait-ing for Thy Word, Set my soul a - fire, Lord, Set my soul a - fire.

A Soul Winner for Jesus

J. W. F.

J. W. Ferrill

1. I want to be a soul winner for Je-sus ev'-ry day, He does so much for me;
2. I want to be a soul winner and bring the lost to Christ, That they His grace may know;
3. I want to be a soul winner till Jesus calls for me, To lay my burdens down;

I want to aid the lost sinner to leave his erring way, And be from bondage free.
I want to live for Christ ever, and do His blessed will, Be-cause He loves me so.
I want to hear Him say, servant, "You've gathered many sheaves, Receive a starry crown."

Chorus

A soul.......... winner for Je - sus, A soul.... .... winner for
winner for Je -sus   Christ the Lord,   winner for Je- sus

Je - sus, O let me be each day; A soul............. win-ner for
Christ the Lord,   win-ner for Je- sus

Je - sus, A soul........winner for Je - sus, He's done so much for me.
Christ the Lord,   winner for Je-sus   Christ the Lord,

407 To the Work!

William H. Doane

1. To the work! to the work! we are serv-ants of God, Let us fol-low the
2. To the work! to the work! let the hun-gry be fed, To the foun-tain of
3. To the work! to the work! there is la-bor for all, For the king-dom of
4. To the work! to the work! in the strength of the Lord, And a robe and a

path that our Mas-ter has trod; With the balm of His coun-sel our
life let the wea-ry be led; In the cross and its ban-ner our
dark-ness and er-ror shall fall; And the name of Je-ho-vah ex-
crown shall our la-bor re-ward When the home of the faith-ful our

strength to re-new, Let us do with our might what our hands find to do.
glo-ry shall be, While we her-ald the ti-dings, "Sal-va-tion is free!"
alt-ed shall be In the loud swell-ing cho-rus, "Sal-va-tion is free!"
dwell-ing shall be And we shout with the ran-somed, "Sal-va-tion is free!"

CHORUS

Toil-ing on, toil-ing on, Toil-ing
Toil-ing on, toil-ing on,

on, toil-ing on; Let us hope,
Toil-ing on, toil-ing on; and trust,

To the Work!

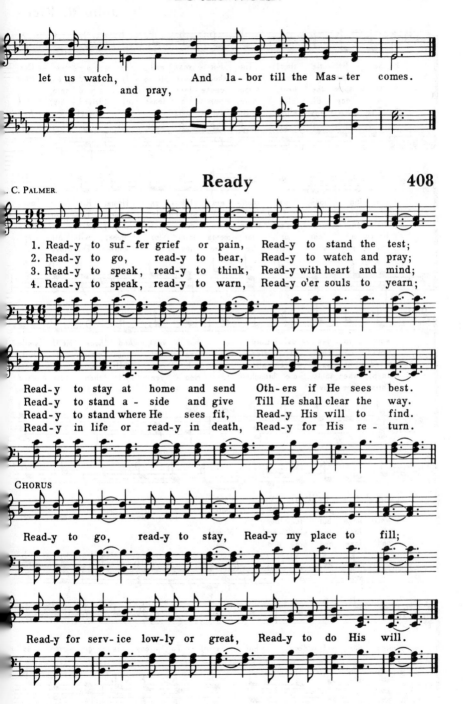

let us watch, and pray, And la-bor till the Mas-ter comes.

Ready

408

C. PALMER.

1. Read-y to suf-fer grief or pain, Read-y to stand the test;
2. Read-y to go, read-y to bear, Read-y to watch and pray;
3. Read-y to speak, read-y to think, Read-y with heart and mind;
4. Read-y to speak, read-y to warn, Read-y o'er souls to yearn;

Read-y to stay at home and send Oth-ers if He sees best.
Read-y to stand a - side and give Till He shall clear the way.
Read-y to stand where He sees fit, Read-y His will to find.
Read-y in life or read-y in death, Read-y for His re - turn.

CHORUS

Read-y to go, read-y to stay, Read-y my place to fill;

Read-y for serv-ice low-ly or great, Read-y to do His will.

409 So Little Time

by John R. Rice

1. So lit-tle time! The har-vest will be o - ver. Our
2. How man-y times I should have strong-ly plead-ed; How
3. De - spite the heat, the cease-less toil, the hard-ship, The
4. A day of plea - sure, or a feast of friend-ship; A
5. The har-vest white, with rea-pers few is wast-ing And

reap-ing done, we reap-ers tak - en Home. Re - port our
of - ten did I feel to strict-ly warn. The Spir - it
brok-en heart o'er those we can-not win; Mis - un-der-
house or car or gar-ments fair or fame, will all be
man - y souls will die and nev - er know The love of

work to Jes - us, Lord of har - vest, And hope He'll smile
moved, oh had I pled for Jes - us! The grain is fall-
stood be-cause we're oft pe - cul - iar, Still no re - grets
trash, when souls are brought to Hea - ven. And then how sad
Christ, the joy of sins for - giv - en. Oh let us weep

Chorus:

and that He'll say, "Well done!"
en, lost ones not re - born.
we'll have but for our sin.   To - day we reap, or
to face the slack - ers' blame!
and love and pray and go!

miss our gol - den har - vest! To - day is gi - ven us

So Little Time

lost souls to win. Oh then to save some dear ones from the

burn - ing. To - day we'll go to bring some sin - ner in.

Copyright 1962 by John R. Rice

The Call for Reapers   410

John O. Thompson

J. B. O. Clemm

1. Far   and   near the fields are teem-ing With the waves of ri - pened grain;
2. Send them forth with morn's first beaming, Send them in   the   noon-tide's glare;
3. O   thou, whom thy Lord is   send-ing, Gath - er now the sheaves of gold;

FINE

Far   and   near their gold is gleam-ing O'er the sun - ny slope and plain.
When the   sun's last rays are gleam-ing, Bid them gath - er ev - ery-where.
Heavenward then at   eve-ning wend- ing, Thou shalt come with joy un - told.

D.S.—*Send them now the sheaves to gath - er, Ere the har - vest - time pass by.*

REFRAIN   D.S.

Lord of har - vest, send forth reap-ers! Hear us, Lord, to   Thee we cry;

Shall I Empty-Handed Be?

Rev. N. A. McAulay.
Maud Frazer.

John P. Hillis.

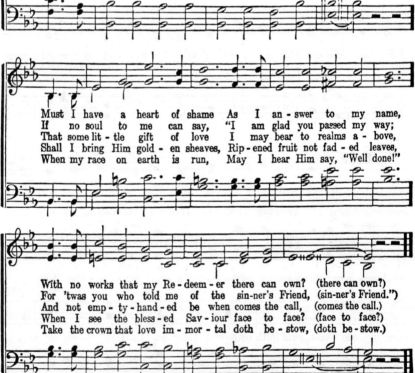

1. Shall I emp - ty - hand - ed be When be - side the crys - tal sea
2. What re - gret must then be mine When I meet my Lord Di - vine,
3. If my grat - i - tude I'd show Un - to Him who loves me so,
4. When the har - vest days are past, Shall I hear Him say at last,
5. When the books are o - pened wide, And the deeds of all are tried,

I shall stand be - fore the ev - er - last - ing throne?
If I've wast - ed all the tal - ents He doth lend?
Let me la - bor till the eve - ning shad - ows fall;
"Wel - come, toil - er, I've pre - pared for thee a place?"
May I have a rec - ord whit - er than the snow;

Must I have a heart of shame As I an - swer to my name,
If no soul to me can say, "I am glad you passed my way;
That some lit - tle gift of love I may bear to realms a - bove,
Shall I bring Him gold - en sheaves, Rip - ened fruit not fad - ed leaves,
When my race on earth is run, May I hear Him say, "Well done!"

With no works that my Re - deem - er there can own? (there can own?)
For 'twas you who told me of the sin - ner's Friend, (sin - ner's Friend.")
And not emp - ty - hand - ed be when comes the call, (comes the call.)
When I see the bless - ed Sav - iour face to face? (face to face?)
Take the crown that love im - mor - tal doth be - stow, (doth be - stow.)

I'll Wish I Had Given Him More

412

G. R. A.

Grace Reese Adkins

1. By and by when I look on His face, Beau - ti - ful face,
2. By and by when He holds out His hands, Wel - com - ing hands,
3. In the light of that heav - en - ly place, Light from His face,

thorn-shad - owed face; By and by when I look on His face, I'll
nail - riv - en hands; By and by when He holds out His hands. I'll
beau - ti - ful face; In the light of that heav - en - ly place, I'll

Chorus

wish I had giv - en Him more. More, so much more,—

More of my life than I e'er gave be - fore— By and by when I
More of my love than I e'er gave be - fore— By and by when He
Treas-ures un-bound - ed for Him I a - dore— By and by when I

look on His face, I'll wish I had giv - en Him more.—
holds out His hands, I'll wish I had giv - en Him more.—
look on His face, I'll wish I had giv - en Him more.—

413 Bring Them In

Alexcenah Thomas

William A. Ogden

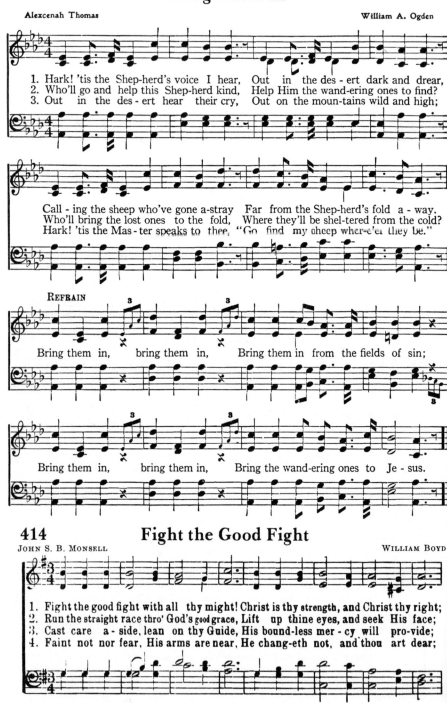

1. Hark! 'tis the Shep-herd's voice I hear, Out in the des-ert dark and drear,
2. Who'll go and help this Shep-herd kind, Help Him the wand-ering ones to find?
3. Out in the des-ert hear their cry, Out on the moun-tains wild and high;

Call-ing the sheep who've gone a-stray Far from the Shep-herd's fold a-way.
Who'll bring the lost ones to the fold, Where they'll be shel-tered from the cold?
Hark! 'tis the Mas-ter speaks to thee, "Go find my sheep wher-e'er they be."

REFRAIN

Bring them in, bring them in, Bring them in from the fields of sin;

Bring them in, bring them in, Bring the wand-ering ones to Je-sus.

414 Fight the Good Fight

JOHN S. B. MONSELL

WILLIAM BOYD

1. Fight the good fight with all thy might! Christ is thy strength, and Christ thy right;
2. Run the straight race thro' God's good grace, Lift up thine eyes, and seek His face;
3. Cast care a-side, lean on thy Guide, His bound-less mer-cy will pro-vide;
4. Faint not nor fear, His arms are near, He chang-eth not, and thou art dear;

Fight the Good Fight

Lay hold on life, and it shall be Thy joy and crown e - ter - nal - ly.
Life with its way be - fore us lies, Christ is the path, and Christ the prize.
Trust, and thy trust-ing soul shall prove Christ is its life, and Christ its love.
On - ly be - lieve, and thou shalt see That Christ is all in all to thee. A-MEN.

Little Is Much When God Is in It 415

Mrs. F. W. S.

Mrs. F. W. SUFFIELD

mp

1. In the har-vest field now rip-ened There's a work for all to do.
2. Does the place you're call'd to la-bor Seem so small and lit-tle known?
3. Are you laid a - side from serv-ice, Bod - y worn from toil and care?
4. When the con-flict here is end-ed, And our race on earth is run,

Hark! the voice of God is call-ing, To the har-vest call-ing you.
It is great if God is in it, And He'll not for-get His own.
You can still be in the bat - tle, In the sa - cred place of prayer.
He will say, if we are faith-ful, "Wel-come home, My child; well done."

CHORUS

f

Lit-tle is much when God is in it; La-bor not for wealth or fame.

mf

There's a crown, and you can win it If you'll go in Je - sus' name.

8va

Our Best

S. C. Kirk

Grant C. Tullar

1. Hear ye the Mas-ter's call, "Give Me thy best!" For, be it great or small,
2. Wait not for men to laud, Heed not their slight; Win-ning the smile of God
3. Night soon comes on a-pace, Day has-tens by; Workman and work must face

That is His test. Do then the best you can, Not for re-ward, Not for the
Brings its de-light! Aid-ing the good and true Ne'er goes un-blest, All that we
Test-ing on high. Oh, may we in that day Find rest, sweet rest, Which God has

REFRAIN

praise of man, But for the Lord.
think or do, Be it the best. Ev-ery work for Je-sus will be blest,
prom-ised those Who do their best.

But He asks from ev-ery-one His best. Our tal-ents may be few,

These may be small, But un-to Him is due Our best, our all.

When the Battle's Over

417

Isaac Watts, D.D.

English. Arr. by Wm. B. Blake

1. Am I a sol-dier of the cross, A fol-lower of the Lamb,
And shall I fear to own His cause, Or blush to speak His name?

2. Must I be car-ried to the skies On flow-ery beds of ease,
While oth-ers fought to win the prize, And sailed thro' blood-y seas?

3. Sure I must fight if I would reign, In-crease my cour-age, Lord;
I'll bear the toil, en-dure the pain, Sup-port-ed by Thy Word.

Chorus

And when the bat-tle's o-ver we shall wear a crown! Yes,
we shall wear a crown! Yes, we shall wear a crown! And when the bat-tle's
o-ver we shall wear a crown In the new Je-ru-sa-lem.

Fine

D. S.

Wear a crown, wear a crown, Wear a bright and shin-ing crown;
Wear a crown, wear a crown,

418   Who Is on the Lord's Side?

FRANCES R. HAVERGAL

C. LUISE REICHARDT
Arr. by John Goss

1. Who is on the Lord's side? Who will serve the King? Who will
2. Not for weight of glo - ry, Not for crown and palm, En - ter
3. Je - sus, Thou hast bought us, Not with gold or gem, But with
4. Fierce may be the con - flict, Strong may be the foe, But the

be His help - ers, Oth - er lives to bring? Who will leave the
we the ar - my, Raise the war-rior - psalm; But for Love that
Thine own life blood, For Thy di - a - dem; With Thy bless - ing
King's own ar - my None can o - ver - throw; Round His stan - dard

world's side? Who will face the foe? Who is on the
claim - eth Lives for whom He died: He whom Je - sus
fill - ing Each who comes to Thee, Thou hast made us
rang - ing, Vic - t'ry is se - cure, For His truth un -

Lords side? Who for Him will go? By Thy call of mer - cy,
nam - eth Must be on His side. By Thy love con-strain - ing,
will - ing, Thou hast made us free. By Thy grand re - demp - tion,
chang - ing Makes the tri - umph sure. Joy-ful - ly en - list - ing,

By Thy grace di - vine, We are on the Lord's side— Sav-ior, we are Thine!

The Banner of the Cross

Daniel W. Whittle

James McGranahan

1. There's a roy-al ban-ner giv-en for dis-play To the sol-diers
2. Though the foe may rage and gath-er as the flood, Let the stand-ard
3. O-ver land and sea, wher-ev-er man may dwell, Make the glo-rious
4. When the glo-ry dawns—'tis draw-ing ver-y near—It is has-t'ning

of the King; As an en-sign fair we lift it up to-day,
be dis-played; And be-neath its folds, as sol-diers of the Lord,
ti-dings known; Of the crim-son ban-ner now the sto-ry tell,
day by day— Then be-fore our King the foe shall dis-ap-pear,

While as ran-somed ones we sing.
For the truth be not dis-mayed!
While the Lord shall claim His own!
And the cross the world shall sway!

Chorus

March-ing on, . . . march-ing
on, on,

on, . . . For Christ count ev-'ry-thing but loss! . . . . . . And to
on, on, ev-'ry-thing, ev-'ry-thing but loss!

crown Him King, toil and sing 'Neath the ban-ner of the cross!
we'll Be-neath

Loyalty to Christ

E. TAYLOR CASSEL

FLORA H. CASSEL

1. From o-ver hill and plain There comes the signal strain, 'Tis loy-al-ty, loy-al-ty,
2. O hear, ye brave, the sound That moves the earth around, 'Tis loy-al-ty, loy-al-ty,
3. Come, join our loy-al throng, We'll rout the giant wrong, 'Tis loy-al-ty, loy-al-ty,
4. The strength of youth we lay At Je-sus' feet to-day, 'Tis loy-al-ty, loy-al-ty,

loy - al - ty to Christ; Its mu-sic rolls a-long, The hills take up the song,
loy - al - ty to Christ; A - rise to dare and do, Ring out the watch-word true,
loy - al - ty to Christ; Where Satan's banners float We'll send the bu-gle note,
loy - al - ty to Christ; His gos-pel we'll pro-claim Thro'-out the world's domain,

CHORUS.

Of loy-al-ty, loy-al-ty, Yes, loy - al-ty to Christ. "On to vic-to-ry! On to

vic-to-ry!" Cries our great Commander; "On!" . . . We'll move at His command,
great Commander; "On!"

We'll soon possess the land, Thro' loyalty, loyalty, Yes, loy-al-ty to Christ. A - MEN.

Sound the Battle Cry

WILLIAM F. SHERWIN

WILLIAM F. SHERWIN

1. Sound the bat-tle cry! See, the foe is nigh; Raise the standard high
2. Strong to meet the foe, Marching on we go, While our cause we know,
3. O! Thou God of all, Hear us when we call, Help us one and all

For the Lord; Gird your ar-mor on, Stand firm, ev-'ry one; Rest your
Must pre-vail; Shield and banner bright, Gleam-ing in the light; Bat-tling
By Thy grace; When the bat-tle's done, And the vic-t'ry's won, May we

CHORUS ff

cause up-on His ho-ly word.
for the right We ne'er can fail. Rouse, then, sol-diers, ral-ly round the
wear the crown Be-fore Thy face.

ban-ner, Read-y, stead-y, pass the word a-long; On-ward, for-ward,

shout a-loud Ho-san-na! Christ is Cap-tain of the might-y throng.

422 Onward, Christian Soldiers

Sabine Baring-Gould

Arthur S. Sullivan

1. On-ward, Chris-tian sol - diers, March-ing as to war, With the cross of
2. At the sign of tri - umph Sa-tan's host doth flee; On, then, Chris-tian
3. Like a might-y ar - my Moves the Church of God; Broth-ers, we are
4. On-ward, then, ye peo - ple, Join our hap-py throng; Blend with ours your

Je - sus Go - ing on be - fore! Christ, the roy-al Mas - ter, Leads a -
sol - diers, On to vic to - ry! Hell's foun-da-tions quiv - er At the
tread - ing Where the saints have trod. We are not di - vid - ed, All one
voic - es In the tri-umph song. Glo - ry, laud and hon - or Un - to

gainst the foe; For-ward in - to bat - tle See His ban-ner go!
shout of praise; Broth-ers, lift your voic - es, Loud your an-thems raise!
bod - y we— One in hope and doc - trine, One in char - i - ty.
Christ the King— This thru count-less a - ges Men and an-gels sing.

Refrain

On-ward, Chris-tian sol - diers, March-ing as to war,

With the cross of Je - sus Go - ing on be - fore!

Soldiers of Christ, Arise!

CHARLES WESLEY, ARR.

GEORGE J. ELVEY

1. Sol - diers of Christ, a - rise, And put your ar - mor on,
2. Stand then in His great might, With all His strength en - dued,
3. Leave no un-guard - ed place, No weak - ness of the soul,

Strong in the strength which God sup-plies Through His e - ter - nal Son;
And take, to arm you for the fight, The pan - o - ply of God;
Take ev - 'ry vir - tue, ev - 'ry grace, And fort - i - fy the whole,

Strong in the Lord of hosts. And in His might - y pow'r,
That hav - ing all things done, And all your con - flicts past,
From strength to strength go on, Wres - tle and fight and pray,

Who in the strength of Je - sus trusts Is more than con - quer - or.
Ye may o'er-come through Christ a - lone, And stand en - tire at last.
Tread all the pow'rs of dark - ness down, And win the well-fought day.

424 Victory Through Grace

FANNY J. CROSBY

JOHN R. SWENEY

1. Con-quer-ing now and still to con-quer, Rid-eth a King in His might!
2. Con-quer-ing now and still to con-quer, Who is this won-der-ful King?
3. Con-quer-ing now and still to con-quer, Je-sus, Thou Rul-er of all!

Lead-ing the host of all the faith-ful In-to the midst of the fight;
Whence are the ar-mies which He lead-eth, While of His glo-ry they sing?
Thrones and their scep-ters all shall per-ish, Crowns and their splen-dor shall fall,

See them with cour-age ad-vanc-ing, Clad in their bril-liant ar-ray,
He is our Lord and Re-deem-er, Sav-ior and Mon-arch di-vine;
Yet shall the ar-mies Thou lead-est, Faith-ful and true to the last,

Fine

Shout-ing the name of their Lead-er, Hear them ex-ult-ing-ly say:
They are the stars that for-ev-er Bright in His King-dom will shine.
Find in Thy man-sions e-ter-nal Rest, when their war-fare is past.

D.S.— *Yet to the true and the faith-ful Vic-t'ry is prom-ised through grace.*

D.S.

CHORUS

Not to the strong is the bat-tle, Not to the swift is the race,

Hold the Fort

P. P. Bliss

P. P. Bliss

1. Ho, my com-rades! see the sig - nal, Wav - ing in the sky!
2. See the might-y host ad - vanc-ing, Sa - tan lead-ing on;
3. See the glo-rious ban - ner wav-ing! Hear the trump-et blow!
4. Fierce and long the bat - tle rag-es, But our help is near;

Re - in - force-ments now ap - pear-ing, Vic - to - ry is nigh.
Might-y men a - round us fall-ing, Cour - age al - most gone!
In our Lead - er's name we'll tri - umph O - ver ev - 'ry foe.
On - ward comes our great Com-mand - er. Cheer, my com-rades, cheer.

REFRAIN

"Hold the fort, for I am com-ing," Je - sus sig - nals still;

Wave the an - swer back to heav - en, "By Thy grace we will."

The Fight Is On

LELIA N. MORRIS   LELIA N. MORRIS

1. The fight is on— the trum-pet sound is ring-ing out, The cry "To
2. The fight is on— a - rouse, ye sol-diers brave and true! Je - ho - vah
3. The Lord is lead - ing on to cer-tain vic - to - ry, The bow of

arms!" is heard a - far and near; The Lord of hosts is march-ing
leads, and vic - t'ry will as - sure; Go buck - le on the ar - mor
prom - ise spans the east-ern sky; His glo-rious name in ev - 'ry

on to vic - to - ry, The tri - umph of the Christ will soon ap-pear.
God has giv - en you, And in His strength un - to the end en-dure.
land shall hon-ored be, The morn will break— the dawn of peace is nigh.

CHORUS

The fight is on, O Chris-tian sol - dier, And face to face in stern ar - ray,

With ar-mor gleam-ing and col-ors streaming, The right and wrong engage to-day!

The Fight Is On

CHRISTIAN WARFARE

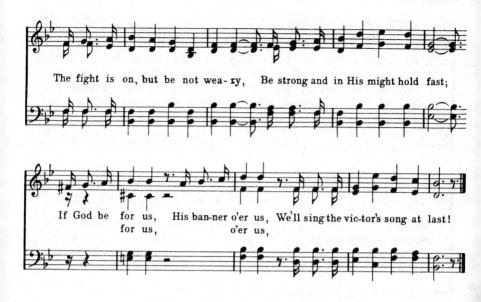

The fight is on, but be not wea-ry, Be strong and in His might hold fast;

If God be for us, His ban-ner o'er us, We'll sing the vic-tor's song at last!
for us, o'er us,

Am I a Soldier of the Cross?

427

ISAAC WATTS

THOMAS A. ARNE

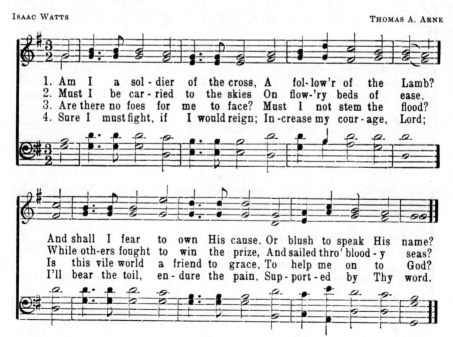

1. Am I a sol - dier of the cross, A fol-low'r of the Lamb?
2. Must I be car - ried to the skies On flow-'ry beds of ease.
3. Are there no foes for me to face? Must I not stem the flood?
4. Sure I must fight, if I would reign; In-crease my cour - age, Lord;

And shall I fear to own His cause. Or blush to speak His name?
While oth-ers fought to win the prize, And sailed thro' blood - y seas?
Is this vile world a friend to grace, To help me on to God?
I'll bear the toil, en - dure the pain, Sup - port - ed by Thy word.

Faith Is the Victory!

JOHN H. YATES

IRA D. SANKEY

1. En-camped a-long the hills of light, Ye Chris-tian sol-diers, rise, And
2. His ban-ner o - ver us is love, Our sword the Word of God; We
3. On ev - 'ry hand the foe we find Drawn up in dread ar - ray; Let
4. To him that o - ver-comes the foe, White rai-ment shall be giv'n; Be-

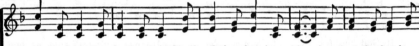

press the bat - tle ere the night Shall veil the glow-ing skies. A-gainst the foe in
tread the road the saints a-bove With shouts of triumph trod. By faith, they like a
tents of ease be left be- hind, And—onward to the fray. Sal-va-tion's helmet
fore the an- gels he shall know His name confessed in heav'n. Then onward from the

vales be-low Let all our strength be hurled; Faith is the vic - to - ry, we know,
whirlwind's breath, Swept on o'er ev-'ry field; The faith by which they conquered Death
on each head, With truth all girt a - bout, The earth shall tremble 'neath our tread,
hills of light, Our hearts with love a-flame; We'll vanquish all the hosts of night,

CHORUS

That o - ver-comes the world.
Is still our shin-ing shield. Faith is the vic - to-ry! Faith is the
And ech - o with our shout.
In Je-sus' conqu'ring name. Faith is the vic - to - ry! Faith is the

Faith Is the Victory!

vic - to - ry! Oh, glo - ri - ous vic - to - ry, That o - ver-comes the world.
vic - to - ry!

Faith of Our Fathers 429

FREDERICK W. FABER

HENRI F. HEMY
ALT. BY JAMES G. WALTON

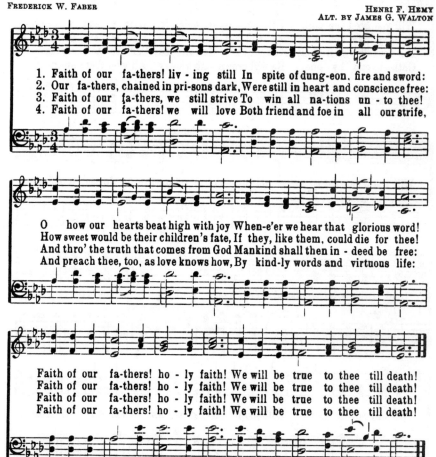

1. Faith of our fa-thers! liv-ing still In spite of dung-eon, fire and sword:
2. Our fa-thers, chained in pri-sons dark, Were still in heart and conscience free:
3. Faith of our fa-thers, we still strive To win all na-tions un - to thee!
4. Faith of our fa-thers! we will love Both friend and foe in all our strife,

O how our hearts beat high with joy When-e'er we hear that glorious word!
How sweet would be their children's fate, If they, like them, could die for thee!
And thro' the truth that comes from God Mankind shall then in - deed be free:
And preach thee, too, as love knows how, By kind-ly words and virtuous life:

Faith of our fa-thers! ho - ly faith! We will be true to thee till death!
Faith of our fa-thers! ho - ly faith! We will be true to thee till death!
Faith of our fa-thers! ho - ly faith! We will be true to thee till death!
Faith of our fa-thers! ho - ly faith! We will be true to thee till death!

430 As a Volunteer

W. S. BROWN

CHARLES H. GABRIEL

1. A call for loy-al sol-diers Comes to one and all; Sol-diers for the con-flict,
2. Yes, Jesus calls for soldiers Who are filled with pow'r, Soldiers who will serve Him
3. He calls you, for He loves you With a heart most kind, He whose heart was broken,
4. And when the war is o-ver, And the vic-t'ry won, When the true and faith-ful

Will you heed the call! Will you an-swer quick-ly, With a read-y cheer,
Ev-'ry day and hour; He will not for-sake you, He is ev-er near;
Bro-ken for man-kind; Now, just now He calls you, Calls in ac-cents clear,
Gath-er one by one, He will crown with glo-ry All who there ap-pear;

CHORUS.

Will you be en-list-ed As a vol-un-teer? A vol-un-teer for Je-sus, A sol-dier

true! Oth-ers have enlisted, Why not you? Je-sus is the Cap-tain,
O why not?

We will nev-er fear; Will you be en-list-ed As a vol-un-teer? A-MEN.

True-Hearted, Whole-Hearted

FRANCES R. HAVERGAL

GEORGE C. STEBBINS

1. True-hearted, whole-hearted, faith-ful and loy - al, King of our lives, by Thy
2. True-hearted, whole-hearted, full - est al - le-giance Yielding henceforth to our
3. True-hearted, whole-hearted, Sav - ior all - glo-rious! Take Thy great pow-er and

grace we will be; Un-der the standard ex - alt - ed and roy - al, Strong in Thy
glo - ri - ous King; Val-iant en-deav-or and lov - ing o-be-dience, Free - ly and
reign there a - lone, O - ver our wills and af-fec-tions vic-to-rious, Free - ly sur-

CHORUS

strength we will bat-tle for Thee. Peal out the watch-word! si - lence it nev-er!
joy - ous - ly now would we bring. Peal out the watch-word! si - lence it nev-er!
ren-dered and whol-ly Thine own.

Song of our spir-its, re - joic - ing and free; Peal out the watch-word!
Song of our spir - its, re - joic-ing and free; Peal out the watch-word!

loy - al for - ev - er, King of our lives, by Thy grace we will be.
loy - al for - ev - er, King of our lives, by Thy grace we will be.

432   Stand Up, Stand Up for Jesus

GEORGE DUFFIELD   ADAM GEIBEL

1. Stand up, stand up for Je - sus, Ye sol - diers of the cross;
2. Stand up, stand up for Je - sus, The trump - et call o - bey;
3. Stand up, stand up for Je - sus. Stand in His strength a - lone;
4. Stand up, stand up for Je - sus, The strife will not be long;

Lift high His roy - al ban - ner, It must not suf - fer loss:
Forth to the might - y con - flict, In this His glo - rious day:
The arm of flesh will fail you, Ye dare not trust your own:
This day the noise of bat - tle, The next, the vic - tor's song:

From vic - t'ry un - to vic - t'ry His ar - my shall He lead,
"Ye that are men now serve Him" A - gainst un - num-bered foes;
Put on the gos - pel ar - mor, Each piece put on with prayer;
To Him that o - ver - com - eth, A crown of life shall be:

rit.

Till ev - 'ry foe is van - quished, And Christ is Lord in - deed.
Let cour-age rise with dan - ger, And strength to strength op - pose.
Where du - ty calls, or dan - ger, Be nev - er want-ing there.
He with the King of glo - ry Shall reign e - ter - nal - ly.

Stand Up, Stand Up for Jesus

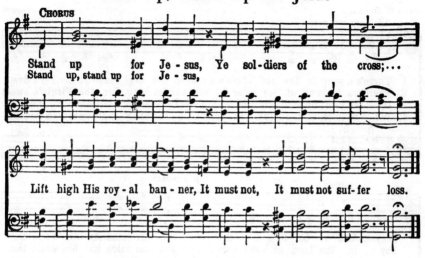

CHORUS

Stand up for Je-sus, Ye sol-diers of the cross;...
Stand up, stand up for Je-sus,

Lift high His roy-al ban-ner, It must not, It must not suf-fer loss.

Stand Up, Stand Up for Jesus 433

GEORGE DUFFIELD   GEORGE J. WEBB

1. Stand up, stand up for Je-sus, Ye sol-diers of the cross, Lift high His
2. Stand up, stand up for Je-sus, The trump-et call o-bey; Forth to the
3. Stand up, stand up for Je-sus, Stand in His strength a-lone; The arm of

roy-al ban-ner, It must not suf-fer loss; From vic-t'ry un-to vic-t'ry, His
might-y con-flict, In this His glo-rious day. "Ye that are men now serve Him,"A-
flesh will fail you—Ye dare not trust your own; Put on the gos-pel ar-mor, And,

ar-my shall He lead, Till ev-'ry foe is van-quished And Christ is Lord in-deed.
gainst un-num-bered foes; Let cour-age rise with dan-ger, And strength to strength oppose.
watching un-to prayer, Where du-ty calls, or dan-ger, Be nev-er want-ing there.

434 **There's a Song in the Air**

JOSIAH G. HOLLAND

KARL P. HARRINGTON

Adante con moto

1. There's a song in the air! There's a star in the sky! There's a mother's deep
2. There's a tu-mult of joy O'er the won-der-ful birth, For the Virgin's sweet
3. In the light of that star Lie the a-ges impearled; And that song from a-
4. We re-joice in the light, And we ech-o the song That comes down thru the

ritard. *piu mosso*

prayer, And a ba-by's low cry! And the star rains its fire while the
boy Is the Lord of the earth. Ay! the star rains its fire while the
far Has swept o-ver the world. Ev-'ry hearth is a-flame, and the
night From the heav-en-ly throng. Ay! we shout to the love-ly e-

ritard.

beau-ti-ful sing, For the man-ger of Beth-le-hem cra-dles a King!
beau-ti-ful sing, For the man-ger of Beth-le-hem cra-dles a King!
beau-ti-ful sing In the homes of the na-tions that Je-sus is King!
van-gel they bring, And we greet in His cra-dle our Sav-iour and King!

435 **I Heard the Bells on Christmas Day**

HENRY W. LONGFELLOW

J. BAPTISTE CALKIN

1. I heard the bells on Christ-mas day Their old fa-mil-iar car-ols play,
2. I thought how, as the day had come, The bel-fries of all Chris-ten-dom
3. And in de-spair I bowed my head: "There is no peace on earth," I said,
4. Then pealed the bells more loud and deep: "God is not dead, nor doth He sleep;
5. Till, ring-ing, sing-ing on its way, The world revolved from night to day,

I Heard the Bells on Christmas Day

And wild and sweet the words re-peat Of peace on earth, good-will to men.
Had rolled a-long th' un-bro-ken song Of peace on earth, good-will to men.
"For hate is strong, and mocks the song Of peace on earth, good-will to men."
The wrong shall fail, the right pre-vail, With peace on earth, good-will to men:"
A voice, a chime, a chant sub-lime, Of peace on earth, good-will to men!

Angels, From the Realms of Glory   436

JAMES MONTGOMERY   HENRY SMART

1. An - gels, from the realms of glo - ry, Wing your flight o'er all the earth;
2. Shep-herds, in the field a - bid-ing, Watching o'er your flocks by night,
3. Sa - ges, leave your con-tem-pla-tions, Bright-er vi-sions beam a - far;
4. Saints, be - fore the al - tar bend-ing, Watching long in hope and fear,

Ye, who sang cre - a - tion's sto - ry, Now pro-claim Mes - si - ah's birth:
God with man is now re - sid-ing, Yon-der shines the In - fant-Light;
Seek the great De - sire of na-tions, Ye have seen His na - tal star;
Sud-den-ly the Lord, de-scend-ing, In His tem - ple shall ap-pear;

Come and wor-ship, come and wor-ship, Wor-ship Christ, the new-born King.

The First Noel

OLD ENGLISH CAROL

TRADITIONAL MELODY FROM
W. SANDY'S "CHRISTMAS CAROLS"

1. The first No - el the angel did say Was to certain poor shepherds in fields as they lay;
2. And by the light of that same Star, Three wise men came from country far;
3. This Star drew nigh to the northwest, O'er Beth - le - hem it took its rest,
4. Then enter-ed in those wise men three, Full rev-'rent-ly up-on their knee,

In fields where they lay keeping their sheep, On a cold winter's night that was so deep.
To seek for a King was their in - tent, And to follow the Star wherever it went.
And there it did both stop and stay, Right o-ver the place where Jesus lay.
And of - fered there in His pres-ence, Their gold, and myrrh, and frank-incense.

REFRAIN.

No - el, No - el, No - el, No - el, Born is the King of Is - ra - el.

438 While Shepherds Watched Their Flocks

NAHUM TATE

GEORGE F. HANDEL

1. While shepherds watched their flocks by night, All seat - ed on the ground, The
2. "Fear not!" said he; for might-y dread Had seized their trou-bled mind, "Glad
3. "To you, in Dav-id's town this day, Is born of Dav-id's line, The
4. "The heav'n-ly Babe you there shall find To hu - man view dis - played, All
5. "All glo - ry be to God on high, And to the earth be peace: Good

While Shepherds Watched Their Flocks

an - gel of the Lord came down, And glo-ry shone a-round, And glo-ry shone a-round.
ti - dings of great joy I bring, To you and all man-kind, To you and all man-kind.
Sav - ior who is Christ the Lord; And this shall be the sign: And this shall be the sign:
mean-ly wrapped in swath-ing-bands, And in a man-ger laid, And in a man-ger laid.
will hence-forth from heav'n to men, Be-gin and nev-er cease, Be-gin and nev-er cease."

Silent Night! Holy Night!

439

JOSEPH MOHR

FRANZ GRUBER

1. Si - lent night, ho - ly night, All is calm, all is bright
2. Si - lent night, ho - ly night, Shep-herds quake at the sight,
3. Si - lent night, ho - ly night, Son of God, love's pure light
4. Si - lent night, ho - ly night, Won-drous star, lend thy light;

Round yon vir - gin moth-er and child. Ho - ly in-fant so ten-der and mild,
Glo - ries stream from heav-en a - far, Heav'n ly hosts sing Al - le - lu - ia;
Ra - diant beams from thy ho-ly face, With the dawn of re - deem-ing grace,
With the an - gels let us sing, Al - le - lu - ia to our King;

Sleep in heav-en-ly peace, Sleep in heav-en-ly peace.
Christ the Sav-ior is born! Christ the Sav-ior is born!
Je - sus, Lord, at thy birth, Je - sus, Lord, at thy birth.
Christ the Sav-ior is born. Christ the Sav-ior is born.

Thou Didst Leave Thy Throne

MARGARET

Emily E. S. Elliott

Timothy R. Matthews

1. Thou didst leave Thy throne And Thy king - ly crown, When Thou
2. Heav-en's arch - es rang When the an - gels sang, Pro-
3. The fox - es found rest, And the birds their nest In the
4. Thou cam - est, O Lord, With the liv - ing word That should
5. When the heav-ens shall ring, And the an - gels sing, At Thy

cam - est to earth for me; But in Beth - le - hem's home
claim - ing Thy roy - al de - gree; But of low - ly birth
shade of the for - est tree; But Thy couch was the sod,
set Thy peo - ple free; But with mock - ing scorn,
com - ing to vic - to - ry, Let Thy voice call me home,

Was there found no room For Thy ho - ly na - tiv - i - ty.
Didst Thou come to earth, And in great hu - mil - i - ty.
O Thou Son of God, In the des - erts of Gal - i - lee.
And with crown of thorn, They bore Thee to Cal - va - ry.
Say - ing, "Yet there is room, There is room at My side for thee."

REFRAIN

1-4. O come to my heart, Lord Je - sus, There is room in my heart for Thee.
5. My heart shall rejoice, Lord Je - sus, When Thou comest and call-est for me.

We Three Kings of Orient Are

JOHN H. HOPKINS

JOHN H. HOPKINS

1. We three kings of O - ri - ent are, Bear-ing gifts we trav-erse a-far
2. Born a King on Beth-le-hem's plain, Gold I bring to crown Him a-gain,
3. Frank-in-cense to of - fer have I, In - cense owns a De - i - ty nigh;
4. Myrrh is mine; its bit - ter per-fume Breathes a life of gath-er-ing gloom;
5. Glo - rious now be - hold Him a - rise, King and God and Sac - ri - fice;

Field and foun - tain, moor and moun-tain, Fol - low-ing yon - der star.
King for - ev - er, ceas-ing nev - er O - ver us all to reign.
Prayer and prais-ing, all men rais - ing, Wor-ship Him, God on high.
Sor-rowing, sigh-ing, bleed-ing, dy - ing, Sealed in the stone-cold tomb.
Al - le - lu - ia, Al - le - lu - ia! Peals through the earth and skies.

REFRAIN *a tempo*

O star of won - der, star of night, Star with loy - - al beau - ty bright,

West-ward lead-ing, still pro-ceed-ing, Guide us to thy per - fect light.

442   Joy to the World!

FROM PSALM 98
ISAAC WATTS

ARR. FROM GEORGE F. HANDEL

1. Joy to the world! the Lord is come; Let earth re-
2. Joy to the world! the Sav - ior reigns; Let men their
3. No more let sins and sor - rows grow, Nor thorns in-
4. He rules the world with truth and grace, And makes the

ceive her King; Let ev - 'ry heart pre - pare Him room,
songs em - ploy; While fields and floods, rocks, hills and plains
fest the ground; He comes to make His bless - ings flow
na - tions prove The glo - ries of His right-eous - ness,

And heav'n and na - ture sing, And heav'n and na - ture
Re - peat the sound - ing joy, Re - peat the sound - ing
Far as the curse is found, Far as the curse is
And won - ders of His love, And won - ders of His

1. And heav'n and na - ture sing,.......... And

sing, And heav'n, and heav'n and na - ture sing.
joy, Re - peat, re - peat the sound - ing joy.
found, Far as, far as the curse is found.
love, And won - ders, and won - ders of His love.

heav'n and na - ture sing,

No Room in the Inn

A. L. SKILTON,

E. GRACE UPDEGRAFF.

1. No beau-ti-ful cham-ber, No soft cra-dle bed, No place but a
2. No sweet con-se-cra-tion, No seek-ing His part, No hu-mil-i-
3. No one to re-ceive Him, No welcome while here, No balm to re-

man-ger, No-where for His head; No prais-es of glad-ness,
a-tion, No place in the heart; No tho't of the Sav-ior,
lieve Him, No staff but a spear; No seek-ing His treas-ure.

No tho't of their sin, No glo-ry but sad-ness, No room in the inn.
No sor-row for sin, No pray'r for His fa-vor, No room in the inn.
No weep-ing for sin, No do-ing His pleasure, No room in the inn.

CHORUS.

No room, no room for Je-sus, Oh, give Him wel-come free, Lest

you should hear at heav-en's gate, "There is no room for thee."

444 Hark! the Herald Angels Sing

CHARLES WESLEY

FELIX MENDELSSOHN-BARTHOLDY
ARR. BY WILLIAM H. CUMMINGS

1. Hark! the her-ald an-gels sing, "Glo-ry to the new-born King;
2. Christ, by high-est Heav'n a-dored, Christ, the ev-er-last-ing Lord:
3. Hail the Heav'n-born Prince of Peace! Hail the Sun of right-eous-ness!
4. Come, De-sire of na-tions, come! Fix in us Thy hum-ble home:

Peace on earth, and mer-cy mild; God and sin-ners rec-on-ciled."
Late in time be-hold Him come, Off-spring of a vir-gin's womb.
Light and life to all He brings, Ris'n with heal-ing in His wings:
Rise, the wom-an's con-qu'ring seed, Bruise in us the ser-pent's head;

Joy-ful, all ye na-tions, rise, Join the tri-umph of the skies;
Veiled in flesh the God-head see, Hail th' in-car-nate De-i-ty!
Mild He lays His glo-ry by, Born that man no more may die;
Ad-am's like-ness now ef-face, Stamp Thine im-age in its place:

With an-gel-ic hosts pro-claim, "Christ is born in Beth-le-hem."
Pleased as man with men to ap-pear, Je-sus our Im-man-uel here.
Born to raise the sons of earth; Born to give them sec-ond birth.
Sec-ond Ad-am from a-bove, Re-in-state us in Thy love.

Hark! the Herald Angels Sing

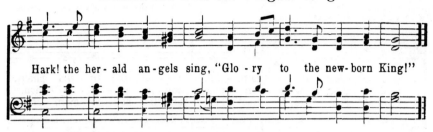

Hark! the her-ald an-gels sing, "Glo-ry to the new-born King!"

O Little Town of Bethlehem 445

PHILLIPS BROOKS

LEWIS H. REDNER

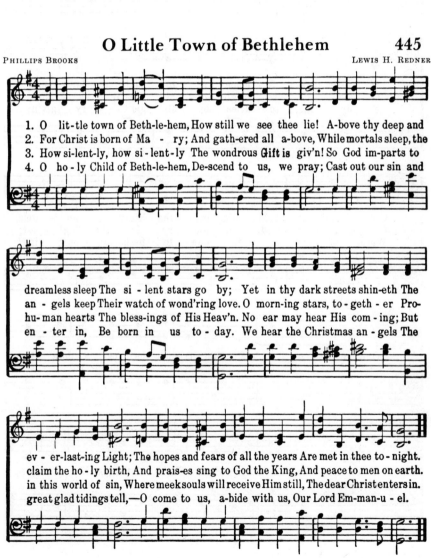

1. O lit-tle town of Beth-le-hem, How still we see thee lie! A-bove thy deep and dreamless sleep The si-lent stars go by; Yet in thy dark streets shin-eth The ev-er-last-ing Light; The hopes and fears of all the years Are met in thee to-night.

2. For Christ is born of Ma-ry; And gath-ered all a-bove, While mortals sleep, the an-gels keep Their watch of wond'ring love. O morn-ing stars, to-geth-er Pro-claim the ho-ly birth, And prais-es sing to God the King, And peace to men on earth.

3. How si-lent-ly, how si-lent-ly The wondrous Gift is giv'n! So God im-parts to hu-man hearts The bless-ings of His Heav'n. No ear may hear His com-ing; But in this world of sin, Where meek souls will receive Him still, The dear Christ enters in.

4. O ho-ly Child of Beth-le-hem, De-scend to us, we pray; Cast out our sin and en-ter in, Be born in us to-day. We hear the Christmas an-gels The great glad tidings tell,—O come to us, a-bide with us, Our Lord Em-man-u-el.

446 O Come, All Ye Faithful

LATIN HYMN
TR. BY FREDERICK OAKELEY

JOHN F. WADE'S "CANTUS DIVERSI"

1. O come, all ye faith - ful, joy - ful and tri - um - phant,
2. ℀ Sing, choirs of an - gels, sing in ex - ul - ta - tion,
3. ℀ Yea, Lord, we greet Thee, born this hap - py morn - ing,

O come ye, O come ye to Beth - le - hem;
O sing, all ye bright hosts of heav'n a - bove;
℀ Je - sus, to Thee be all glo - ry giv'n;

Come and be - hold Him born the King of an - gels;
Glo - ry to God, all glo - ry in the high - est;
Word of the Fa - ther, now in flesh ap - pear - ing;

REFRAIN

O come, let us a - dore Him, O come, let us a - dore Him,

O come, let us a - dore Him, Christ, the Lord. A - MEN.

It Came Upon the Midnight Clear 447

EDMUND H. SEARS   RICHARD S. WILLIS

1. It came up - on the mid-night clear, That glo-rious song of old,
2. Still thro' the clo - ven skies they come, With peace-ful wings un - furled,
3. And ye, be - neath life's crushing load, Whose forms are bend-ing low,
4. For lo, the days are has-t'ning on, By proph-et bards fore-told,

From an - gels bend-ing near the earth To touch their harps of gold:
And still their heav'n-ly mu - sic floats O'er all the wea - ry world:
Who toil a - long the climb-ing way With pain-ful steps and slow,
When with the ev - er - cir - cling years Comes round the age of gold;

"Peace on the earth, good-will to men, From heav'n's all-gracious King:" The
A - bove its sad and low - ly plains They bend on hov-'ring wing: And
Look now! for glad and gold - en hours Come swift-ly on the wing; O
When peace shall o - ver all the earth Its an-cient splen-dors fling, And

world in sol - emn still-ness lay To hear the an - gels sing.
ev - er o'er its Ba - bel sounds The bless - ed an - gels sing.
rest be - side the wea - ry road, And hear the an - gels sing.
the whole world give back the song Which now the an - gels sing. A-MEN.

Crowded Out

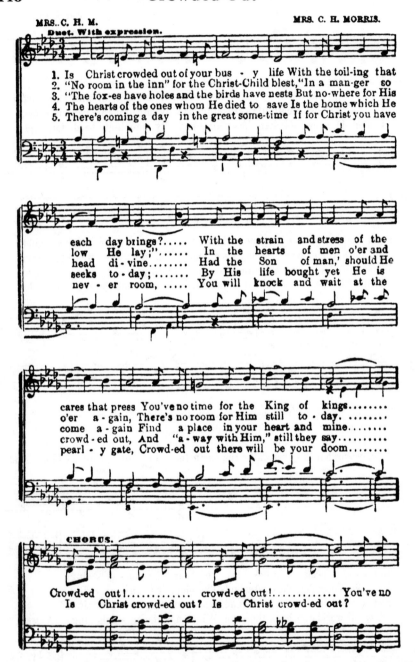

MRS. C. H. M.

MRS. C. H. MORRIS.

Duet. With expression.

1. Is Christ crowded out of your bus - y life With the toil-ing that each day brings?..... With the strain and stress of the cares that press You've no time for the King of kings........

2. "No room in the inn" for the Christ-Child blest, "In a man-ger so low He lay;".... In the hearts of men o'er and o'er a-gain, There's no room for Him still to-day. ....

3. "The fox-es have holes and the birds have nests But no-where for His head di-vine........ Had the Son of man,' should He come a-gain Find a place in your heart and mine........

4. The hearts of the ones whom He died to save Is the home which He seeks to-day; .... By His life bought yet He is crowd-ed out, And "a-way with Him," still they say..........

5. There's coming a day in the great some-time If for Christ you have nev-er room, ... You will knock and wait at the pearl-y gate, Crowd-ed out there will be your doom........

CHORUS.

Crowd-ed out!............. crowd-ed out!............. You've no

Is Christ crowd-ed out? Is Christ crowd-ed out?

Crowded Out

time for His serv-ice, you say;........ While for pleas-ure and
you say:

business you al-ways have time, Is Christ crowded out to - day?

Away in a Manger

MARTIN LUTHER

MARTIN LUTHER

1. A - way in a man-ger, No crib for a bed, The lit - tle Lord
2. The cat - tle are low - ing, The poor ba - by wakes, But lit - tle Lord

Je - sus Laid down His sweet head; The stars in the sky.... Looked
Je - sus, No cry - ing He makes; I love Thee, Lord Je - sus! Look

down where He lay,—The lit - tle Lord Je - sus, A - sleep on the hay.
down from the sky, And stay by my cra - dle To watch lul - la - by.

Count Your Blessings

JOHNSON OATMAN, JR.

EDWIN O. EXCELL

1. When up-on life's bil-lows you are tem - pest-tossed, When you are dis-
2. Are you ev - er bur-dened with a load of care? Does the cross seem
3. When you look at oth-ers with their lands and gold, Think that Christ has
4. So, a - mid the con-flict, whether great or small, Do not be dis-

cour-aged, think-ing all is lost, Count your man-y bless-ings, name them
heav - y you are called to bear? Count your man-y bless-ings, ev - 'ry
prom-ised you His wealth un - told; Count your man-y bless-ings, mon-ey
cour-aged, God is o - ver all; Count your man-y bless-ings, an - gels

one by one, And it will sur-prise you what the Lord hath done.
doubt will fly, And you will be sing-ing as the days go by.
can - not buy Your re-ward in heav-en, nor your home on high.
will at - tend, Help and com-fort give you to your jour - ney's end.

CHORUS.

Count your bless-ings, Name them one by one; Count your
Count your man-y bless-ings, Name them one by one; Count your man-y

bless-ings, See what God hath done; Count your bless-ings,
bless-ings, See what God hath done; Count your man-y bless-ings,

Count Your Blessings

Name them one by one; Count your man-y blessings, See what God hath done.

Thanks to God

451

Anon. (Swedish)
Tr. C. E. BACKSTROM

J. A. HULTMAN

1. Thanks to God for my Re-deem - er, Thanks for all Thou dost pro - vide!
2. Thanks for prayers that Thou hast answered, Thanks for what Thou dost de - ny!
3. Thanks for ros - es by the way - side, Thanks for thorns their stems contain!

Thanks for times now but a mem-'ry, Thanks for Je - sus by my side!
Thanks for storms that I have weathered, Thanks for all Thou dost sup - ply!
Thanks for home and thanks for fire-side, Thanks for hope, that sweet re-frain!

Thanks for pleas-ant, balm - y springtime, Thanks for dark and drear-y fall!
Thanks for pain, and thanks for pleas-ure, Thanks for com - fort in de - spair!
Thanks for joy and thanks for sor - row, Thanks for heav'nly peace with Thee!

Thanks for tears by now for - got - ten, Thanks for peace with-in my soul!
Thanks for grace that none can meas-ure, Thanks for love be-yond com - pare!
Thanks for hope in the to - mor - row, Thanks thro' all e - ter - ni - ty!

We Gather Together

AUTHOR UNKNOWN
TR. BY THEODORE BAKER

NETHERLANDS FOLK SONG
ARR. BY EDWARD KREMSER

1. We gath-er to-geth-er to ask the Lord's bless-ing,
2. Be-side us to guide us, our God with us join-ing,
3. We all do ex-tol Thee, Thou Lead-er in bat-tle,

He chas-tens and has-tens His will to make known;
Or-dain-ing, main-tain-ing His king-dom di-vine;
And pray that Thou still our De-fend-er wilt be.

The wick-ed op-press-ing cease them from dis-tress-ing,
So from the be-gin-ning the fight we were win-ning,
Let Thy con-gre-ga-tion es-cape trib-u-la-tion;

Sing prais-es to His name, He for-gets not His own.
Thou, Lord, wast at our side,— the glo-ry be Thine!
Thy name be ev-er praised. O Lord, make us free! A-MEN.

Great Is Thy Faithfulness 453

Thomas O. Chisholm

William M. Runyan

1. "Great is Thy faith-ful-ness," O God my Fa-ther, There is no shad-ow of
2. Sum-mer and win-ter, and spring-time and harvest, Sun, moon and stars in their
3. Par-don for sin and a peace that en-dur-eth, Thy own dear presence to

turn-ing with Thee; Thou chang-est not, Thy com-pas-sions, they fail not;
cours-es a-bove, Join with all na-ture in man-i-fold wit-ness,
cheer and to guide; Strength for to-day and bright hope for to-mor-row,

Chorus

As Thou hast been Thou for-ev-er wilt be.
To Thy great faith-ful-ness, mer-cy and love. "Great is Thy faith-ful-ness!
Blessings all mine, with ten thou-sand be-side!

Great is Thy faithfulness!" Morning by morning new mercies I see; All I have

rall.

need-ed Thy hand hath provided—"Great is Thy faithfulness," Lord, un-to me!

Favorite hymn of singer Bill Harvey and Dr. Clyde M. Narramore.

Battle Hymn of the Republic

Julia Ward Howe

William Steffe

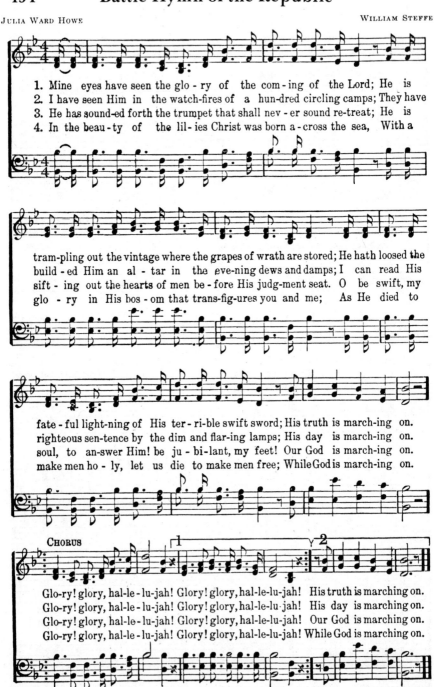

1. Mine eyes have seen the glo - ry of the com - ing of the Lord; He is
2. I have seen Him in the watch-fires of a hun-dred circling camps; They have
3. He has sound-ed forth the trumpet that shall nev - er sound re-treat; He is
4. In the beau-ty of the lil-ies Christ was born a-cross the sea, With a

tram-pling out the vintage where the grapes of wrath are stored; He hath loosed the
build - ed Him an al - tar in the eve-ning dews and damps; I can read His
sift - ing out the hearts of men be - fore His judg-ment seat. O be swift, my
glo - ry in His bos - om that trans-fig-ures you and me; As He died to

fate - ful light-ning of His ter - ri-ble swift sword; His truth is march-ing on.
righteous sen-tence by the dim and flar-ing lamps; His day is march-ing on.
soul, to an-swer Him! be ju - bi-lant, my feet! Our God is march-ing on.
make men ho - ly, let us die to make men free; While God is march-ing on.

Chorus

Glo-ry! glory, hal-le - lu-jah! Glory! glory, hal-le-lu-jah! His truth is marching on.
Glo-ry! glory, hal-le - lu-jah! Glory! glory, hal-le-lu jah! His day is marching on.
Glo-ry! glory, hal-le - lu-jah! Glory! glory, hal-le-lu-jah! Our God is marching on.
Glo-ry! glory, hal-le - lu-jah! Glory! glory, hal-le-lu-jah! While God is marching on.

O Beautiful for Spacious Skies

Katherine L. Bates

Samuel A. Ward

1. O beau - ti - ful for spa-cious skies, For am - ber waves of grain,
2. O beau - ti - ful for pil - grim feet, Whose stern, im-pas-sioned stress
3. O beau - ti - ful for he-roes proved In lib - er - at - ing strife.
4. O beau - ti - ful for pa-triot dream That sees be - yond the years

For pur - ple moun-tain maj - es - ties A - bove the fruit - ed plain!
A thor-ough-fare for free - dom beat A - cross the wil - der - ness!
Who more than self their coun-try loved, And mer - cy more than life!
Thine al - a - bas - ter cit - ies gleam, Undimmed by hu - man tears!

A - mer - i - ca! A - mer - i - ca! God shed His grace on thee,
A - mer - i - ca! A - mer - i - ca! God mend thine ev - 'ry flaw,
A - mer - i - ca! A - mer - i - ca! May God thy gold re - fine,
A - mer - i - ca! A - mer - i - ca! God shed His grace on thee,

And crown thy good with broth - er-hood From sea to shin - ing sea!
Con - firm thy soul in self - con-trol, Thy lib - er - ty in law!
Till all suc - cess be no - ble-ness And ev - 'ry gain di - vine!
And crown thy good with broth - er-hood From sea to shin - ing sea!

456   The Star-Spangled Banner

Francis Scott Key

Attributed to
John Stafford Smith

1. O say, can you see, by the dawn's ear-ly light, What so proud-ly we
2. O thus be it ev - er, when free men shall stand Be - tween their loved

hailed at the twi-light's last gleam-ing, Whose broad stripes and bright stars, thru the
homes and the war's des - o - la - tion! Blest with vic - t'ry and peace, may the

per - il - ous fight, O'er the ram-parts we watched, were so gal-lant-ly stream-ing?
heav'n-res-cued land Praise the Pow'r that hath made and pre-served us a na - tion!

And the rock-ets' red glare, the bombs burst-ing in air, Gave proof thru the
Then con-quer we must, when our cause it is just; And this be our

night that our flag was still there. O say, does that star-span-gled
mot - to: "In God is our trust!" And the star-span-gled ban - ner in

The Star-Spangled Banner

ban - ner yet wave O'er the land of the free and the home of the brave?
tri - umph shall wave O'er the land of the free and the home of the brave!

My Country, 'Tis of Thee   457

SAMUEL FRANCIS SMITH

Source unknown
From *Thesaurus Musicus*

1. My coun - try, 'tis of thee, Sweet land of lib - er - ty,
2. My na - tive coun - try, thee, Land of the no - ble free,
3. Let mu - sic swell the breeze, And ring from all the trees
4. Our fa - thers' God, to Thee, Au - thor of lib - er - ty,

Of thee I sing: Land where my fa - thers died, Land of the
Thy name I love: I love thy rocks and rills, Thy woods and
Sweet free-dom's song: Let mor - tal tongues a - wake, Let all that
To Thee we sing: Long may our land be bright With free-dom's

pil - grims' pride, From ev - 'ry moun-tain side Let free-dom ring!
tem - pled hills; My heart with rap - ture thrills Like that a - bove.
breathe par-take; Let rocks their si - lence break, The sound pro - long.
ho - ly light; Pro - tect us by Thy might, Great God, our King!

458   My Plea

J. L. B.

J. L. BAKER

Should I at the gates__ of heav-en ap-pear To answ-er the
Of all earth-ly treas-ures no-thing I've brought No great deeds of
My sins they are man-y my virt-ues are few The blood of my

chal-lenge what claim hast thou here, What hast thou to of-fer yea
mer-it have I ev-er wrought Tho vile and un-worth-y as
Sav-iour will car-ry me through When Christ in my place died on

what is thy plea? With_ bless-ed as-sur-ance my answ-er would be,
mor-tal could be I've_ noth-ing to of-fer but this is my plea,
cal-va-ry's tree Hal-le-lu-jah that op-ened God's heav-en to me,

CHORUS

All that I have is Je - sus All that I

claim is Je - sus All that I want

All that I need All that I plead is Je - sus.

Jesus in My Heart

J. L. B.

J. L. BAKER

You may won-der why it is I'm al ways hap-py, You may
You may won-der why I seek no earth-ly treas-ure, And the
It is Je-sus who has pur-chased my re-demp-tion, It was

won-der why I'm sing-ing all day long, You may won-der at the
lux-ur-y that gold a-lone can buy, You may won-der why I
Je-sus who trans-formed this heart of mine, He who loved me and from

joy with-in my be-ing That can on-ly find ex-press-ion in my song.
crave no world-ly pleas-ure If you lis-ten I will tell the rea son why.
all my sin has washed me In the foun-tain of His prec-ious Blood di - vine.

CHORUS

It is Je-sus on-ly Je - sus It is Je-sus in my

heart_____ It is Je-sus on-ly Je - sus It is

1

Je - sus in my heart.

2

in my heart.

The Ninety and Nine

ELIZABETH C. CLEPHANE

IRA D. SANKEY

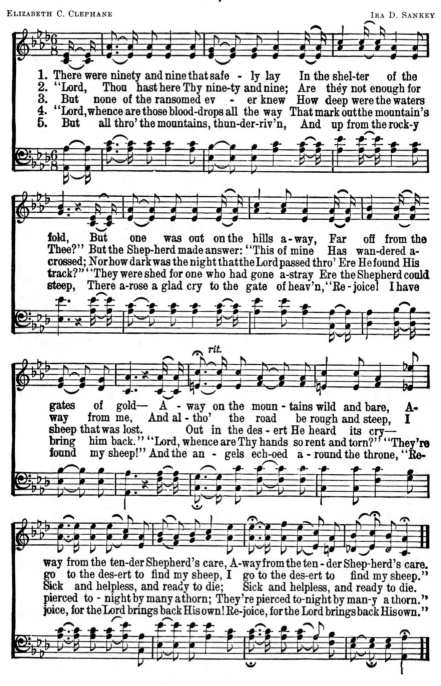

1. There were ninety and nine that safe - ly lay In the shel-ter of the
2. "Lord, Thou hast here Thy nine-ty and nine; Are they not enough for
3. But none of the ransomed ev - er knew How deep were the waters
4. "Lord, whence are those blood-drops all the way That mark out the mountain's
5. But all thro' the mountains, thun-der-riv'n, And up from the rock-y

fold, But one was out on the hills a-way, Far off from the
Thee?" But the Shep-herd made answer: "This of mine Has wan-dered a-
crossed; Nor how dark was the night that the Lord passed thro' Ere He found His
track?" "They were shed for one who had gone a-stray Ere the Shepherd could
steep, There a-rose a glad cry to the gate of heav'n, "Re - joice! I have

rit.

gates of gold— A - way on the moun - tains wild and bare, A-
way from me, And al - tho' the road be rough and steep, I
sheep that was lost. Out in the des - ert He heard its cry—
bring him back." "Lord, whence are Thy hands so rent and torn?" "They're
found my sheep!" And the an - gels ech-oed a - round the throne, "Re-

way from the ten-der Shepherd's care, A-way from the ten - der Shep-herd's care.
go to the des-ert to find my sheep, I go to the des-ert to find my sheep."
Sick and helpless, and ready to die; Sick and helpless, and ready to die.
pierced to - night by many a thorn; They're pierced to-night by man-y a thorn."
joice, for the Lord brings back His own! Re-joice, for the Lord brings back His own."

Lead Me Gently Home, Father

W. L. T.

WILL L. THOMPSON

1. Lead me gen-tly home, Fa-ther, Lead me gen-tly home, When life's toils are
2. Lead me gen-tly home, Fa-ther, Lead me gen-tly home, In life's dark-est
3. Lead me gen-tly home, Fa-ther, Lead me gen-tly home, In temp-ta-tion's

end - ed, and part - ing days have come; Sin no more shall tempt me,
hours, Fa-ther, when life's trou-bles come, Keep my feet from wan-dering,
hour, Fa-ther, when sore tri - als come; Be Thou near to keep me,

rit.

Ne'er from Thee I'll roam, If Thou'lt on - ly lead me, Fa - ther,
Lest from Thee I roam, Lest I fall up - on the way - side,
Take me as Thine own, For I can - not live with - out Thee,

p   CHORUS

Lead me gen-tly home. Lead me gen-tly home, Fa - ther,
Lead me gen-tly home, Fa - ther, Lead me gen - tly

rit.   *p*

lead me gen-tly, Lest I fall up-on the way-side, Lead me gen-tly home.
home, Fa - ther, gen-tly home.

462 Come Unto Me

E. E. HEWITT
SOLO OR UNISON

D. WARD MILAM
Arranged for JOHN T. BENSON Jr.

1. Come, all ye wea-ry and op-pressed, O come and I will give you rest;
2. Come, ye that feel the weight of sin, And I will breathe sweet peace with-in;
3. So ten-der-ly my Sav-iour pleads, For all His own He in-ter-cedes;

I'll bid your anx-ious fears de-part, For I am meek and low-ly in heart,
I'll lift the bur-den from your heart, For-give-ness I will free-ly im-part,
And still He's call-ing, Come to me, And ye shall find rest un-to your soul,

ad lib

For I am meek aud low-ly in heart, And I will give you rest.
For-give-ness I will free-ly im-part, And I will give you rest.
For I am meek and low-ly in heart, And I will give you rest.

CHORUS

Ye that la-bor and are heav-y la-den, Come to me, (to me,) Come, come,
Take my yoke, my

Come Unto Me

Come......and learn of me;.... My yoke is eas - y, My
yoke up-on you, and learn, and learn of me, of me; For my yoke is eas-y, and My
For my yoke is eas - y, My

bur - - den is light,..... My yoke is eas - y, My
bur-den is light, My bur-den is light, For My yoke is eas-y and My
bur - - den is light,.......... For My yoke is eas-y and My

rit.

bur - den is light.....Come, come, Come and I will give you rest.
burden is light, My burden is light, Come, O come,

Isn't He Wonderful? **463**

S. Jones   Arranged

Is - n't He won - der-ful, won - der-ful, won - der - ful? Is - n't

Je - sus my Lord won - der-ful? Eyes have seen; ears have heard;

It's re-cord - ed in God's Word. Is - n't Je - sus my Lord won - der-ful?

Still Sweeter Every Day

W. C. Martin

C. Austin Miles

1. To Je - sus ev - 'ry day I find my heart is clos - er drawn; He's
2. His glo - ry broke up - on me when I saw Him from a - far; He's
3. My heart is some-times heav-y, but He comes with sweet re - lief; He

fair - er than the glo - ry of the gold and pur - ple dawn; He's all my
fair - er than the lil - y, bright - er than the morn-ing star; He fills and
folds me to His bos - om when I droop with blighting grief; I love the

fan - cy pic-tures in its fair-est dreams, and more; Each day He grows still
sat - is - fies my long-ing spir - it o'er and o'er; Each day He grows still
Christ who all my bur-dens in His bod - y bore; Each day He grows still

CHORUS

sweet-er than He was the day be - fore. The half . . . . can-not be
sweet-er than He was the day be - fore.
sweet-er than He was the day be - fore. The half can-not be fan-cied on this

fan - cied this side . . . . the gold-en shore; Oh,
side the gold-en shore, The half can-not be fan - cied on this side the golden shore; Oh,

Still Sweeter Every Day

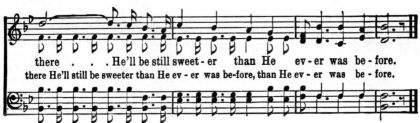

there . . . He'll be still sweet-er than He ev-er was be-fore.
there He'll still be sweeter than He ev-er was be-fore, than He ev-er was be-fore.

Cleanse Me

465

J. EDWIN ORR

MAORI MELODY

1. Search me, O God, and know my heart to-day; Try me, O
2. I praise Thee, Lord, for cleans-ing me from sin: Ful-fill Thy
3. Lord, take my life, and make it whol-ly Thine: Fill my poor
4. O Ho-ly Ghost, re-viv-al comes from Thee: Send a re-

Sav-ior, know my thoughts, I pray: See if there be some wick-ed
Word, and make me pure with-in; Fill me with fire, where once I
heart with Thy great love di-vine; Take all my will, my pas-sion,
viv-al—start the work in me: Thy Word de-clares Thou wilt sup-

way in me: Cleanse me from ev-'ry sin, and set me free.
burned with shame: Grant my de-sire to mag-ni-fy Thy name.
self and pride; I now sur-ren-der: Lord, in me a-bide.
ply our need: For bless-ing now, O Lord, I hum-bly plead.

466 O Perfect Love

DOROTHY F. GURNEY

JOSEPH BARNBY

1. O per-fect Love, all hu-man thought tran-scend-ing,
2. O per-fect Life, be Thou their full as-sur-ance
3. Grant them the joy which bright-ens earth-ly sor-row,
4. Hear us, O Fa-ther, gra-cious and for-giv-ing,

Low-ly we kneel in prayer be-fore Thy throne,
Of ten-der char-i-ty and stead-fast faith,
Grant them the peace which calms all earth-ly strife,
Through Je-sus Christ, Thy co-e-ter-nal Word,

That theirs may be the love which knows no end-ing,
Of pa-tient hope, and qui-et, brave en-dur-ance,
And to life's day the glo-rious, un-known mor-row
Who, with the Ho-ly Ghost, by all things liv-ing

Whom Thou for-ev-er-more dost join in one.
With child-like trust that fears nor pain nor death.
That dawns up-on e-ter-nal love and life.
Now and to end-less a-ges art a-dored. A-MEN.

Lead Me, Saviour

F. M. D.

FRANK M. DAVIS

With expression

1. Sav-iour, lead me, lest I stray, Gen-tly lead me all the way;
2. Thou the ref-uge of my soul, When life's stormy billows roll,
3. Sav-iour, lead me, then at last, When the storm of life is past,

1. Sav - iour, lead me, lest I stray, Gen - tly lead me all the way;

I am safe when by Thy side, I would in Thy love a-bide.
I am safe when Thou art nigh, All my hopes on Thee re-ly.
To the land of end-less day, Where all tears are wiped away.

I am safe when by Thy side, I would in Thy love a-bide.

CHORUS

Lead me, lead me, Sav - iour, lead me, lest I stray; .... Gen - tly
lest I stray;

rit. e dim.

down the stream of time, Lead me, Sav-iour, all the way.
stream of time, all the way.

468   O Happy Day

Philip Doddridge

Arr. by L.B. Harris

1. O hap-py day that fixed my choice On Thee, my
2. O hap-py bond that seals my vows To Him who
3. 'Tis done, the great trans-ac-tion's done! I am my

Sav-iour and) (Well may this glow-ing
Sav-iour and my God! (the liv-ing God!) Well may this glow-ing heart re-
mer its all my love! (yes, all my love!) Let cheer-ful an-thems fill His
Lord's and He is mine; (He's tru-ly mine;) He drew me and I fol-lowed

heart re-joice, And tell its rap-tures) He taught me
joice, And tell its rap-tures all a-broad. (a-broad.)
house, While to that sa-cred shrine I move. (I move.)
on, Charmed to con-fess the voice di-vine. (di-vine.)

CHORUS

He taught me how to pray, to watch and pray, And live re-
He taught me how to pray, to watch and pray, And
taught me how to pray, to watch and pray, And live re-

-ing ev-'ry day; O hap-py day, O hap-py
joic-ing ev-'ry day; O hap-py day, O hap-py
live re-joic-ing ev-'ry pass-ing day; O hal-le-lu-jah,

joic-ing ev-'ry pass-ing day; Hap-py day, blest

day, When Je-sus washed my sins a-way.
O hap-py day, When Je-sus washed my sins a-way, my sins a-way.

hap-py day,

Mrs. FRANK A. BRECK   GRANT COLFAX TULLAR

1. There was One who was will-ing to die in my stead, That a
2. He is ten-der and lov-ing and pa-tient with me, While He
3. I will cling to my Sav-ior and nev-er de-part—I will

soul so un-wor-thy might live; And the path to the cross He was
cleans-es my heart of the dross; But "there's no con-dem-na-tion"—I
joy-ful-ly jour-ney each day. With a song on my lips and a

REFRAIN

will-ing to tread, All the sins of my life to for-give.
know I am free, For my sins are all nailed to the cross. They are nailed to the cross,
song in my heart, That my sins have been tak-en a-way.

pp

They are nailed to the cross, O how much He was will-ing to bear! With what

rit.

an-guish and loss Je-sus went to the cross! But He carried my sins with Him there.

Friendship With Jesus

Rev. J. C. Ludgate

1. A friend of Je - sus, oh, what bliss That one so weak as I
2. A friend when oth. - er friend-ships cease, A friend when oth - ers fail;
3. A friend to lead me in the dark, A friend who knows the way;
4. A friend when sick - ness lays me low, A friend when death draws near;
5. A friend when life's rough voyage is o'er, A friend when death is past;

Should ev - er have a friend like this To lead me to the sky.
A friend who gives me joy and peace, A friend who will pre - vail.
A friend to steer my weak, frail bark, A friend my debts to pay.
A friend as thro' the vale I go, A friend to help and cheer.
A friend to greet on heav - en's shore, A friend when home at last.

CHORUS

Friend - ship with Je - sus, Fel - low - ship di - vine;

rit.

Oh, what bless-ed sweet com-mun - ion, Je - sus is a friend of mine.

Almost

P. P. B.

P. P. Bilhorn

Slowly

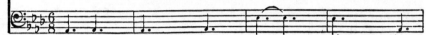

1. Al - most I trust-ed in Je - sus, Al - most I turned from my sin;
2. Al - most I said, "Je - sus, save me," Al - most sub - mit - ted my will;
3. Al - most, but still I re - sist - ed, Al - most, but nev - er be - lieved;
4. Al - most at one time I yield - ed, Al - most at one time was saved;
5. Al - most,—why lon-ger re - fuse Him? Al - most, O lost one, be - lieve;

rit.

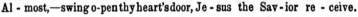

Al - most I yield - ed com - plete - ly To the sweet striv-ing with-in.
Al - most per-suad-ed to serve Him, But I re - ject - ed Him still.
Al - most, but wait - ed and wait - ed, Till the sweet Spir-it was grieved.
Al - most, but drift - ed and drift - ed; Sa - tan thus held me en - slaved.
Al - most,—swing o-pen thy heart's door, Je - sus the Sav - ior re - ceive.

CHORUS *Faster*

Now is the time to re - ceive Him, Now is the time to be saved;

Now, while the Spir - it is plead - ing, Now, Je - sus wait-eth to save.

472 Ivory Palaces

HENRY BARRACLOUGH

HENRY BARRACLOUGH

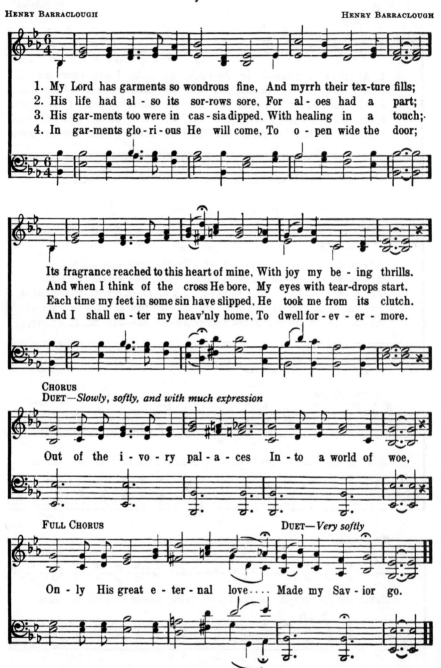

1. My Lord has garments so wondrous fine, And myrrh their tex-ture fills;
2. His life had al - so its sor-rows sore, For al - oes had a part;
3. His gar-ments too were in cas - sia dipped. With healing in a touch;·
4. In gar-ments glo - ri - ous He will come, To o - pen wide the door;

Its fragrance reached to this heart of mine, With joy my be - ing thrills.
And when I think of the cross He bore, My eyes with tear-drops start.
Each time my feet in some sin have slipped, He took me from its clutch.
And I shall en - ter my heav'nly home, To dwell for - ev - er - more.

CHORUS
DUET—*Slowly, softly, and with much expression*

Out of the i - vo - ry pal - a - ces In - to a world of woe,

FULL CHORUS

DUET—*Very softly*

On - ly His great e - ter - nal love.... Made my Sav - ior go.

Jesus, Lover of My Soul

CHARLES WESLEY   REFUGE   JOSEPH P. HOLBROOK

1. Je - sus, Lov - er of my soul, Let me to Thy bos - om fly,
2. Oth - er ref - uge have I none; Hangs my help - less soul on Thee;
3. Thou, O Christ, art all I want; More than all in Thee I find:
4. Plen-teous grace with Thee is found, Grace to cov - er all my sin;

While the near - er wa - ters roll, While the tem - pest still is high!
Leave, O leave me not a - lone, Still sup - port and com-fort me:
Raise the fall - en, cheer the faint, Heal the sick, and lead the blind.
Let the heal - ing streams a-bound; Make me, keep me pure with-in.

Hide me, O my Sav - iour, hide, Till the storm of life is past;
All my trust on Thee is stayed, All my help from Thee I bring;
Just and ho - ly is Thy name, I am all un - right-eous-ness;
Thou of life the foun - tain art, Free - ly let me take of Thee;

Safe in - to the ha - ven guide, O re - ceive my soul at last.
Cov - er my de - fense-less head With the shad - ow of Thy wing.
False, and full of sin I am, Thou art full of truth and grace.
Spring Thou up with - in my heart, Rise to all e - ter - ni - ty.

474 The Stranger of Galilee

Mrs. C. H. MORRIS   Mrs. C. H. MORRIS

Solo or Quartet

1. In fan-cy I stood by the shore, one day, Of the beau-ti-ful murm'ring
2. His look of com-pas-sion, His words of love, They shall nev-er for-got-ten
3. I heard Him speak peace to the an-gry waves, Of that tur-bu-lent, rag-ing
4. Come ye, who are driv-en, and tempest tossed, And His gra-cious sal-va-tion

1. Of the beau - - - ti-ful

sea; . . . I saw the great crowds as they thronged the way Of the Stranger of
be, . . . When sin-sick and helpless He saw me there, This Stranger of
sea; . . . And lo! at His word are the wa-ters stilled, This Stranger of
see; . . . He'll qui-et life's storms with His "Peace, be still!" This Stranger of

murm'ring sea;   1. Of the Stran - - -

Gal-i-lee; . . . I saw how the man who was blind from birth, In a
Gal-i-lee; . . . He show'd me His hand and His riv-en side, And He
Gal-i-lee; . . . A peace-ful, a qui-et, and ho-ly calm, Now and
Gal-i-lee; . . . He bids me to go and the sto-ry tell What He

ger of Gal-i-lee;

The Stranger of Galilee

mo-ment was made to see; . . . The lame was made whole by the matchless skill
whispered "It was for thee!" . . My bur-den fell off at the pierc-ed feet
ev - er a-bides with me; . . . He hold-eth my life in His might-y hands,
ev - er to you will be, . . . If on - ly you let Him with you a - bide,
1. mo - - ment was made to see;

CHORUS

Of the Stranger of Gal - i - lee.
Of the Stranger of Gal - i - lee. And I felt I could love Him for-
This Stranger of Gal - i - lee.
This Stranger of Gal - i - lee. (4 v.) Oh, my friend, won't you love Him for-

ff   *p*   *rit.*   *a tempo*

ev - - - er, So gra-cious and ten-der was He! I
ev - - - er? So gra-cious and ten-der was He! . . . . Ac-
ev - er and ev - er, so ten - der was He!

cres.   *rit. e dim.*

claimed Him that day as my Sav - ior, This Stranger of Gal - i - lee.
cept Him to-day as your Sav - ior, This Stranger of Gal - i - lee.
Lord and my Sav-ior,

His Eye Is on the Sparrow

CIVILLA D. MARTIN

CHARLES H. GABRIEL

1. Why should I feel discouraged, Why should the shadows come, Why should my
2. "Let not your heart be troubled," His ten-der word I hear, And rest-ing
3. When-ev-er I am temp-ted, When-ev-er clouds a - rise, When songs give

heart be lonely And long for Heav'n and home, When Jesus is my portion? My
on His goodness, I lose my doubts and fears; Tho' by the path He leadeth But
place to sighing, When hope within me dies, I draw the clo-ser to Him, From

constant Friend is He: His eye is on the spar-row, And I know He watches
one step I may see: His eye is on the spar-row, And I know He watches
care He sets me free; His eye is on the spar-row, And I know He cares for

me; His eye is on the sparrow, And I know He watches me.
me; His eye is on the sparrow, And I know He watches me.
me; His eye is on the sparrow, And I know He cares for me.

His Eye Is on the Sparrow

Chorus.

I sing be-cause I'm hap-py (I'm hap-py), I sing because I'm free (I'm free),

rall.

For His eye is on the spar-row, And I know He watch-es me.

All for Jesus

476

Rev. J. B. Atchinson.

E. O. Excell.

FINE

1. { All, yes, all I give to Je - sus, It be-longs to Him;
     All my heart I give to Je - sus, It be-longs to Him;

2. { All, yes, all I give to Je - sus, It be-longs to Him;
     All my voice I give to Je - sus, It be-longs to Him;

3. { All, yes, all I give to Je - sus, It be-longs to Him;
     All my love I give to Je - sus, It be-longs to Him;

4. | All, yes, all I give to Je - sus, It be-longs to Him;
     All my life I give to Je - sus, It be-longs to Him,

D. C.—Ev - er more His good-ness tell - ing, It be-longs to Him.
Sing-ing o'er and o'er the sto - ry, It be-longs to Him.
For His watch-care nev - er ceas - ing, It be-longs to Him.
Ev - er-more I'll hon - or Je - sus; All be-longs to Him.

D. C.

Ev - er-more to be His dwell - ing, Ev - er-more His prais - es swell-ing,
Plead - ing for the young and hoar - y, Tell - ing of His pow'r and glo - ry,
Lov - ing Him for love un - ceas-ing, For His mer - cy e'er in - creas-ing,
Hour by hour I'll live for Je - sus, Day by day I'll work for Je - sus,

477 Though Your Sins Be As Scarlet

FANNY J. CROSBY

WILLIAM H. DOANE

1. "Tho' your sins be as scar-let, They shall be as white as snow;
2. Hear the voice that en-treats you, O re-turn ye un-to God!
3. He'll for-give your trans-gres-sions, And re-mem-ber them no more;

Tho' your sins be as scar-let, They shall be as white as snow;
Hear the voice that en-treats you, O re-turn ye un-to God!
He'll for-give your trans-gres-sions, And re-mem-ber them no more;

Tho' they be red . . . . . like crim-son, They shall be as wool!"
He is of great . . . . com-pas-sion, And of won-drous love;
"Look un-to Me, ... ye peo-ple," Saith the Lord your God!

"Tho' your sins be as scar-let, Tho' your sins be as scar-let,
Hear the voice that en-treats you, Hear the voice that en-treats you,
He'll for-give your trans-gres-sions, He'll for-give your trans-gres-sions,

They shall be as white as snow, They shall be as white as snow."
O re-turn ye un-to God! O re-turn ye un-to God!
And re-mem-ber them no more, And re-mem-ber them no more.

He Will Hold Me Fast

ADA R. HABERSHON

ROBERT HARKNESS

1. When I fear my faith will fail, Christ will hold me fast;
2. I could nev-er keep my hold, He will hold me fast;
3. I am pre-cious in His sight, He will hold me fast;
4. He'll not let my soul be lost, Christ will hold me fast;

When the tempt-er would pre-vail, He can hold me fast...
For my love is oft-en cold, He must hold me fast...
Those He saves are His de-light, He will hold me fast...
Bought by Him at such a cost, He will hold me fast...

rall.

REFRAIN *a tempo*

He will hold me fast, He will hold me fast;
hold me fast, hold me fast;

rall.

For my Sav-ior loves me so, He will hold me fast.

479

Ship Ahoy!

M. J. Cartwright

D. B. Towner

Effective Solo

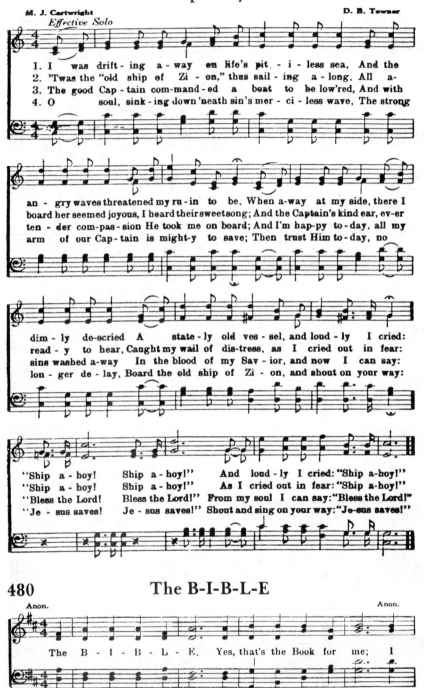

1. I was drift-ing a-way on life's pit-i-less sea, And the
2. 'Twas the "old ship of Zi-on," thus sail-ing a-long, All a-
3. The good Cap-tain com-mand-ed a boat to be low'red, And with
4. O soul, sink-ing down 'neath sin's mer-ci-less wave, The strong

an-gry waves threatened my ru-in to be, When a-way at my side, there I
board her seemed joyous, I heard their sweet song; And the Captain's kind ear, ev-er
ten-der com-pas-sion He took me on board; And I'm hap-py to-day, all my
arm of our Cap-tain is might-y to save; Then trust Him to-day, no

dim-ly de-scried A state-ly old ves-sel, and loud-ly I cried:
read-y to hear, Caught my wail of dis-tress, as I cried out in fear:
sins washed a-way In the blood of my Sav-ior, and now I can say:
lon-ger de-lay, Board the old ship of Zi-on, and shout on your way:

"Ship a-hoy! Ship a-hoy!" And loud-ly I cried: "Ship a-hoy!"
"Ship a-hoy! Ship a-hoy!" As I cried out in fear: "Ship a-hoy!"
"Bless the Lord! Bless the Lord!" From my soul I can say: "Bless the Lord!"
"Je-sus saves! Je-sus saves!" Shout and sing on your way: "Je-sus saves!"

480

The B-I-B-L-E

Anon.

Anon.

The B-I-B-L-E, Yes, that's the Book for me; I

The B-I-B-L-E

stand a - lone on the Word of God: The B - I - B - L - E.

Jesus Bids Us Shine 481

SUSAN WARNER

EDWIN O. EXCELL

1. Je - sus bids us shine, With a clear, pure light, Like a lit - tle
2. Je - sus bids us shine, First of all for Him; Well He sees and
3. Je - sus bids us shine, Then, for all a - round Man - y kinds of
4. Je - sus bids us shine, As we work for Him, Bring-ing those that

can - dle Burn - ing in the night; In this world of dark - ness
knows it If our light is dim; He looks down from heav - en,
dark - ness In this world a - bound— Sin, and want, and sor - row:
wan - der From the paths of sin; He will ev - er help us,

We must shine, You in your small cor - ner, And I in mine.
Sees us shine, You in your small cor - ner, And I in mine.
We must shine, You in your small cor - ner, And I in mine.
If we shine, You in your small cor - ner, And I in mine.

482   'Tis Marvelous and Wonderful

Mrs. C. H. M.

Mrs. C. H. Morris

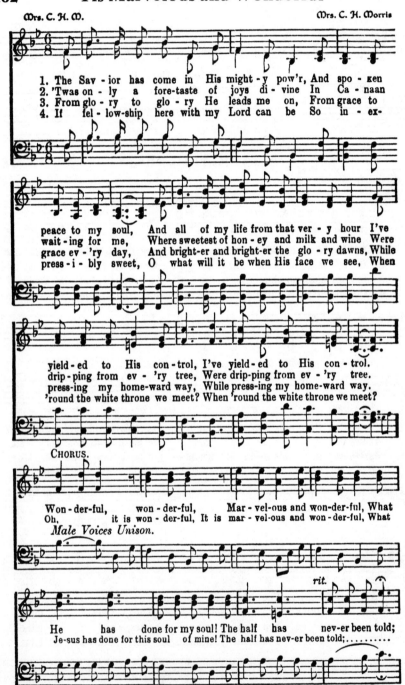

1. The Sav-ior has come in His might-y pow'r, And spo-ken
2. 'Twas on-ly a fore-taste of joys di-vine In Ca-naan
3. From glo-ry to glo-ry He leads me on, From grace to
4. If fel-low-ship here with my Lord can be So in-ex-

peace to my soul, And all of my life from that ver-y hour I've
wait-ing for me, Where sweetest of hon-ey and milk and wine Were
grace ev-'ry day, And bright-er and bright-er the glo-ry dawns, While
press-i-bly sweet, O what will it be when His face we see, When

yield-ed to His con-trol, I've yield-ed to His con-trol.
drip-ping from ev-'ry tree, Were drip-ping from ev-'ry tree.
press-ing my home-ward way, While press-ing my home-ward way.
'round the white throne we meet? When 'round the white throne we meet?

CHORUS.

Won-der-ful, won-der-ful, Mar-vel-ous and won-der-ful, What
Oh, it is won-der-ful, It is mar-vel-ous and won-der-ful, What

Male Voices Unison.

rit.

He has done for my soul! The half has nev-er been told;
Je-sus has done for this soul of mine! The half has nev-er been told;..........

'Tis Marvelous and Wonderful

a tempo.

Oh,...... it is won-der-ful, It is mar-vel-ous and won-der-ful,
Won-der-ful,

rit.

What Je-sus has done for this soul of mine! The half has nev-er been told.

Resting in His Promise   483

Words and music by Evangelist John R. Rice

Copyright, 1960, by John R. Rice

1. All my sins were laid on Je - sus; On the cross my debt He paid.
2. Now there is no con-dem-na-tion; Not a blot my rec-ord bears.
3. "I have tak-en life e-ter-nal; I am now a son of God.
4. "I will nev-er leave, for-sake thee," None can take me from His hand.

Chorus: Rest-ing sweet-ly in His pro-mise, Rest my soul on what He said.

Then He cried out, "It is fin-ished!" Ere He in the tomb was laid.
For my sins the blood all cov-ers, Je-sus' right-eous robe I wear.
Of God's na-ture now par-tak-er, Now no fear of judg-ment's rod.
So the Sav-iour's pro-mise claim-ing, Now I live in Beu-lah Land.

Trust-ing ful-ly, whol-ly trust-ing, In the price my Sav-iour paid.

484   All Hail, Immanuel!

D. R. Van Sickle   Charles H. Gabriel

1. All hail to Thee, Im-man-u-el, We cast . . . our crowns be-fore Thee;
2. All hail to Thee, Im-man-u-el, The ran - somed hosts surround Thee;
3. All hail to Thee, Im-man-u-el, Our ris - - en King and Sav - ior!

Let ev - 'ry heart o - bey Thy will, And ev - - - 'ry voice a-
And earth - ly mon-archs clam - or forth Their Sov - - 'reign King to
Thy foes are van-quished, and Thou art Om - nip - - - o - tent for-

dore Thee. In praise to Thee, our Sav - ior King, The vi - brant
crown Thee. While those re-deemed in a - ges gone, As - sem - bled
ev - er. Death, sin and hell no lon - ger reign, And Sa - tan's

chords of Heav - en ring, And ech - o back the might - y strain:
round the great white throne, Break forth in - to im - mor - tal song:
pow'r is burst in twain; E - ter - nal glo - ry to Thy Name:

All hail! all hail! All hail! all hail! Im-man-u-el!
All hail! all hail!

All Hail, Immanuel!

CHORUS.

Hail! . . . . . Im-man-u-el! Im-man-u-el! Hail! . . . . .

Hail to the King we love so well! Hail! Im-man-u-el Hail to the King we love so well!

Hail!

Im-man-u-el! Im-man-u-el!

Hail! Im-man-u-el! Glo-ry and honor and majesty, Wisdom and power be
Hail! . . . . . Glo - - ry and maj-es-ty, Wis - dom be

rit.

Hail! . . . . . . Im-

un - to Thee, Now and ev - er - more! . . . Hail to the King we love so well!

man-u-el! Im-man-u-el! Hail! . . . . . Im-man-u-el! Im-man-u-el!

Hail! Im - man-u-el! Hail to the King we love so well! Hail! Im - man-u-el!
Hail! . . . . . . Hail! . . . . .

King of kings and Lord of lords, All hail, Im-man-u-el! A-MEN.

485   **Onward, Christian Soldiers**

SABINE BARING-GOULD

W. H. JUDE

UNISON *Tempo di marcia*

1. On-ward, Chris-tian sol - - diers! Marching as to war,
2. On-ward, then, ye peo - - ple! Join our hap-py throng,

With the Cross of Je - sus Go - ing on be - fore.
Blend with ours your voic - es In the tri - umph - song;

Christ, the roy - al Mas - ter, Leads a-gainst the foe;
Glo - ry, laud, and hon - or Un - to Christ the King,

For-ward in - to bat - tle, See, His ban - ner go!
This thro' count-less a - ges Men and an - gels sing.

CHORUS *All Parts*

Onward, Christian sol - diers! Marching as to war, With the Cross of Je - sus

Onward, Christian Soldiers

Go-ing on be - fore. Marching, marching, Marching as to war, With the Cross of Je - sus Go-ing on be - fore. A - MEN.

FINE Final ending only.

MALE VOICES *Unison*

At the sign of tri - umph Satan's host doth flee; On, then, Christian
Crowns and thrones may per-ish, Kingdoms rise and wane, But the cross of

ALL VOICES

sol - diers, On to vic-to-ry! Hell's foun-da-tions quiv-er At the
Je - sus Constant will remain; Gates of hell can nev - er 'Gainst the

D.S. to Chorus

shout, at the shout of praise; Brothers, lift your voices, Loud your anthems raise.
cross, 'gainst the cross prevail; We have Christ's own promise, And that cannot fail.

From Every Stormy Wind

H. Stowell (Solo Obligato) S. Wilder

1. From ev - 'ry storm - y wind that blows, From ev - 'ry
2. There is a place where Je - sus sheds The oil of

Accompanying voices pp

3. There is a scene where spir - its blend, Where friend holds
4. Oh, let my hand for - get her skill, My tongue be

swell - ing tide of woes, There is a calm, a
glad - ness on our heads; A place than all be-

fel - low - ship with friend; Tho' sun - dered far, by
si - lent, cold, and still, This bound - ing heart for-

sure re - treat: 'Tis found be - neath the mer - cy - seat.
sides more sweet: It is the blood-bought mer - cy - seat.

faith they meet A - round one com - mon mer - cy - seat.
get to beat, If I for - get the mer - cy - seat!

WILLIAM S. PITTS

WILLIAM S. PITTS

1. There's a church in the val-ley by the wild-wood, No love-li-er
2. Oh, come to the church in the wild-wood, To the trees where the
3. How sweet on a clear Sun-day morn-ing, To list to the
4. From the church in the val-ley by the wild-wood, When day fades a-

spot in the dale; No place is so dear to my child-hood As the
wild flow-ers bloom; Where the part-ing hymn will be chant-ed, We will
clear ring-ing bell; Its tones so sweet-ly are call-ing, Oh,
way in-to night, I would fain from this spot of my child-hood Wing my

D.S.—*No spot is so dear to my child-hood As the*

FINE CHORUS

lit-tle brown church in the vale.
weep by the side of the tomb.
come to the church in the vale.
way to the man-sions of light.

Come to the

Oh, come, come, come, come, come, come,

lit-tle brown church in the vale.

D.S.

church in the wild - wood, Oh, come to the church in the vale;
come, come, come, come, come, come, come, come, come, come, come, come, come;

God So Loved the World

J. STAINER

Andante ma non lento

God so loved the world, God so loved the world, that He gave His
world, that He

on - ly be - got - ten Son, that who-so be-liev-eth, be-liev-eth in Him should not

per - ish, should not per-ish, but have ev-er-last - ing life. For God sent not His

Son in - to the world to con-demn the world, God sent not His Son in - to the

world to con-demn the world; But that the world thro' Him might be sav - ed.

God So Loved the World

Christt Is King

CHARLES R. SCOVILLE

DE LOSS SMITH

1. Come, friends sing, of the faith that's so dear to me, . . .
2. Cru - ci - fied, thus He suf-fered and bled for me, . . .
3. At His feet, on old Ol - i - vet's Hill they say, . . .

Re - vealed thro' God's Son, in Gal - i - lee; He brought
Death and the grave won sin's vic - to - ry; Then the
Cloud char - iots halt - ed, took Christ a - way; Then the

peace on earth and good will to the sons of men,
sky grew dark and the tem-ple veil rent in twain,
an - gels came and to wond'ring dis - ci - ples said

Go tell it to the world, her King reigns a - - gain.
Rocks rent, and an - gels came, for He lived a - - gain.
He'll come, and earth and sea shall yield up their dead.

Christ Is King

CHORUS *Unison*

I am so hap-py in Je - sus, Cap-tiv-i-ty's Cap-tor is

He; . . . . An-gels re-joice when a soul's saved, Some day we

like Him shall be, . . . Sor-row and joy have the same Lord,

Val-ley of shad-ows shall sing; . . . Death has its life, its door

Harmony

o-pens in heav-en e - ter-nal-ly, Christ is King . . . .

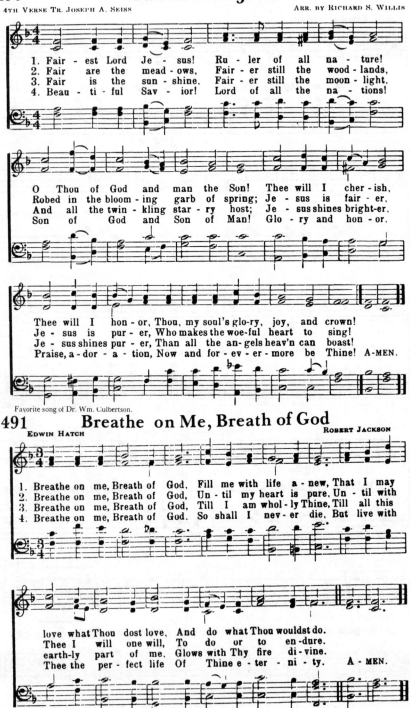

490   Fairest Lord Jesus

4TH VERSE TR. JOSEPH A. SEISS   ARR. BY RICHARD S. WILLIS

1. Fair - est Lord Je - sus! Ru - ler of all na - ture!
2. Fair are the mead - ows, Fair - er still the wood - lands,
3. Fair is the sun - shine, Fair - er still the moon - light,
4. Beau - ti - ful Sav - ior! Lord of all the na - tions!

O Thou of God and man the Son! Thee will I cher - ish,
Robed in the bloom - ing garb of spring; Je - sus is fair - er,
And all the twin - kling star - ry host; Je - sus shines bright - er,
Son of God and Son of Man! Glo - ry and hon - or,

Thee will I hon - or, Thou, my soul's glo - ry, joy, and crown!
Je - sus is pur - er, Who makes the woe - ful heart to sing!
Je - sus shines pur - er, Than all the an - gels heav'n can boast!
Praise, a - dor - a - tion, Now and for - ev - er - more be Thine! A - MEN.

Favorite song of Dr. Wm. Culbertson.

491   Breathe on Me, Breath of God

EDWIN HATCH   ROBERT JACKSON

1. Breathe on me, Breath of God, Fill me with life a - new, That I may
2. Breathe on me, Breath of God, Un - til my heart is pure, Un - til with
3. Breathe on me, Breath of God, Till I am whol - ly Thine, Till all this
4. Breathe on me, Breath of God, So shall I nev - er die, But live with

love what Thou dost love, And do what Thou wouldst do.
Thee I will one will, To do or to en - dure.
earth - ly part of me, Glows with Thy fire di - vine.
Thee the per - fect life Of Thine e - ter - ni - ty. A - MEN.

This Is My Father's World

MALTBIE D. BABCOCK

FRANKLIN L. SHEPPARD

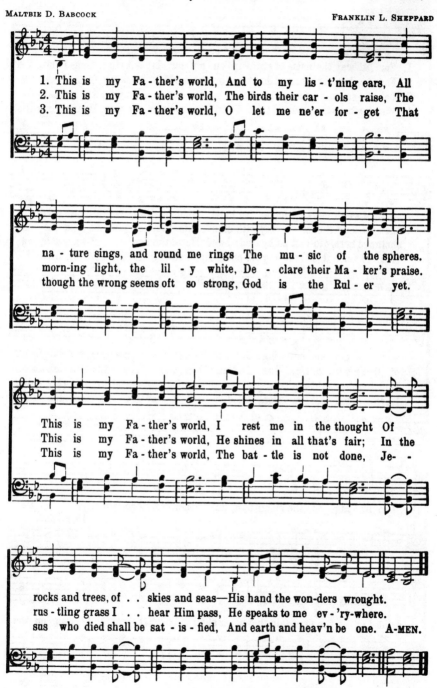

1. This is my Fa-ther's world, And to my lis-t'ning ears, All
2. This is my Fa-ther's world, The birds their car-ols raise, The
3. This is my Fa-ther's world, O let me ne'er for-get That

na-ture sings, and round me rings The mu-sic of the spheres.
morn-ing light, the lil-y white, De-clare their Ma-ker's praise.
though the wrong seems oft so strong, God is the Rul-er yet.

This is my Fa-ther's world, I rest me in the thought Of
This is my Fa-ther's world, He shines in all that's fair; In the
This is my Fa-ther's world, The bat-tle is not done, Je- -

rocks and trees, of . . skies and seas—His hand the won-ders wrought.
rus-tling grass I . . hear Him pass, He speaks to me ev-'ry-where.
sus who died shall be sat-is-fied, And earth and heav'n be one. A-MEN.

493 Dwelling in Beulah Land

C. AUSTIN MILES   C. AUSTIN MILES

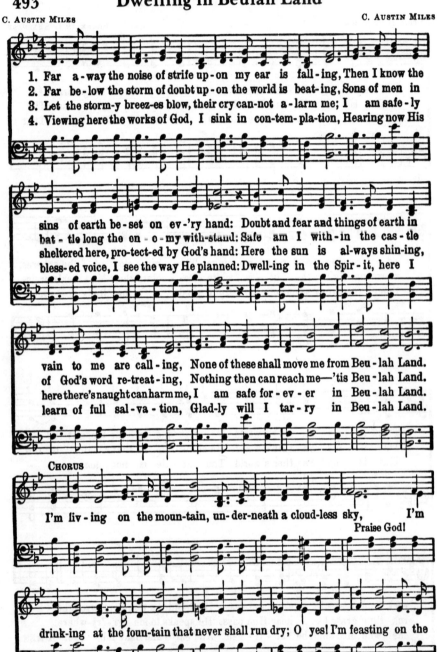

1. Far a-way the noise of strife up-on my ear is fall-ing, Then I know the
2. Far be-low the storm of doubt up-on the world is beat-ing, Sons of men in
3. Let the storm-y breez-es blow, their cry can-not a-larm me; I am safe-ly
4. Viewing here the works of God, I sink in con-tem-pla-tion, Hearing now His

sins of earth be-set on ev-'ry hand: Doubt and fear and things of earth in
bat-tle long the on - o-my with-stand: Safe am I with-in the cas-tle
sheltered here, pro-tect-ed by God's hand: Here the sun is al-ways shin-ing,
bless-ed voice, I see the way He planned: Dwell-ing in the Spir-it, here I

vain to me are call-ing, None of these shall move me from Beu-lah Land.
of God's word re-treat-ing, Nothing then can reach me—'tis Beu-lah Land.
here there's naught can harm me, I am safe for-ev-er in Beu-lah Land.
learn of full sal-va-tion, Glad-ly will I tar-ry in Beu-lah Land.

CHORUS

I'm liv-ing on the moun-tain, un-der-neath a cloud-less sky,   I'm
                                                          Praise God!

drink-ing at the foun-tain that never shall run dry; O yes! I'm feasting on the

Dwelling in Beulah Land

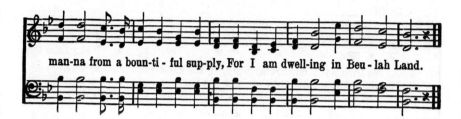

man-na from a boun-ti-ful sup-ply, For I am dwell-ing in Beu-lah Land.

All I Need

494

UNKNOWN

1. Je-sus Christ is made to me, All I need, all I need,
2. He re-deemed me when He died, All I need, all I need,
3. He's the treas-ure of my soul, All I need, all I need,
4. Je-sus is my all in all, All I need, all I need,
5. Glo-ry, Glo-ry to the Lamb, All I need, all I need,

He a-lone is all my plea, He is all I need.
I with Him was cru-ci-fied, He is all I need.
He hath cleansed and made me whole, He is all I need.
While He keeps I can-not fall, He is all I need.
By His Spir-it sealed I am, He is all I need.

Chorus:

Wis-dom, right-eous-ness and power, Hol-i-ness this ver-y hour

My re-demp-tion full and free, He is all I need.

495 The Lights of Home

Fanny J. Crosby.

Chas. H. Marsh.

DUET.

1. O the friends that now are wait-ing, In the cloud-less realms of day,
2. They have laid a - side their ar - mor For the robe of spot-less white;
3. On those dear fa - mil - iar fac - es There will be no trace of care;

Who are call - ing me to fol-low Where their steps have led the way;
And with Je - sus they are walk-ing Where the riv - er spark-les bright.
Ev - 'ry sigh was hush'd for - ev - er At the pal-ace gate so fair.

They have laid a - side their ar-mor, And their earth-ly course is run;
We have la - bored here to - geth-er, We have la - bored side by side,
I shall see them, I shall know them, I shall hear their song of love,

They have kept the faith with patience And their crown of life is won.
Just a lit - tle while be - fore me They have cross'd the roll - ing tide.
And we'll all sing hal - le - lu - jah In our Fa-ther's house a - bove.

REFRAIN.

They are call-ing, gen-tly call - ing, Sweet-ly call - ing me to come,

The Lights of Home

rit.

And I'm look-ing thro' the shad-ows For the bless-ed lights of home.

All Your Anxiety   496

Andante con espress.

Words and air by Lieut. Col. E. H. Joy

1. Is there a heart o'er-bound by sor-row? Is there a life weighed down by care?
2. No oth-er Friend so keen to help you; No oth-er Friend so quick to hear;
3. Come then, at once, de-lay no long-er; Heed His en-treat-y, kind and sweet;

Come to the cross, each bur-den bear-ing, All your anx-i-e-ty—leave it there.
No oth-er place to leave your bur-den; No oth-er one to hear your prayer.
You need not fear a dis-ap-point-ment, You shall find peace at the mer-cy-seat.

CHORUS

All your anx-i-e-ty, all your care, Bring to the Mer-cy-seat, leave it there;

Nev-er a bur-den He can-not bear, Nev-er a Friend like Je-sus.

497

Sing As You Ride

Wm. H. Rice

Arr. by Mrs. W. H. R.

Unknown

Sing as you ride in the round-up of life. Sing as you ride thro' the day and the night. Sing as you ride, for with Christ by your side He will nev-er once fail to the end of the trail, So just sing as you ride.

Copyright, 1946, by Wm. H. Rice. Used by Permission.

498

Where Could I Go?

Copyright, 1940, by Stamps–Baxter Co. in "Golden Key"

J. B. C.

J. B. Coats

1. Liv - ing be-low in this old sin-ful world, Hard-ly a com-fort can af-ford;
2. Neighbors are kind, I love them ev-'ry one, We get a-long in sweet ac-cord;
3. Life here is grand with friends I love so dear, Com-fort I get from God's own word;

Cho. *Where could I go, O where could I go; Seek-ing a ref-uge for my soul?*

D. C. for Chorus

Striv-ing a-lone to face temp-ta-tions sore,
But when my soul needs manna from a-bove, Where could I go but to the Lord?
Yet when I face the chill-ing hand of death,

Need - ing a friend to help me in the end, Where could I go but to the Lord?

Brethren, We Have Met to Worship 499

GEORGE ATKINS

Attr. to William Moore
in *Columbian Harmony*

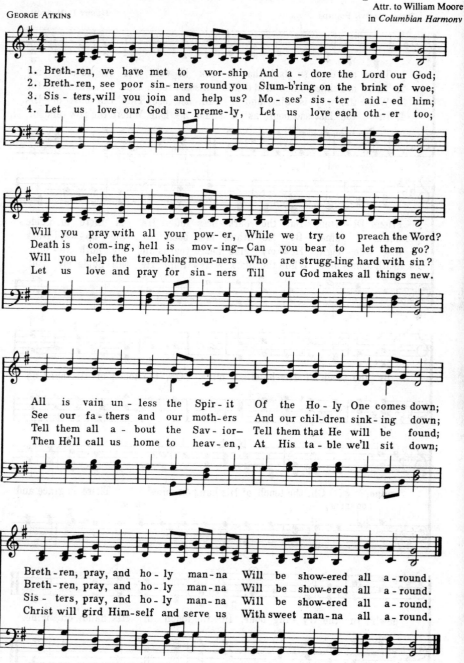

1. Breth-ren, we have met to wor-ship And a - dore the Lord our God;
2. Breth-ren, see poor sin- ners round you Slum-b'ring on the brink of woe;
3. Sis - ters, will you join and help us? Mo - ses' sis - ter aid - ed him;
4. Let us love our God su-preme-ly, Let us love each oth - er too;

Will you pray with all your pow-er, While we try to preach the Word?
Death is com-ing, hell is mov-ing— Can you bear to let them go?
Will you help the trem-bling mour-ners Who are strugg-ling hard with sin?
Let us love and pray for sin - ners Till our God makes all things new.

All is vain un - less the Spir-it Of the Ho - ly One comes down;
See our fa - thers and our moth-ers And our chil-dren sink-ing down;
Tell them all a - bout the Sav - ior— Tell them that He will be found;
Then He'll call us home to heav-en, At His ta - ble we'll sit down;

Breth - ren, pray, and ho - ly man - na Will be show-ered all a - round.
Breth - ren, pray, and ho - ly man - na Will be show-ered all a - round.
Sis - ters, pray, and ho - ly man - na Will be show-ered all a - round.
Christ will gird Him-self and serve us With sweet man - na all a - round.

500   The Touch of His Hand on Mine

JESSIE BROWN POUNDS   HENRY P. MORTON

1. There are days so dark that I seek in vain For the face of my
2. There are times, when tired of the toil-some road, That for ways of the
3. When the way is dim, and I can-not see Thro' the mist of His
4. In the last sad hour, as I stand a-lone Where the pow-ers of

Friend Di-vine; But tho' dark-ness hide, He is there to guide
world I pine; But He draws me back to the up-ward track
wise de-sign, How my glad heart yearns and my faith re-turns
death com-bine, While the dark waves roll He will guide my soul

CHORUS.

By the touch of His hand on mine. Oh, the touch of His hand on
mine, Oh, the touch of His hand on mine! There is grace and
on mine, on mine!

pow'r, in the try-ing hour, In the touch of His hand on mine.

Here Am I

J.R.R.

John R. Rice

1. We should pray the Lord of Har-vest, "Reap- ers send in-to Thy field."
2. Ho - ly Fa - ther, send a se-raph, From the al - tar take a coal.
3. Not four months a - way the har-vest, Fields are white: lift up your eyes.
4. Pluck as em - bers from the burn-ing Souls for whom the Sav-iour died.

Few are reap-ers; white and wast-ing Are the fields, How rich the yield.
Cleanse my lips, I hear "Whom shall I Send to gar -ner pre-cious souls?"
Fruit for life e - ter - nal ga-ther, Rich the wag - es for such prize.
Oh, then send me, Christ of mer-cy, To the doomed and lost out- side.

Chorus

Here am I! (O Lord, send me) Here am I! (I wait on Thee) Send me forth, O

With emphasis - - - - - - - -

Lord of Har-vest, Breathe on me Thy Ho-ly Spir-it. Here am I! (O Lord, send me)

Here am I! (I wait on Thee) Send me forth to win some pre-cious soul to-day.

Awakening Chorus

Charlotte G. Homer.

Chas. H. Gabriel.

1. A - wake! a - wake! and sing the bless-ed sto - ry; A -
A-wake! a-wake!
2. Ring out! ring out! O bells of joy and glad-ness! Re-
Ring out! ring out!

wake! a - wake! and let your song of praise a-rise; A-wake! a-
A-wake! a-wake! A-wake!
peat, re - peat a - new the sto-ry o'er a-gain, Till all the
Re-peat, re-peat, Till all

wake! the earth is full of glo - ry, And light is beam - ing
a-wake! And light is beam-ing
earth shall lose its weight of sad-ness, And shout a - new the
the earth, And shout a-new

MALE VOICES IN UNISON.

from the ra-diant skies; The rocks and rills, the vales and hills re-sound with
glo - ri - ous re-frain; With an-gels in the heights sing of the great sal-

FULL HARMONY.

glad - ness, All na - ture joins to sing the triumph song. The Lord Je-
va - tion He wrest - ed from the hand of sin and death.

Awakening Chorus

UNISON.

ho - vah reigns and sin is back-ward hurled! Re - joice! re-
sin is back-ward hurled!

joice! lift heart and voice, Je - ho - vah reigns!

FULL HARMONY.

Pro-claim His sov-'reign pow'r to all the world, And let His
pow'r to all the world, And let His

glo - - rious ban-ner be un-furled! Je - ho - vah reigns!
grand and glo-rious ban - ner be un - furled! Je - ho - vah reigns! Je - ho - vah reigns!

Re-joice! re-joice! re-joice! Je - ho - vah reigns! A-MEN.
Re-joice! re-joice! re-joice!

Hallelujah Chorus

(The Vocal Score is complete and uniform with the Messiah edition)

CEORGE FREDERICK HANDEL

Hal - le - lu - jah! Hal - le - lu - jah! Hal - le - lu - jah! Hal - le - lu - jah! Hal - le - lu jah!

Hal - le - lu - jah! Hal - le - lu - jah! Hal - le - lu - jah! Hal - le - lu - jah! Hal - le - lu - jah!

for the Lord God om-nip-o-tent reign-eth. Hal - le - lu - jah! Hal-le-lu-jah! Hal-le-

lu - jah! Hal-le - lu - jah! for the Lord God om-nip - o - tent reign-eth. Hal-le-

Hallelujah Chorus

Hallelujah Chorus

Hal-le-lu-jah! Hal-le-lu-jah! Hal-le-lu-jah! Hal-le-lu-jah! Hal-le-lu-jah! Hal-

for   the Lord God om-nip - o - tent reign - eth. Hallelujah!

for   the Lord God om-nip - o - tent reign - eth.   Hal-

Hallelujah! Hallelujah! Hallelujah! Hallelujah! Hallelujah! Hal-le-

le - lu - jah!   The king-dom of this world   is be-be-

Hal-le-lu-jah!

le - lu - jah!   is be-be-

lu-jah! Hal-le-lu-jah!

come the king-dom of our Lord, and of His Christ, and of His Christ;

come   And He shall

And He shall reign for ev - er and ev - - -

reign for ev - er and ev - er,   for ev - er and ev - er,   and He shall

Hallelujah Chorus

Hallelujah Chorus

Hallelujah Chorus

504   PSALM 1

BLESSED *is* the man that walketh not in the counsel of the ungodly, nor standeth in the way of sinners, nor sitteth in the seat of the scornful.

But his delight *is* in the law of the LORD; and in his law doth he meditate day and night.

And he shall be like a tree planted by the rivers of water, that bringeth forth his fruit in his season; his leaf also shall not wither; and whatsoever he doeth shall prosper.

The ungodly *are* not so: but *are* like the chaff which the wind driveth away.

Therefore the ungodly shall not stand in the judgment, nor sinners in the congregation of the righteous.

For the LORD knoweth the way of the righteous: but the way of the ungodly shall perish.

505   PSALM 19

To the chief Musician, A Psalm of David

THE heavens declare the glory of God; and the firmament sheweth his handywork.

Day unto day uttereth speech, and night unto night sheweth knowledge.

There is no speech nor language, *where* their voice is not heard.

Their line is gone out through all the earth, and their words to the end of the world. In them hath he set a tabernacle for the sun,

Which *is* as a bridegroom coming out of his chamber, *and* rejoiceth as a strong man to run a race.

His going forth *is* from the end of the heaven, and his circuit unto the ends of it: and there is nothing hid from the heat thereof.

The law of the LORD *is* perfect, converting the soul: the testimony of the LORD *is* sure, making wise the simple.

The statutes of the LORD *are* right, rejoicing the heart: the commandment of the LORD *is* pure, enlightening the eyes.

The fear of the LORD *is* clean, enduring for ever: the judgments of the LORD *are* true *and* righteous altogether.

More to be desired *are they* than gold, yea, than much fine gold: sweeter also than honey and the honeycomb.

Moreover by them is thy servant warned: *and* in keeping of them *there is* great reward.

Who can understand *his* errors? cleanse thou me from secret *faults.*

Keep back thy servant also from presumptuous *sins;* let them not have dominion over me: then shall I be upright, and I shall be innocent from the great transgression.

Let the words of my mouth, and the meditation of my heart, be acceptable in thy sight, O LORD, my strength, and my redeemer.

PSALM 23

506

A Psalm of David

THE LORD *is* my shepherd; I shall not want.

He maketh me to lie down in green pastures: he leadeth me beside the still waters.

He restoreth my soul: he leadeth me in the paths of righteousness for his name's sake.

Yea, though I walk through the valley of the shadow of death, I will fear no evil: for thou *art* with me; thy rod and thy staff they comfort me.

Thou preparest a table before me in the presence of mine enemies: thou anointest my head with oil; my cup runneth over.

Surely goodness and mercy shall follow me all the days of my life: and I will dwell in the house of the LORD for ever.

507   PSALM 34

A Psalm of David, when he changed his behaviour before Abimelech; who drove him away, and he departed

I WILL bless the LORD at all times: his praise *shall* continually *be* in my mouth.

My soul shall make her boast in the LORD: the humble shall hear *thereof,* and be glad.

O magnify the LORD with me, and let us exalt his name together.

I sought the LORD, and he heard me, and delivered me from all my fears.

They looked unto him, and were lightened: and their faces were not ashamed.

This poor man cried, and the

LORD heard *him*, and saved him out of all his troubles.

The angel of the LORD encampeth round about them that fear him, and delivereth them.

O taste and see that the LORD *is* good: blessed *is* the man *that* trusteth in him.

O fear the LORD, ye his saints: for *there is* no want to them that fear him.

The young lions do lack, and suffer hunger: but they that seek the LORD shall not want any good *thing*.

Come, ye children, hearken unto me: I will teach you the fear of the LORD.

What man *is he that* desireth life, *ana* loveth *many* days, that he may see good?

Keep thy tongue from evil, and thy lips from speaking guile.

Depart from evil, and do good; seek peace, and pursue it.

The eyes of the LORD *are* upon the righteous, and his ears *are open* unto their cry.

The face of the LORD *is* against them that do evil, to cut off the remembrance of them from the earth.

The righteous cry, and the LORD heareth, and delivereth them out of all their troubles.

The LORD *is* nigh unto them that are of a broken heart; and saveth such as be of a contrite spirit.

Many *are* the afflictions of the righteous: but the LORD delivereth him out of them all.

He keepeth all his bones: not one of them is broken.

Evil shall slay the wicked: and they that hate the righteous shall be desolate.

The LORD redeemeth the soul of his servants: and none of them that trust in him shall be desolate.

PSALM 37

508

A Psalm of David

FRET not thyself because of evildoers, neither be thou envious against the workers of iniquity.

For they shall soon be cut down like the grass, and wither as the green herb.

Trust in the LORD, and do good; so shalt thou dwell in the land, and verily thou shalt be fed.

Delight thyself also in the LORD; and he shall give thee the desires of thine heart.

Commit thy way unto the LORD; trust also in him; and he shall bring *it* to pass.

And he shall bring forth thy righteousness as the light, and thy judgment as the noonday.

Rest in the LORD, and wait patiently for him: fret not thyself because of him who prospereth in his way, because of the man who bringeth wicked devices to pass.

Cease from anger, and forsake wrath: fret not thyself in any wise to do evil.

For evildoers shall be cut off: but those that wait upon the LORD, they shall inherit the earth.

For yet a little while, and the wicked *shall* not *be:* yea, thou shalt diligently consider his place, and it *shall* not *be.*

But the meek shall inherit the earth; and shall delight themselves in the abundance of peace.

The wicked plotteth against the just, and gnasheth upon him with his teeth.

The Lord shall laugh at him: for he seeth that his day is coming.

The wicked have drawn out the sword, and have bent their bow, to cast down the poor and needy, *and* to slay such as be of upright conversation.

Their sword shall enter into their own heart, and their bows shall be broken.

A little that a righteous man hath *is* better than the riches of many wicked.

For the arms of the wicked shall be broken: but the LORD upholdeth the righteous.

The LORD knoweth the days of the upright: and their inheritance shall be for ever.

They shall not be ashamed in the evil time: and in the days of famine they shall be satisfied.

But the wicked shall perish, and the enemies of the LORD *shall be* as the fat of lambs: they shall consume; into smoke shall they consume away.

The wicked borroweth, and payeth not again: but the righteous sheweth mercy, and giveth.

For *such as* be blessed of him shall inherit the earth; and *they that be* cursed of him shall be cut off.

The steps of a *good* man are ordered by the LORD: and he delighteth in his way.

Though he fall, he shall not be utterly cast down: for the LORD upholdeth *him with* his hand.

I have been young, and *now* am old; yet have I not seen the righteous forsaken, nor his seed begging bread.

He is ever merciful, and lendeth; and his seed *is* blessed.

Depart from evil, and do good; and dwell for evermore.

For the LORD loveth judgment, and forsaketh not his saints; they are preserved for ever: but the seed of the wicked shall be cut off.

The righteous shall inherit the land, and dwell therein for ever.

The mouth of the righteous speaketh wisdom, and his tongue talketh of judgment.

The law of his God *is* in his heart; none of his steps shall slide.

The wicked watcheth the righteous, and seeketh to slay him.

The LORD will not leave him in his hand, nor condemn him when he is judged.

Wait on the LORD, and keep his way, and he shall exalt thee to inherit the land: when the wicked are cut off, thou shall see *it*.

I have seen the wicked in great power, and spreading himself like a green bay tree.

Yet he passed away, and, lo, he *was* not: yea, I sought him, but he could not be found.

Mark the perfect *man*, and behold the upright: for the end of *that* man *is* peace.

But the transgressors shall be destroyed together: the end of the wicked shall be cut off.

But the salvation of the righteous *is* of the LORD: *he is* their strength in the time of trouble.

And the LORD shall help them, and deliver them: he shall deliver them from the wicked, and save them, because they trust in him.

PSALM 91

509

H E that dwelleth in the secret place of the most High shall abide under the shadow of the Almighty.

I will say of the LORD, *He is* my refuge and my fortress: my God; in him will I trust.

Surely he shall deliver thee from the snare of the fowler, *and* from the noisome pestilence.

He shall cover thee with his feathers, and under his wings shalt thou trust: his truth *shall be thy* shield and buckler.

Thou shalt not be afraid for the terror by night; *nor* for the arrow *that* flieth by day;

Nor for the pestilence *that* walketh in darkness; *nor* for the destruction *that* wasteth at noonday.

A thousand shall fall at thy side, and ten thousand at thy right hand; *but* it shall not come nigh thee.

Only with thine eyes shalt thou behold and see the reward of the wicked.

Because thou hast made the LORD, *which is* my refuge, *even* the most High, thy habitation;

There shall no evil befall thee, neither shall any plague come nigh thy dwelling.

For he shall give his angels charge over thee, to keep thee in all thy ways.

They shall bear thee up in *their* hands, lest thou dash thy foot against a stone.

Thou shalt tread upon the lion and adder: the young lion and the dragon shalt thou trample under feet.

Because he hath set his love upon me, therefore will I deliver him: I will set him on high, because he hath known my name.

He shall call upon me, and I will answer him: I *will be* with him in trouble; I will deliver him, and honour him.

With long life will I satisfy him, and shew him my salvation.

PSALM 100

510

A Psalm of praise

M AKE a joyful noise unto the LORD, all ye lands.

Serve the LORD with gladness: come before his presence with singing.

Know ye that the LORD he *is* God: *it is* he *that* hath made us, and not we ourselves; *we are* his people, and the sheep of his pasture.

Enter into his gates with thanksgiving, *and* into his courts with praise: be thankful unto him, *and* bless his name.

For the LORD *is* good; his mercy

is everlasting; and his truth *endureth* to all generations.

PSALM 103

511

A Psalm of David

BLESS the LORD, O my soul: and all that is within me, *bless* his holy name.

Bless the LORD, O my soul, and forget not all his benefits:

Who forgiveth all thine iniquities; who healeth all thy diseases;

Who redeemeth thy life from destruction; who crowneth thee with lovingkindness and tender mercies;

Who satisfieth thy mouth with good *things; so that* thy youth is renewed like the eagle's.

The LORD executeth righteousness and judgment for all that are oppressed.

He made known his ways unto Moses, his acts unto the children of Israel.

The LORD *is* merciful and gracious, slow to anger, and plenteous in mercy.

He will not always chide: neither will he keep *his anger* for ever.

He hath not dealt with us after our sins; nor rewarded us according to our iniquities.

For as the heaven is high above the earth, *so* great is his mercy toward them that fear him.

As far as the east is from the west, *so* far hath he removed our transgressions from us.

Like as a father pitieth *his* children, *so* the LORD pitieth them that fear him.

For he knoweth our frame; he remembereth that we *are* dust.

As *for* man, his days *are* as grass; as a flower of the field, so he flourisheth.

For the wind passeth over it, and it is gone; and the place thereof shall know it no more.

But the mercy of the LORD *is* from everlasting to everlasting upon them that fear him, and his righteousness unto children's children;

To such as keep his covenant, and to those that remember his commandments to do them.

The LORD hath prepared his throne in the heavens; and his kingdom ruleth over all.

Bless the LORD, ye his angels, that excel in strength, that do his commandments, hearkening unto the voice of his word.

Bless ye the LORD, all *ye* his hosts; *ye* ministers of his, that do his pleasure.

Bless the LORD, all his works in all places of his dominion: bless the LORD, O my soul.

PSALM 126

512

A Song of degrees

WHEN the LORD turned again the captivity of Zion, we were like them that dream.

Then was our mouth filled with laughter, and our tongue with singing: then said they among the heathen, The LORD hath done great things for them.

The LORD hath done great things for us; *whereof* we are glad.

Turn again our captivity, O LORD, as the streams in the south.

They that sow in tears shall reap in joy.

He that goeth forth and weepeth, bearing precious seed, shall doubtless come again with rejoicing, bringing his sheaves *with him.*

PSALM 127

513

A Song of degrees for Solomon

EXCEPT the LORD build the house, they labour in vain that build it: except the LORD keep the city, the watchman waketh *but* in vain.

It is vain for you to rise up early, to sit up late, to eat the bread of sorrows: *for* so he giveth his beloved sleep.

Lo, children *are* an heritage of the LORD: *and* the fruit of the womb *is his* reward.

As arrows *are* in the hand of a mighty man; so *are* children of the youth.

Happy *is* the man that hath his quiver full of them: they shall not be ashamed, but they shall speak with the enemies in the gate.

THE BEATITUDES

514 Matthew 5:1-12

AND seeing the multitudes, he went up into a mountain: and when he was set, his disciples came unto him: And he opened his mouth, and taught them, saying,

Blessed *are* the poor in spirit: for theirs is the kingdom of heaven.

Blessed *are* they that mourn: for they shall be comforted.

Blessed *are* the meek: for they shall inherit the earth.

Blessed *are* they which do hunger and thirst after righteousness: for they shall be filled.

Blessed *are* the merciful: for they shall obtain mercy.

Blessed *are* the pure in heart: for they shall see God.

Blessed *are* the peacemakers: for they shall be called the children of God.

Blessed *are* they which are persecuted for righteousness' sake: for theirs is the kingdom of heaven.

Blessed are ye, when *men* shall revile you, and persecute *you*, and shall say all manner of evil against you falsely, for my sake.

Rejoice, and be exceeding glad: for great *is* your reward in heaven: for so persecuted they the prophets which were before you.

THE LORD'S PRAYER

515 Matthew 6:9-13

After this manner therefore pray ye: Our Father which art in heaven, Hallowed be thy name.

Thy kingdom come. Thy will be done in earth, as *it is* in heaven.

Give us this day our daily bread.

And forgive us our debts, as we forgive our debtors.

And lead us not into temptation, but deliver us from evil: For thine is the kingdom, and the power, and the glory, for ever. Amen.

CHRIST'S RESURRECTION

516 Matthew 28:1-20

IN the end of the sabbath, as it began to dawn toward the first *day* of the week, came Mary Magdalene and the other Mary to see the sepulchre.

And, behold, there was a great earthquake: for the angel of the Lord descended from heaven, and came and rolled back the stone from the door, and sat upon it.

His countenance was like lightning, and his raiment white as snow:

And for fear of him the keepers did shake, and became as dead *men*.

And the angel answered and said unto the women, Fear not ye: for I know that ye seek Jesus, which was crucified.

He is not here: for he is risen, as he said. Come, see the place where the Lord lay.

And go quickly, and tell his disciples that he is risen from the dead; and, behold, he goeth before you into Galilee; there shall ye see him: lo, I have told you.

And they departed quickly from the sepulchre with fear and great joy; and did run to bring his disciples word.

And as they went to tell his disciples, behold, Jesus met them, saying, All hail. And they came and held him by the feet, and worshipped him.

Then said Jesus unto them, Be not afraid: go tell my brethren that they go into Galilee, and there shall they see me.

Now when they were going, behold, some of the watch came into the city, and shewed unto the chief priests all the things that were done.

And when they were assembled with the elders, and had taken counsel, they gave large money unto the soldiers,

Saying, Say ye, His disciples came by night, and stole him *away* while we slept.

And if this come to the governor's ears, we will persuade him, and secure you.

So they took the money, and did as they were taught: and this saying is commonly reported among the Jews until this day.

Then the eleven disciples went away into Galilee, into a mountain where Jesus had appointed them.

And when they saw him, they worshipped him: but some doubted.

And Jesus came and spake unto them, saying, All power is given unto me in heaven and in earth.

Go ye therefore, and teach all nations, baptizing them in the name of the Father, and of the Son, and of the Holy Ghost:

Teaching them to observe all things whatsoever I have commanded you: and, lo, I am with you alway, *even* unto the end of the world. Amen.

THE TRIUMPHAL ENTRY

517   Mark 11:1-11

AND when they came nigh to Jerusalem, unto Beth'-pha-ge and Bethany, at the mount of Olives, he sendeth forth two of his disciples,

And saith unto them, Go your way into the village over against you: and as soon as ye be entered into it, ye shall find a colt tied, whereon never man sat; loose him, and bring *him.*

And if any man say unto you, Why do ye this? say ye that the Lord hath need of him; and straightway he will send him hither.

And they went their way, and found the colt tied by the door without in a place where two ways met; and they loose him.

And certain of them that stood there said unto them, What do ye, loosing the colt?

And they said unto them even as Jesus had commanded: and they let them go.

And they brought the colt to Jesus, and cast their garments on him; and he sat upon him.

And many spread their garments in the way: and others cut down branches off the trees, and strawed *them* in the way.

And they that went before, and they that followed, cried, saying, Hosanna; Blessed *is* he that cometh in the name of the Lord:

Blesed *be* the kingdom of our father David, that cometh in the name of the Lord: Hosanna in the highest.

And Jesus entered into Jerusalem, and into the temple: and when he had looked round about upon all things, and now the eventide was come, he went out unto Bethany with the twelve.

THE SECOND COMING

518   Mark 13:32-37

But of that day and *that* hour knoweth no man, no, not the angels which are in heaven, neither the Son, but the Father.

Take ye heed, watch and pray: for ye know not when the time is.

For the Son of man is as a man taking a far journey, who left his house, and gave authority to his servants, and to every man his work, and commanded the porter to watch.

Watch ye therefore: for ye know not when the master of the house cometh, at even, or at midnight, or at the cockcrowing, or in the morning:

Lest coming suddenly he find you sleeping.

And what I say unto you I say unto all, Watch.

THE BIRTH OF CHRIST

519   Luke 2:1-20

AND it came to pass in those days, that there went out a decree from Cæsar Augustus, that all the world should be taxed.

(*And* this taxing was first made when Cy-re'-ni-us was governor of Syria.)

And all went to be taxed, every one into his own city.

And Joseph also went up from Galilee, out of the city of Nazareth, into Judæa, unto the city of David, which is called Bethlehem; (because he was of the house and lineage of David:)

To be taxed with Mary his espoused wife, being great with child.

And so it was, that, while they were there, the days were accomplished that she should be delivered.

And she brought forth her firstborn son, and wrapped him in swaddling clothes, and laid him in a manger; because there was no room for them in the inn.

And there were in the same country shepherds abiding in the field, keeping watch over their flock by night.

And, lo, the angel of the Lord came upon them, and the glory of the Lord shone round about them: and they were sore afraid.

And the angel said unto them, Fear not: for, behold, I bring you good tidings of great joy, which shall be to all people.

For unto you is born this day in the city of David a Saviour, which is Christ the Lord.

And this *shall be* a sign unto you; Ye shall find the babe wrapped in swaddling clothes, lying in a manger.

And suddenly there was with the angel a multitude of the heavenly host praising God, and saying,

Glory to God in the highest, and on earth peace, good will toward men.

And it came to pass, as the angels were gone away from them into heaven, the shepherds said one to another, Let us now go even unto Bethlehem, and see this thing which is come to pass, which the Lord hath made known unto us.

And they came with haste, and found Mary, and Joseph, and the babe lying in a manger.

And when they had seen *it*, they made known abroad the saying which was told them concerning this child.

And all they that heard *it* wondered at those things which were told them by the shepherds.

But Mary kept all these things, and pondered *them* in her heart.

And the shepherds returned, glorifying and praising God for all the things that they had heard and seen, as it was told unto them.

A LESSON ON PRAYER

520   Luke 11:1-13

AND it came to pass, that, as he was praying in a certain place, when he ceased, one of his disciples said unto him, Lord, teach us to pray, as John also taught his disciples.

And he said unto them, When ye pray, say, Our Father which art in heaven, Hallowed be thy name. Thy kingdom come. Thy will be done, as in heaven, so in earth.

Give us day by day our daily bread.

And forgive us our sins; for we also forgive every one that is indebted to us. And lead us not into temptation; but deliver us from evil.

And he said unto them, Which of you shall have a friend, and shall go unto him at midnight, and say unto him, Friend, lend me three loaves;

For a friend of mine in his journey is come to me, and I have nothing to set before him?

And he from within shall answer and say, Trouble me not: the door is now shut, and my children are with m.e in bed; I cannot rise and give thee.

I say unto you, Though he will not rise and give him, because he is his friend, yet because of his importunity he will rise and give him as many as he needeth.

And I say unto you, Ask, and it shall be given you; seek, and ye shall find; knock, and it shall be opened unto you.

For every one that asketh receiveth; and he that seeketh findeth; and to him that knocketh it shall be op~ned.

If a son shall ask bread of any of you that is a father, will he give him a stone? or if *he ask* a fish, will he for a fish give him a serpent?

Or if he shall ask an egg, will he offer him a scorpion?

If ye then, being evil, know how to give good gifts unto your children: how much more shall *your* heavenly Father give the Holy Spirit to them that ask him?

LOST SHEEP, LOST COIN, PRODIGAL SON

521   Luke 15:1-32

THEN drew near unto him all the publicans and sinners for to hear him.

And the Pharisees and scribes murmured, saying, This man receiveth sinners, and eateth with them.

And he spake this parable unto them, saying,

What man of you, having an hundred sheep, if he lose one of them, doth not leave the ninety and nine in the wilderness, and go after that which is lost, until he find it?

And when he hath found *it*, he layeth *it* on his shoulders, rejoicing.

And when he cometh home, he calleth together *his* friends and neighbours, saying unto them, Rejoice with me; for I have found my sheep which was lost.

I say unto you, that likewise joy shall be in heaven over one sinner that repenteth, more than over ninety and nine just persons, which need no repentance.

Either what woman having ten pieces of silver, if she lose one piece, doth not light a candle, and sweep the house, and seek diligently till she find *it*?

And when she hath found *it*, she calleth *her* friends and *her* neighbours together, saying, Rejoice with me; for

I have found the piece which I had lost.

Likewise, I say unto you there is joy in the presence of the angels of God over one sinner that repenteth.

And he said, A certain man had two sons:

And the younger of them said to *his* father, Father, give me the portion of goods that falleth *to me*. And he divided unto them *his* living.

And not many days after the younger son gathered all together, and took his journey into a far country, and there wasted his substance with riotous living.

And when he had spent all, there arose a mighty famine in that land; and he began to be in want.

And he went and joined himself to a citizen of that country; and he sent him into his fields to feed swine.

And he would fain have filled his belly with the husks that the swine did eat: and no man gave unto him.

And when he came to himself, he said, How many hired servants of my father's have bread enough and to spare, and I perish with hunger!

I will arise and go to my father, and will say unto him, Father, I have sinned against heaven, and before thee,

And am no more worthy to be called thy son: make me as one of thy hired servants.

And he arose, and came to his father. But when he was yet a great way off, his father saw him, and had compassion, and ran, and fell on his neck, and kissed him.

And the son said unto him, Father, I have sinned against heaven, and in thy sight, and am no more worthy to be called thy son.

But the father said to his servants, Bring forth the best robe, and put *it* on him; and put a ring on his hand, and shoes on *his* feet:

And bring hither the fatted calf, and kill *it*; and let us eat, and be merry:

For this my son was dead, and is alive again; he was lost, and is found. And they began to be merry.

Now his elder son was in the field: and as he came and drew nigh to the house, he heard musick and dancing.

And he called one of the servants, and asked what these things meant.

And he said unto him, Thy broth-er is come; and thy father hath killed the fatted calf, because he hath received him safe and sound.

And he was angry, and would not go in: therefore came his father out, and intreated him.

And he answering said to *his* father, Lo, these many years do I serve thee, neither transgressed I at any time thy commandment: and yet thou never gavest me a kid, that I might make merry with my friends:

But as soon as this thy son was come, which hath devoured thy living with harlots, thou hast killed for him the fatted calf.

And he said unto him, Son, thou art ever with me, and all that I have is thine.

It was meet that we should make merry, and be glad: for this thy brother was dead, and is alive again; and was lost, and is found.

THE WORD MADE FLESH

522   John 1:1-14

IN the beginning was the Word, and the Word was with God, and the Word was God.

The same was in the beginning with God.

All things were made by him; and without him was not any thing made that was made.

In him was life; and the life was the light of men.

And the light shineth in darkness; and the darkness comprehended it not.

There was a man sent from God, whose name *was* John.

The same came for a witness, to bear witness of the Light, that all *men* through him might believe.

He was not that Light, but *was sent* to bear witness of that Light.

That was the true Light, which lighteth every man that cometh into the world.

He was in the world, and the world was made by him, and the world knew him not.

He came unto his own, and his own received him not.

But as many as received him, to them gave he power to become the sons of God, *even* to them that believe on his name:

Which were born, not of blood, nor of the will of the flesh, nor of the will of man, but of God.

And the Word was made flesh, and dwelt among us, (and we beheld his glory, the glory as of the only begotten of the Father,) full of grace and truth.

THE NEW BIRTH

523 John 3:1-18

THERE was a man of the Pharisees, named Nic-o-de'-mus, a ruler of the Jews:

The same came to Jesus by night, and said unto him, Rabbi, we know that thou art a teacher come from God: for no man can do these miracles that thou doest, except God be with him.

Jesus answered and said unto him, Verily, verily, I say unto thee, Except a man be born again, he cannot see the kingdom of God.

Nic-o-de'-mus saith unto him, How can a man be born when he is old? can he enter the second time into his mother's womb, and be born?

Jesus answered, Verily, verily, I say unto thee, Except a man be born of water and of the Spirit, he cannot enter into the kingdom of God.

That which is born of the flesh is flesh; and that which is born of the Spirit is spirit.

Marvel not that I said unto thee, Ye must be born again.

The wind bloweth where it listeth, and thou hearest the sound thereof, but canst not tell whence it cometh, and whither it goeth: so is every one that is born of the Spirit.

Nic-o-de'-mus answered and said unto him, How can these things be?

Jesus answered and said unto him, Art thou a master of Israel, and knowest not these things?

Verily, verily, I say unto thee, We speak that we do know, and testify that we have seen; and ye receive not our witness.

If I have told you earthly things, and ye believe not, how shall ye believe, if I tell you of heavenly things?

And no man hath ascended up to heaven, but he that came down from heaven, even the Son of man which is in heaven.

And as Moses lifted up the serpent in the wilderness, even so must the Son of man be lifted up:

That whosoever believeth in him should not perish, but have eternal life.

For God so loved the world, that he gave his only begotten Son, that whosoever believeth in him should not perish, but have everlasting life.

For God sent not his Son into the world to condemn the world; but that the world through him might be saved.

He that believeth on him is not condemned: but he that believeth not is condemned already, because he hath not believed in the name of the only begotten Son of God.

HEAVENLY MANSIONS

524 John 14:1-16

LET not your heart be troubled: ye believe in God, believe also in me.

In my Father's house are many mansions: if it were not so, I would have told you. I go to prepare a place for you.

And if I go and prepare a place for you, I will come again, and receive you unto myself; that where I am, there ye may be also.

And whither I go ye know, and the way ye know.

Thomas saith unto him, Lord, we know not whither thou goest; and how can we know the way?

Jesus saith unto him, I am the way, the truth, and the life: no man cometh unto the Father, but by me.

If ye had known me, ye should have known my Father also: and from henceforth ye know him, and have seen him.

Philip saith unto him, Lord, shew us the Father, and it sufficeth us.

Jesus saith unto him, Have I been so long time with you, and yet hast thou not known me, Philip? he that hath seen me hath seen the Father; and how sayest thou then, Shew us the Father?

Believest thou not that I am in the Father, and the Father in me? the words that I speak unto you I speak not of myself: but the Father that dwelleth in me, he doeth the works.

Believe me that I am in the Father, and the Father in me: or else believe me for the very works' sake.

Verily, verily, I say unto you, He that believeth on me, the works that I do shall he do also; and greater *works* than these shall he do; because I go unto my Father.

And whatsoever ye shall ask in my name, that will I do, that the Father may be glorified in the Son.

If ye shall ask any thing in my name, I will do *it*.

If ye love me, keep my commandments.

And I will pray the Father, and he shall give you another Comforter, that he may abide with you for ever;

THE HOLY SPIRIT
525   John 14:16-18

And I will pray the Father, and he shall give you another Comforter, that he may abide with you for ever; *Even* the Spirit of truth; whom the world cannot receive, because it seeth him not, neither knoweth him: but ye know him; for he dwelleth with you, and shall be in you.

I will not leave you comfortless: I will come to you.

John 16:5-15

But now I go my way to him that sent me; and none of you asketh me, Whither goest thou?

But because I have said these things unto you, sorrow hath filled your heart.

Nevertheless I tell you the truth; It is expedient for you that I go away: for if I go not away, the Comforter will not come unto you; but if I depart, I will send him unto you.

And when he is come, he will reprove the world of sin, and of righteousness, and of judgment:

Of sin, because they believe not on me;

Of righteousness, because I go to my Father, and ye see me no more;

Of judgment, because the prince of this world is judged.

I have yet many things to say unto you, but ye cannot bear them now.

Howbeit when he, the Spirit of truth, is come, he will guide you into all truth: for he shall not speak of himself; but whatsoever he shall hear, *that* shall he speak: and he will shew you things to come.

He shall glorify me: for he shall receive of mine, and shall shew *it* unto you.

All things that the Father hath are mine: therefore said I, that he shall take of mine, and shall shew *it* unto you.

THE VINE AND BRANCHES
526   John 15:1-20

I AM the true vine, and my Father is the husbandman.

Every branch in me that beareth not fruit he taketh away: and every *branch* that beareth fruit, he purgeth it, that it may bring forth more fruit.

Now ye are clean through the word which I have spoken unto you.

Abide in me, and I in you. As the branch cannot bear fruit of itself, except it abide in the vine; no more can ye, except ye abide in me.

I am the vine, ye *are* the branches: He that abideth in me, and I in him, the same bringeth forth much fruit: for without me ye can do nothing.

If a man abide not in me, he is cast forth as a branch, and is withered; and men gather them, and cast *them* into the fire, and they are burned.

If ye abide in me, and my words abide in you, ye shall ask what ye will, and it shall be done unto you.

Herein is my Father glorified, that ye bear much fruit; so shall ye be my disciples.

As the Father hath loved me, so have I loved you: continue ye in my love.

If ye keep my commandments, ye shall abide in my love; even as I have kept my Father's commandments, and abide in his love.

These things have I spoken unto you, that my joy might remain in you, and *that* your joy might be full.

This is my commandment, That ye love one another, as I have loved you.

Greater love hath no man than this, that a man lay down his life for his friends.

Ye are my friends, if ye do whatsoever I command you.

Henceforth I call you not servants; for the servant knoweth not what his lord doeth: but I have called you friends; for all things that I have heard of my Father I have made known unto you.

Ye have not chosen me, but I have chosen you, and ordained you, that ye should go and bring forth fruit, and *that* your fruit should remain: that whatsoever ye shall ask of the Father in my name, he may give it you.

These things I command you, that ye love one another.

If the world hate you, ye know that it hated me before *it hated* you.

If ye were of the world, the world would love his own: but because ye are not of the world, but I have chosen you out of the world, therefore the world hateth you.

Remember the word that I said unto you, The servant is not greater than his lord. If they have persecuted me, they will also persecute you; if they have kept my saying, they will keep yours also.

THE CRUCIFIXION
John 19:1-6, 16-19
527

THEN Pilate therefore took Jesus, and scourged him.

And the soldiers platted a crown of thorns, and put it on his head, and they put on him a purple robe,

And said, Hail, King of the Jews! and they smote him with their hands.

Pilate therefore went forth again, and saith unto them, Behold, I bring him forth to you, that ye may know that I find no fault in him.

Then came Jesus forth, wearing the crown of thorns, and the purple robe. And *Pilate* saith unto them, Behold the man!

When the chief priests therefore and officers saw him, they cried out, saying, Crucify *him*, crucify *him*. Pilate saith unto them, Take ye him, and crucify *him*: for I find no fault in him.

Then delivered he him therefore unto them to be crucified. And they took Jesus, and led *him* away.

And he bearing his cross went forth into a place called *the place* of a skull, which is called in the Hebrew Gol'-go-tha:

Where they crucified him, and two other with him, on either side one, and Jesus in the midst.

And Pilate wrote a title, and put *it* on the cross. And the writing was, JESUS OF NAZARETH THE KING OF THE JEWS.

THE RESURRECTED CHRIST
John 20:19-31
528

Then the same day at evening, being the first *day* of the week, when the doors were shut where the disciples were assembled for fear of the Jews, came Jesus and stood in the midst, and saith unto them, Peace *be* unto you.

And when he had so said, he shewed unto them *his* hands and his side. Then were the disciples glad, when they saw the Lord.

Then said Jesus to them again, Peace *be* unto you: as *my* Father hath sent me, even so send I you.

And when he had said this, he breathed on *them*, and saith unto them, Receive ye the Holy Ghost:

Whose soever sins ye remit, they are remitted unto them; *and* whose soever *sins* ye retain, they are retained.

But Thomas, one of the twelve, called Did'-y-mus, was not with them when Jesus came.

The other disciples therefore said unto him, We have seen the Lord. But he said unto them, Except I shall see in his hands the print of the nails, and put my finger into the print of the nails, and thrust my hand into his side, I will not believe.

And after eight days again his disciples were within, and Thomas with them: *then* came Jesus, the doors being shut, and stood in the midst, and said, Peace *be* unto you.

Then saith he to Thomas, Reach hither thy finger, and behold my hands; and reach hither thy hand, and thrust *it* into my side: and be not faithless, but believing.

And Thomas answered and said unto him, My Lord and my God.

Jesus saith unto him, Thomas, because thou hast seen me, thou hast believed: blessed *are* they that have not seen, and *yet* have believed.

And many other signs truly did Jesus in the presence of his disciples, which are not written in this book:

But these are written, that ye might believe that Jesus is the Christ, the Son of God; and that believing ye might have life through his name.

THE GREAT COMMISSION

529 Acts 1:1-14

THE former treatise have I made, O The-oph'-i-lus, of all that Jesus began both to do and teach,

Until the day in which he was taken up, after that he through the Holy Ghost had given commandments unto the apostles whom he had chosen:

To whom also he shewed himself alive after his passion by many infallible proofs, being seen of them forty days, and speaking of the things pertaining to the kingdom of God:

And, being assembled together with *them*, commanded them that they should not depart from Jerusalem, but wait for the promise of the Father, which, *saith he*, ye have heard of me.

For John truly baptized with water; but ye shall be baptized with the Holy Ghost not many days hence.

When they therefore were come together, they asked of him, saying, Lord, wilt thou at this time restore again the kingdom to Israel?

And he said unto them, It is not for you to know the times or the seasons, which the Father hath put in his own power.

But ye shall receive power, after that the Holy Ghost is come upon you: and ye shall be witnesses unto me both in Jerusalem, and in all Judæa, and in Sa-ma'-ri-a, and unto the uttermost part of the earth.

And when he had spoken these things, while they beheld, he was taken up; and a cloud received him out of their sight.

And while they looked stedfastly toward heaven as he went up, behold, two men stood by them in white apparel;

Which also said, Ye men of Galilee, why stand ye gazing up into heaven? this same Jesus, which is taken up from you into heaven, shall so come in like manner as ye have seen him go into heaven.

Then returned they unto Jerusalem from the mount called Olivet, which is from Jerusalem a sabbath day's journey.

And when they were come in, they went up into an upper room, where abode both Peter, and James, and John, and Andrew, Philip, and Thomas, Bartholomew, and Matthew, James *the son* of Al-phæ'-us, and Simon Ze-lo'-tes, and Judas *the brother* of James.

These all continued with one accord in prayer and supplication, with the women, and Mary the mother of Jesus, and with his brethren.

ALL HAVE SINNED

530 Romans 3:9-24

What then? are we better *than they?* No, in no wise: for we have before proved both Jews and Gentiles, that they are all under sin;

As it is written, There is none righteous, no, not one:

There is none that understandeth, there is none that seeketh after God.

They are all gone out of the way, they are together become unprofitable; there is none that doeth good, no, not one.

Their throat *is* an open sepulchre; with their tongues they have used deceit; the poison of asps *is* under their lips:

Whose mouth *is* full of cursing and bitterness:

Their feet *are* swift to shed blood:

Destruction and misery *are* in their ways:

And the way of peace have they not known:

There is no fear of God before their eyes.

Now we know that what things soever the law saith, it saith to them who are under the law: that every mouth may be stopped, and all the world may become guilty before God.

Therefore by the deeds of the law there shall no flesh be justified in his sight: for by the law *is* the knowledge of sin.

But now the righteousness of God without the law is manifested, being witnessed by the law and the prophets;

Even the righteousness of God *which is* by faith of Jesus Christ unto all and upon all them that believe: for there is no difference:

For all have sinned, and come short of the glory of God;

Being justified freely by his grace through the redemption that is in Christ Jesus:

NO CONDEMNATION, NO SEPARATION

531 Romans 8:28-39

And we know that all things work together for good to them that love God, to them who are the called according to *his* purpose.

For whom he did foreknow, he also did predestinate *to be* conformed to the image of his Son, that he might be the firstborn among many brethren.

Moreover whom he did predestinate, them he also called: and whom he called, them he also justified: and whom he justified, them he also glorified.

What shall we then say to these things? If God *be* for *us,* who *can be* against us?

He that spared not his own Son, but delivered him up for us all, how shall he not with him also freely give us all things?

Who shall lay any thing to the charge of God's elect? *It is* God that justifieth.

Who *is* he that condemneth? *It is* Christ that died, yea rather, that is risen again, who is even at the right hand of God, who also maketh intercession for us.

Who shall separate us from the love of Christ? *shall* tribulation, or distress, or persecution, or famine, or nakedness, or peril, or sword?

As it is written, For thy sake we are killed all the day long; we are accounted as sheep for the slaughter.

Nay, in all these things we are more than conquerors through him that loved us.

For I am persuaded, that neither death, nor life, nor angels, nor principalities, nor powers, nor things present, nor things to come,

Nor height, nor depth, nor any other creature, shall be able to separate us from the love of God, which is in Christ Jesus our Lord.

HOW TO BE SAVED

532 Romans 10:1-13

BRETHREN, my heart's desire and prayer to God for Israel is, that they might be saved.

For I bear them record that they have a zeal of God, but not according to knowledge.

For they being ignorant of God's righteousness, and going about to establish their own righteousness, have not submitted themselves unto the righteousness of God.

For Christ *is* the end of the law for righteousness to every one that believeth.

For Moses describeth the righteousness which is of the law, That the man which doeth those things shall live by them.

But the righteousness which is of faith speaketh on this wise, Say not in thine heart, Who shall ascend into heaven? (that is, to bring Christ down *from above:)*

Or, Who shall descend into the deep? (that is, to bring up Christ again from the dead.)

But what saith it? The word is nigh thee, *even* in thy mouth, and in thy heart: that is, the word of faith, which we preach;

That if thou shalt confess with thy mouth the Lord Jesus, and shalt believe in thine heart that God hath raised him from the dead, thou shalt be saved.

For with the heart man believeth unto righteousness; and with the mouth confession is made unto salvation.

For the scripture saith, Whosoever believeth on him shall not be ashamed.

For there is no difference between the Jew and the Greek: for the same Lord over all is rich unto all that call upon him.

For whosoever shall call upon the name of the Lord shall be saved.

CONSECRATION

533 Romans 12:1-21

I BESEECH you therefore, brethren, by the mercies of God, that ye present your bodies a living sacrifice, holy, acceptable unto God, *which is* your reasonable service.

And be not conformed to this world: but be ye transformed by the renewing of your mind, that ye may prove what *is* that good, and acceptable, and perfect, will of God.

For I say, through the grace given unto me, to every man that is among you, not to think *of himself* more highly than he ought to think; but to think soberly, according as God hath dealt to every man the measure of faith.

For as we have many members in one body, and all members have not the same office:

So we, *being* many, are one body in Christ, and every one members one of another.

Having then gifts differing according to the grace that is given to us, whether prophecy, *let us prophesy* according to the proportion of faith;

Or ministry, *let us wait* on *our* ministering: or he that teacheth, on teaching;

Or he that exhorteth, on exhortation: he that giveth, *let him do it* with simplicity; he that ruleth, with diligence; he that sheweth mercy, with cheerfulness.

Let love be without dissimulation. Abhor that which is evil; cleave to that which is good.

Be kindly affectioned one to another with brotherly love; in honour preferring one another;

Not slothful in business; fervent in spirit; serving the Lord;

Rejoicing in hope; patient in tribulation; continuing instant in prayer;

Distributing to the necessity of saints; given to hospitality.

Bless them which persecute you: bless, and curse not.

Rejoice with them that do rejoice, and weep with them that weep.

Be of the same mind one toward another. Mind not high things, but condescend to men of low estate. Be not wise in your own conceits.

Recompense to no man evil for evil. Provide things honest in the sight of all men.

If it be possible, as much as lieth in you, live peaceably with all men.

Dearly beloved, avenge not yourselves, but *rather* give place unto wrath: for it is written, Vengeance *is* mine; I will repay, saith the Lord.

Therefore if thine enemy hunger, feed him; if he thirst, give him drink: for in so doing thou shalt heap coals of fire on his head.

Be not overcome of evil, but overcome evil with good.

GOVERNMENT OR-DAINED OF GOD
Romans 13:1-7

534

LET every soul be subject unto the higher powers. For there is no power but of God: the powers that be are ordained of God.

Whosoever therefore resisteth the power, resisteth the ordinance of God: and they that resist shall receive to themselves damnation.

For rulers are not a terror to good works, but to the evil. Wilt thou then not be afraid of the power? do that which is good, and thou shalt have praise of the same:

For he is the minister of God to thee for good. But if thou do that which is evil, be afraid; for he beareth not the sword in vain: for he is the minister of God, a revenger to *execute* wrath upon him that doeth evil.

Wherefore *ye* must needs be subject, not only for wrath, but also for conscience sake.

For for this cause pay ye tribute also: for they are God's ministers, attending continually upon this very thing.

Render therefore to all their dues: tribute to whom tribute *is due;* custom to whom custom; fear to whom fear; honour to whom honour.

THE JUDGMENT SEAT OF CHRIST
I Corinthians 3:10-15

535

According to the grace of God which is given unto me, as a wise masterbuilder, I have laid the foundation, and another buildeth thereon. But let every man take heed how he buildeth thereupon.

For other foundation can no man lay than that is laid, which is Jesus Christ.

Now if any man build upon this foundation gold, silver, precious stones, wood, hay, stubble;

Every man's work shall be made manifest: for the day shall declare it, because it shall be revealed by fire; and the fire shall try every man's work of what sort it is.

If any man's work abide which

he hath built thereupon, he shall receive a reward.

If any man's work shall be burned, he shall suffer loss: but he himself shall be saved; yet so as by fire.

CHRISTIAN LOVE

536 I Corinthians 13:1-13

THOUGH I speak with the tongues of men and of angels, and have not charity, I am become *as* sounding brass, or a tinkling cymbal.

And though I have *the gift of* prophecy, and understand all mysteries, and all knowledge; and though I have all faith, so that I could remove mountains, and have not charity, I am nothing.

And though I bestow all my goods to feed *the poor*, and though I give my body to be burned, and have not charity, it profiteth me nothing.

Charity suffereth long, *and* is kind; charity envieth not; charity vaunteth not itself, is not puffed up,

Doth not behave itself unseemly, seeketh not her own, is not easily provoked, thinketh no evil;

Rejoiceth not in iniquity, but rejoiceth in the truth;

Beareth all things, believeth all things, hopeth all things, endureth all things.

Charity never faileth: but whether *there be* prophecies, they shall fail; whether *there be* tongues, they shall cease; whether *there be* knowledge, it shall vanish away.

For we know in part, and we prophesy in part.

But when that which is perfect is come, then that which is in part shall be done away.

When I was a child, I spake as a child, I understood as a child, I thought as a child: but when I became a man, I put away childish things.

For now we see through a glass, darkly; but then face to face: now I know in part; but then shall I know even as also I am known.

And now abideth faith, hope, charity, these three; but the greatest of these *is* charity.

CHRISTIAN RESURRECTION

I Corinthians 15:1-25

537

MOREOVER, brethren, I declare unto you the gospel which I preached unto you, which also ye have received, and wherein ye stand;

By which also ye are saved, if ye keep in memory what I preached unto you, unless ye have believed in vain.

For I delivered unto you first of all that which I also received, how that Christ died for our sins according to the scriptures;

And that he was buried, and that he rose again the third day according to the scriptures:

And that he was seen of Ce'-phas, then of the twelve:

After that, he was seen of above five hundred brethren at once; of whom the greater part remain unto this present, but some are fallen asleep.

After that, he was seen of James; then of all the apostles.

And last of all he was seen of me also, as of one born out of due time.

For I am the least of the apostles, that am not meet to be called an apostle, because I persecuted the church of God.

But by the grace of God I am what I am: and his grace which *was* bestowed upon me was not in vain; but I laboured more abundantly than they all: yet not I, but the grace of God which was with me.

Therefore whether *it were* I or they, so we preach, and so ye believed.

Now if Christ be preached that he rose from the dead, how say some among you that there is no resurrection of the dead?

But if there be no resurrection of the dead, then is Christ not risen:

And if Christ be not risen, then *is* our preaching vain, and your faith *is* also vain.

Yea, and we are found false witnesses of God; because we have testified of God that he raised up Christ: whom he raised not up, if so be that the dead rise not.

For if the dead rise not, then is not Christ raised:

And if Christ be not raised, your faith *is* vain; ye are yet in your sins.

Then they also which are fallen asleep in Christ are perished.

If in this life only we have hope in Christ, we are of all men most miserable.

But now is Christ risen from the dead, *and* become the firstfruits of them that slept.

For since by man *came* death, by man *came* also the resurrection of the dead.

For as in Adam all die, even so in Christ shall all be made alive.

But every man in his own order: Christ the firstfruits; afterward they that are Christ's at his coming.

Then *cometh* the end, when he shall have delivered up the kingdom to God, even the Father; when he shall have put down all rule and all authority and power.

For he must reign, till he hath put all enemies under his feet.

CHRISTIAN SEPA-RATION

538 II Corinthians 6:14-18

Be ye not unequally yoked together with unbelievers: for what fellowship hath righteousness with unrighteousness? and what communion hath light with darkness?

And what concord hath Christ with Be'-li-al? or what part hath he that believeth with an infidel?

And what agreement hath the temple of God with idols? for ye are the temple of the living God; as God hath said, I will dwell in them, and walk in *them;* and I will be their God, and they shall be my people.

Wherefore come out from among them, and be ye separate, saith the Lord, and touch not the unclean *thing;* and I will receive you,

And will be a Father unto you, and ye shall be my sons and daughters, saith the Lord Almighty.

CHRISTIAN GIVING

II Corinthians 8:1-7

539

MOREOVER, brethren, we do you to wit of the grace of God bestowed on the churches of Macedonia;

How that in a great trial of affliction the abundance of their joy and their deep poverty abounded unto the riches of their liberality.

For to *their* power, I bear record, yea, and beyond *their* power *they were* willing of themselves;

Praying us with much intreaty that we would receive the gift, and *take upon us* the fellowship of the ministering to the saints.

And *this they did,* not as we hoped, but first gave their own selves to the Lord, and unto us by the will of God.

Insomuch that we desired Titus, that as he had begun, so he would also finish in you the same grace also.

Therefore, as ye abound in every *thing, in* faith, and utterance, and knowledge, and *in* all diligence, and *in* your love to us, *see* that ye abound in this grace also.

II Corinthians 9:6-8

But this I *say,* He which soweth sparingly shall reap also sparingly; and he which soweth bountifully shall reap also bountifully.

Every man according as he purposeth in his heart, *so let him give;* not grudgingly, or of necessity: for God loveth a cheerful giver.

And God *is* able to make all grace abound toward you; that ye, always having all sufficiency in all *things,* may abound to every good work:

WALK IN THE SPIRIT

Galatians 5:16-26

540

This I say then, Walk in the Spirit, and ye shall not fulfil the lust of the flesh.

For the flesh lusteth against the Spirit, and the Spirit against the flesh: and these are contrary the one to the other: so that ye cannot do the things that ye would.

But if ye be led of the Spirit, ye are not under the law.

Now the works of the flesh are manifest, which are *these;* Adultery, fornication, uncleanness, lasciviousness,

Idolatry, witchcraft, hatred, variance, emulations, wrath, strife, seditions, heresies,

Envyings, murders, drunkenness, revellings, and such like: of the which I tell you before, as I have also told *you* in time past, that they which do such things shall not inherit the kingdom of God.

But the fruit of the Spirit is love, joy, peace, longsuffering, gentleness, goodness, faith,

Meekness, temperance: against such there is no law.

And they that are Christ's have crucified the flesh with the affections and lusts.

If we live in the Spirit, let us also walk in the Spirit.

Let us not be desirous of vain glory, provoking one another, envying one another.

SOWING AND REAPING

541 Galatians 6:1-9

BRETHREN, if a man be overtaken in a fault, ye which are spiritual, restore such an one in the spirit of meekness; considering thyself, lest thou also be tempted.

Bear ye one another's burdens, and so fulfil the law of Christ.

For if a man think himself to be something, when he is nothing, he deceiveth himself.

But let every man prove his own work, and then shall he have rejoicing in himself alone, and not in another.

For every man shall bear his own burden.

Let him that is taught in the word communicate unto him that teacheth in all good things.

Be not deceived; God is not mocked: for whatsoever a man soweth, that shall he also reap.

For he that soweth to his flesh shall of the flesh reap corruption; but he that soweth to the Spirit shall of the Spirit reap life everlasting.

And let us not be weary in well doing: for in due season we shall reap, if we faint not.

THE NEW MAN

542 Ephesians 4:17-32

This I say therefore, and testify in the Lord, that ye henceforth walk not as other Gentiles walk, in the vanity of their mind,

Having the understanding darkened, being alienated from the life of God through the ignorance that is in them, because of the blindness of their heart:

Who being past feeling have given themselves over unto lasciviousness, to work all uncleanness with greediness.

But ye have not so learned Christ;

If so be that ye have heard him, and have been taught by him, as the truth is in Jesus:

That ye put off concerning the former conversation the old man, which is corrupt according to the deceitful lusts;

And be renewed in the spirit of your mind;

And that ye put on the new man, which after God is created in righteousness and true holiness.

Wherefore putting away lying, speak every man truth with his neighbour: for we are members one of another.

Be ye angry, and sin not: let not the sun go down upon your wrath:

Neither give place to the devil.

Let him that stole steal no more: but rather let him labour, working with *his* hands the thing which is good, that he may have to give to him that needeth.

Let no corrupt communication proceed out of your mouth, but that which is good to the use of edifying, that it may minister grace unto the hearers.

And grieve not the holy Spirit of God, whereby ye are sealed unto the day of redemption.

Let all bitterness, and wrath, and anger, and clamour, and evil speaking, be put away from you, with all malice:

And be ye kind one to another, tenderhearted, forgiving one another, even as God for Christ's sake hath forgiven you.

HUSBAND AND WIFE

543 Ephesians 5:18-33

And be not drunk with wine, wherein is excess; but be filled with the Spirit;

Speaking to yourselves in psalms and hymns and spiritual songs, singing and making melody in your heart to the Lord;

Giving thanks always for all

things unto God and the Father in the name of our Lord Jesus Christ;

Submitting yourselves one to another in the fear of God.

Wives, submit yourselves unto your own husbands, as unto the Lord.

For the husband is the head of the wife, even as Christ is the head of the church: and he is the saviour of the body.

Therefore as the church is subject unto Christ, so let the wives be to their own husbands in every thing.

Husbands, love your wives, even as Christ also loved the church, and gave himself for it;

That he might sanctify and cleanse it with the washing of water by the word,

That he might present it to himself a glorious church, not having spot, or wrinkle, or any such thing; but that it should be holy and without blemish.

So ought men to love their wives as their own bodies. He that loveth his wife loveth himself.

For no man ever yet hated his own flesh; but nourisheth and cherisheth it, even as the Lord the church:

For we are members of his body, of his flesh, and of his bones.

For this cause shall a man leave his father and mother, and shall be joined unto his wife, and they two shall be one flesh.

This is a great mystery: but I speak concerning Christ and the church.

Nevertheless let every one of you in particular so love his wife even as himself; and the wife see that she reverence her husband.

I Peter 3:1-12

LIKEWISE, ye wives, be in subjection to your own husbands; that, if any obey not the word, they also may without the word be won by the conversation of the wives;

While they behold your chaste conversation coupled with fear.

Whose adorning let it not be that outward adorning of plaiting the hair, and of wearing of gold, or of putting on of apparel;

But let it be the hidden man of the heart, in that which is not corruptible, even the ornament of a meek and quiet

spirit, which is in the sight of God of great price.

For after this manner in the old time the holy women also, who trusted in God, adorned themselves, being in subjection unto their own husbands:

Even as Sara obeyed Abraham, calling him lord: whose daughters ye are, as long as ye do well, and are not afraid with any amazement.

Likewise, ye husbands, dwell with them according to knowledge, giving honour unto the wife, as unto the weaker vessel, and as being heirs together of the grace of life; that your prayers be not hindered.

Finally, be ye all of one mind, having compassion one of another, love as brethren, be pitiful, be courteous:

Not rendering evil for evil, or railing for railing: but contrariwise blessing; knowing that ye are thereunto called, that ye should inherit a blessing.

For he that will love life, and see good days, let him refrain his tongue from evil, and his lips that they speak no guile:

Let him eschew evil, and do good; let him seek peace, and ensue it.

For the eyes of the Lord are over the righteous, and his ears are open unto their prayers: but the face of the Lord is against them that do evil.

CHRIST'S RETURN
I Thessalonians 4:13-18

544

But I would not have you to be ignorant, brethren, concerning them which are asleep, that ye sorrow not, even as others which have no hope.

For if we believe that Jesus died and rose again, even so them also which sleep in Jesus will God bring with him.

For this we say unto you by the word of the Lord, that we which are alive and remain unto the coming of the Lord shall not prevent them which are asleep.

For the Lord himself shall descend from heaven with a shout, with the voice of the archangel, and with the trump of God: and the dead in Christ shall rise first:

Then we which are alive and remain shall be caught up together with them in the clouds to meet the Lord in the air: and so shall we ever be with the Lord.

Wherefore comfort one another with these words.

PAUL'S FAREWELL
II Timothy 4:1-8

545

I CHARGE *thee* therefore before God, and the Lord Jesus Christ, who shall judge the quick and the dead at his appearing and his kingdom;

Preach the word; be instant in season, out of season; reprove, rebuke, exhort with all longsuffering and doctrine.

For the time will come when they will not endure sound doctrine; but after their own lusts shall they heap to themselves teachers, having itching ears;

And they shall turn away *their* ears from the truth, and shall be turned unto fables.

But watch thou in all things, endure afflictions, do the work of an evangelist, make full proof of thy ministry.

For I am now ready to be offered, and the time of my departure is at hand.

I have fought a good fight, I have finished *my* course, I have kept the faith:

Henceforth there is laid up for me a crown of righteousness, which the Lord, the righteous judge, shall give me at that day: and not to me only, but unto all them also that love his appearing.

BEARING CHRIST'S REPROACH
Hebrews 13:1-17

546

L ET brotherly love continue.
Be not forgetful to entertain strangers: for thereby some have entertained angels unawares.

Remember them that are in bonds, as bound with them; *and* them which suffer adversity, as being yourselves also in the body.

Marriage *is* honourable in all, and the bed undefiled: but whoremongers and adulterers God will judge.

Let your conversation *be* without covetousness; *and be* content with such things as ye have: for he hath said, I will never leave thee, nor forsake thee.

So that we may boldly say, The Lord *is* my helper, and I will not fear what man shall do unto me.

Remember them which have the rule over you, who have spoken unto you the word of God: whose faith follow, considering the end of *their* conversation.

Jesus Christ the same yesterday, and to day, and for ever.

Be not carried about with divers and strange doctrines. For *it is* a good thing that the heart be established with grace; not with meats, which have not profited them that have been occupied therein.

We have an altar, whereof they have no right to eat which serve the tabernacle.

For the bodies of those beasts, whose blood is brought into the sanctuary by the high priest for sin, are burned without the camp.

Wherefore Jesus also, that he might sanctify the people with his own blood, suffered without the gate.

Let us go forth therefore unto him without the camp, bearing his reproach.

For here have we no continuing city, but we seek one to come.

By him therefore let us offer the sacrifice of praise to God continually, that is, the fruit of *our* lips giving thanks to his name.

But to do good and to communicate forget not: for with such sacrifices God is well pleased.

Obey them that have the rule over you, and submit yourselves: for they watch for your souls, as they that must give account, that they may do it with joy, and not with grief: for that *is* unprofitable for you.

DRAW NIGH TO GOD
James 4:1-11

547

F ROM whence *come* wars and fightings among you? *come they* not hence, *even* of your lusts that war in your members?

Ye lust, and have not: ye kill, and desire to have, and cannot obtain: ye fight and war, yet ye have not, because ye ask not.

Ye ask, and receive not, because ye ask amiss, that ye may consume *it* upon your lusts.

Ye adulterers and adulteresses,

know ye not that the friendship of the world is enmity with God? whosoever therefore will be a friend of the world is the enemy of God.

Do ye think that the scripture saith in vain, The spirit that dwelleth in us lusteth to envy?

But he giveth more grace. Wherefore he saith, God resisteth the proud, but giveth grace unto the humble.

Submit yourselves therefore to God. Resist the devil, and he will flee from you.

Draw nigh to God, and he will draw nigh to you. Cleanse *your* hands, *ye* sinners; and purify *your* hearts, *ye* double minded.

Be afflicted, and mourn, and weep: let your laughter be turned to mourning, and *your* joy to heaviness.

Humble yourselves in the sight of the Lord, and he shall lift you up.

Speak not evil one of another, brethren. He that speaketh evil of *his* brother, and judgeth his brother, speaketh evil of the law, and judgeth the law: but if thou judge the law, thou art not a doer of the law, but a judge.

INSPIRATION OF SCRIPTURE

548   Matthew 4:4

But he answered and said, It is written, Man shall not live by bread alone, but by every word that proceedeth out of the mouth of God.

Matthew 5:17-18

Think not that I am come to destroy the law, or the prophets: I am not come to destroy, but to fulfil.

For verily I say unto you, Till heaven and earth pass, one jot or one tittle shall in no wise pass from the law, till all be fulfilled.

II Timothy 3:14-17

But continue thou in the things which thou hast learned and hast been assured of, knowing of whom thou hast learned *them;*

And that from a child thou hast known the holy scriptures, which are able to make thee wise unto salvation through faith which is in Christ Jesus.

All scripture *is* given by inspiration of God, and *is* profitable for doctrine, for reproof, for correction, for instruction in righteousness:

That the man of God may be perfect, throughly furnished unto all good works.

I Peter 1:23-25

Being born again, not of corruptible seed, but of incorruptible, by the word of God, which liveth and abideth for ever.

For all flesh *is* as grass, and all the glory of man as the flower of grass. The grass withereth, and the flower thereof falleth away:

But the word of the Lord endureth for ever. And this is the word which by the gospel is preached unto you.

II Peter 1:19-21

We have also a more sure word of prophecy; whereunto ye do well that ye take heed, as unto a light that shineth in a dark place, until the day dawn, and the day star arise in your hearts:

Knowing this first, that no prophecy of the scripture is of any private interpretation.

For the prophecy came not in old time by the will of man: but holy men of God spake *as they were* moved by the Holy Ghost.

TOPICAL INDEX

TOPICAL INDEX

TOPICAL INDEX

GENERAL INDEX

GENERAL INDEX

GENERAL INDEX

GENERAL INDEX

GENERAL INDEX

GENERAL INDEX

GENERAL INDEX

GENERAL INDEX

Favorite Song of Christian Leaders

SELECTIONS FROM SCRIPTURE INDEX